Core Connections Algebra 2
Second Edition*, Version 4.0, Volume 2

Managing Editors / Authors

Judy Kysh (Both Editions)
San Francisco State University
San Francisco, CA

Evra Baldinger (First Edition)
University of California, Berkeley
Berkeley, CA

Michael Kassarjian (2nd Edition)
CPM Educational Program
Encino, CA

Contributing Authors

Karen Arth
Central High School East
Fresno, CA

Mark Atkinson
North Salem High School
Salem, OR

Carlos Cabana
San Lorenzo High School
San Lorenzo, CA

John Cooper
Del Oro High School
Loomis, CA

Elizabeth Coyner
Christian Brothers High School
Sacramento, CA

Scott Coyner
Christian Brothers High School
Sacramento, CA

Dolores Dean
Holy Family High School
Broomfield, CO

Ernest Derrera
Roosevelt High School
Johnston, CO

Leslie Dietiker
Michigan State University
East Lansing, MI

Misty Nikula
Whatcom Day Acadamy
Bellingham, WA

Bob Petersen
Rosemont High School
Sacramento, CA

Norm Prokup
The College Preparatory School
Oakland, CA

Barbara Shreve
San Lorenzo High School
San Lorenzo, CA

Estelle Woodbury
San Lorenzo High School
San Lorenzo, CA

Karen Wootton
CPM Educational Program
Odenton, MD

Technical Managers

Hannah Coyner
Sacramento, CA

Sarah Maile
Sacramento, CA

Claire Taylor
Sacramento, CA

Program Directors

Elizabeth Coyner
CPM Educational Program
Sacramento, CA

Leslie Dietiker, Ph.D.
Boston University
Boston, MA

Lori Hamada
CPM Educational Program
Fresno, CA

Brian Hoey
CPM Educational Program
Sacramento, CA

Michael Kassarjian
CPM Educational Program
Kensington, CA

Judy Kysh, Ph.D.
Departments of Education and
Mathematics San Francisco
State University, CA

Tom Sallee, Ph.D.
Department of Mathematics
University of California, Davis

Karen Wootton
CPM Educational Program
Odenton, MD

*Based on *Algebra 2 Connections*

e-book Manager
Carol Cho
Director of Technology
Martinez, CA

e-book Programmers
Rakesh Khanna
Daniel Kleinsinger
Kevin Stein

e-book Assistants
Debbie Dodd
Shirley Paulsen
Wendy Papciak
Anna Poehlmann
Jordan Wight

Assessment Manager
Karen Wootton
Director of Assessment
Odenton, MD

Assessment Website
Elizabeth Fong
Michael Huang
Daniel Kleinsinger

Illustration
Kevin Coffey
San Francisco, CA

Homework Help Manager
Bob Petersen
CPM Educational Program

Homework Help Website
Carol Cho
Director of Technology

Parent Guide with Extra Practice
Bob Petersen (Managing Editor)
CPM Educational Program
Sacramento, CA

Scott Coyner
Christian Brothers High School
Sacramento, CA

Brian Hoey
Christian Brothers High School
Sacramento, CA

Sarah Maile
CPM Educational Program
Sacramento, CA

Karen Wooton
CPM Educational Program
Odenton, MD

Technical Manager
Rebecca Harlow
Sarah Maile

Technical Assistants

Stephanie Achondo
Eric Baxter
Diego Breedlove
Carrie Cai
Mary Coyner
Bethany Firch
Rebecca Harlow
Leslie Lai
Michael Li
James McCardle
Wendy Papciak
Iris Perez
Eduardo Ramirez
Andrea Smith
Christy Van Beek
Alex Yu

Robert Ainsworth
Rebecca Bobell
Duncan Breedlove
Alex Contreras
Carmen de la Cruz
Elizabeth Fong
Dana Kimball
Keith Lee
Jerry Luo
Nyssa Muheim
Atlanta Parrott
Steven Pham
John Ramos
Rachel Smith
Megan Walters

Erica Andrews
Delenn Breedlove
Elizabeth Burke
Hannah Coyner
Matthew Donahue
Miguel Francisco
Madeline Kimball
Michael Leong
Eli Marable
Alexandra Murphy
Ryan Peabody
Anna Poehlmann
Ali Rivera
Claire Taylor
Sarah Wong

3 4 5 6 7 8   18 17 16 15 14   Version 4.0

Printed in the United States of America   ISBN: 978-1-60328-114-0

A Note to Students:

Welcome to a new year of math! In this course, you will learn to use new models and methods to think about problems as well as solve them. You will be developing powerful mathematical tools and learning new ways of thinking about and investigating situations. You will be making connections, discovering relationships, figuring out what strategies can be used to solve problems, and explaining your thinking. Learning to think in these ways and communicate about your thinking is useful in mathematical contexts, other subjects in school, and situations outside the classroom. The mathematics you have learned in the past will be valuable for learning in this course. That work, and what you learn in this course, will prepare you for future courses.

In meeting the challenges of this course, you will not be learning alone. You will cooperate with other students as a member of a study team. Being a part of a team means speaking up and interacting with other people. You will explain your ideas, listen to what others have to say, and ask questions if there is something you do not understand. In this course, a single problem can often be solved several ways. You will see problems in different ways than your teammates do. Each of you has something to contribute while you work on the lessons in this course.

Together, your team will complete problems and activities that will help you discover mathematical ideas and develop solution methods. Your teacher will support you as you work, but will not take away your opportunity to think and investigate for yourself. Each topic will be revisited many times and will connect to other topics. If something is not clear to you the first time you work on it, you will have more chances to build your understanding as the course continues.

Learning math this way has an advantage: as long as you actively participate, make sure everyone in your study team is involved, and ask good questions, you will find yourself understanding mathematics at a deeper level than ever before. By the end of this course, you will have a powerful set of mathematical tools to use to solve new problems. With your teammates you will meet mathematical challenges you would not have known how to approach before.

In addition to the support provided by your teacher and your study team, CPM has also created online resources to help you, including help with homework, and a parent guide with extra practice. You will find these resources and more at www.cpm.org.

We wish you well and are confident that you will enjoy this next year of learning!

Sincerely,
The CPM Team

Core Connections Algebra 2
Student Edition

Volume 1

Volume 2

Chapter 6   3-D Graphing and Logarithms

In this chapter, you will learn to extend your mathematical thinking to three dimensions and you will further your understanding of logarithms, which will give you the tools to solve a murder mystery.

In the first section, you will expand your understanding of graphing equations and systems of equations to three dimensions and you will broaden your understanding of solutions to include solutions to systems in three dimensions.

In Section 6.2, you will return to logarithms to learn more about their properties and why they are useful. You will construct an exponential function to model a situation, and you will use logarithms to solve a mathematical murder mystery.

Guiding Question

Mathematically proficient students make sense of problems and persevere in solving them.

As you work through this chapter, ask yourself:

How can I apply what I learned about graphs and equations in two dimensions to three-dimensional situations?

Chapter Outline

Section 6.1 In this section, you will learn how to graph points, equations, and systems of equations in three dimensions. You will solve three-dimensional systems of equations. You will learn how to use systems of three equations in three variables to solve problems, including finding the equation of a parabola passing through any three points.

Section 6.2 You will learn some important properties of logarithms that will enable you to solve equations. You will then use these skills to solve a murder mystery, "The Mystery of the Cooling Corpse."

6.1.1 How can I plot points in three dimensions?

Creating a Three-Dimensional Model

In geometry, you worked with objects that existed in different dimensions. You considered lines and line segments, which have only one dimension: length. You also looked at flat shapes like circles, rectangles, and trapezoids that have two dimensions: length and width. Prisms, cones, and most objects that you encounter in the real world have volume, and therefore have three dimensions: length, width and height.

When you worked with graphs in Algebra 1, you represented points, the number line, and curves on a **two-dimensional** (flat) surface called the xy-plane. So far, you have only been able to represent relationships with at most two unknowns, usually the variables x and y. However, many problems, like some that you may have done in homework problems in Chapter 6, have more than two unknowns. Today, you and your team will build a model that will help you graph in three dimensions. As you work on this lesson, consider the following questions with your team:

How can we plot a point in three dimensions?

How can we write the coordinates of a point in three dimensions?

How can we show three dimensions on flat paper?

6-1.   Consider when it is appropriate to graph a situation in one, two, and/or three dimensions. It may be helpful to think about your experience representing numbers and relationships on a number line or an xy-plane, and how you can adapt your knowledge to work in three dimensions. Discuss each question with your team before writing your response.

   a.   How can you represent the solution to $x = 5$ graphically? Can you think of more than one way?

   b.   How can you represent the solutions to $x + 2y = 5$ graphically?

   c.   How could you represent the solutions to $x + 2y + z = 5$? What would the solutions look like? Discuss these questions with your team and write down any ideas that you have.

6-2.   To graph solutions to equations with three variables, you need to use a three-dimensional coordinate system. Obtain a Lesson 6.1.1A or 6.1.1B Resource Page from your teacher. Use scissors to cut out the region indicated on the page. Then fold along each of the axes and use tape to attach the dashed edge to the z-axis. Be sure that the grid ends up on the *inside* of your model (rather than the outside). The result should look similar to the diagram at right.

6-3.   Place a penny (or other marker) on the bottom surface of your model at the point where $x = 4$ and $y = 2$. Now lift your marker straight up so that it you are holding it 3 units above the bottom of the model.

   a.   With your team, find a way to write the coordinates of this point.

   b.   In your model, find the point where $x = 3$, $y = 4$, and $z = 2$. Use your team's method to write the coordinates for this point.

   c.   The model you have created is only a portion of the entire coordinate system used to represent three dimensions mathematically. How many of these models would you have to put together to create a model that represents the entire three-dimensional coordinate system? Think about the regions you would need to graph points like $(5, -2, -7)$ or $(-1, -2, -4)$.

6-4.   Use cubes to build each shape described below inside your three-dimensional model. Make sure that one corner of each shape you build lies at the **origin** (at the point $(0, 0, 0)$).

   a.   Build a $2 \times 2 \times 2$ cube. Use coordinates to name the vertex that is farthest from the origin.

   b.   Build a rectangular prism that is 2 units in length along the x-axis, 1 unit in length along the y-axis, and 3 units in length along the z-axis. Use coordinates to name the vertex that is farthest from the origin.

   c.   Draw and label a three-dimensional coordinate system on isometric dot paper, as shown at right. Now add the prism from part (b) to the drawing. On your dot paper, label the coordinates of *all* of the vertices.

6-5.   Build a rectangular prism that will have vertices in your model at $(1, 0, 0)$, $(0, 0, 4)$, and $(0, 3, 0)$.

   a.   Find the coordinates of the other five vertices.

   b.   Move the rectangular prism so that three vertices are at $(-1, 0, 0)$, $(0, 0, 4)$, and $(0, 3, 0)$. Now where are the other vertices?

   c.   Is it possible to build another rectangular prism that has the same coordinates for the vertex farthest from the origin as the prism in part (b)? Be sure to justify your conclusion.

Core Connections Algebra 2

6-6.　　On isometric dot paper, draw a three-dimensional coordinate system and plot the following points: $(0,1,-1)$, $(1,2,0)$, and $(2,3,1)$.

　　a.　What do you notice about the three points?

　　b.　With your team, find a strategy to make each point clearly different from the others. Be prepared to share your strategy with the class.

　　c.　Identify the coordinates of two points that appear to be the same as $(-2,0,0)$.

6-7.　　LEARNING LOG

In your Learning Log, show and explain how to graph points in three dimensions. Include clear pictures to illustrate your method. Title this entry "Plotting Points in *xyz*-Space" and label it with today's date.

6-8.　　Make a table like the one below. Choose points in each of the locations listed at the top of the table and write in the coordinates of the points you have chosen.

	Points on the *x*-axis	Points on the *y*-axis	Points on the *z*-axis	Points not on the *x*-, *y*-, or *z*-axes
1st point	(, ,)	(, ,)	(, ,)	(, ,)
2nd point	(, ,)	(, ,)	(, ,)	(, ,)
3rd point	(, ,)	(, ,)	(, ,)	(, ,)
4th point	(, ,)	(, ,)	(, ,)	(, ,)

　　a.　What do you notice about the coordinates of the points on the *x*-axis?

　　b.　Make a conjecture about the coordinates of points that lie on any of the coordinate axes.

6-9.　　Solve the system of equations at right.

$$3x + 8 = 2$$
$$7x + 3y = 1$$

6-10.   Each cube below is 1 cm on a side.

(I)   (II)   (III)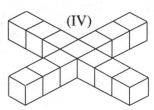

?

a.   Based on the pattern, find the volume of Figure III.

b.   If the pattern continues, write an expression to represent the volume of Figure *N*. What kind of sequence is this?

6-11.   Solve each exponential equation for *x*.

a. $10^x = 16$ b. $10^x = 41$ c. $3^x = 729$ d. $10^x = 101$

6-12.   Rewrite each expression below as an equivalent expression without negative exponents.

a. 5^{-2} b. xy^{-2} c. $(xy)^{-2}$ d. $a^3b^4a^{-4}b^6$

6-13.   Multiply or divide and simplify each of the following expressions.

a. $\dfrac{3x}{x^2+2x+1} \div \dfrac{3}{x^2+2x+1}$ b. $\dfrac{3}{x-1} \cdot \dfrac{2}{x-2}$

6-14.   Given the two points $(-2, 0)$ and $(0, 1)$, complete parts (a) through (c) below.

a.   Find the slope of the line that passes through these two points.

b.   Find the slope of the line perpendicular to the line that passes through these two points.

c.   Describe the relationship between the slopes of perpendicular lines.

6-15.   The cost of food has been increasing by 4% per year for many years. To find the cost of an item 15 years ago, Heather said, *"Take the current price and divide it by* $(1.04)^{15}$ *."*

Her friend Elissa said, *"No, you should take the current price and multiply it by* $(0.96)^{15}$ *!"*

Explain who is correct and why.

6.1.2 How can I graph an equation in three dimensions?

Graphing Equations in Three Dimensions

In the past, you have used the two-dimensional Cartesian coordinate system (*x*- and *y*-axes) to graph equations involving two variables. In Lesson 6.1.1, you used a three-dimensional coordinate system to plot points. Today you will use the three-dimensional coordinate system to graph equations that have three variables. As you are working through the lesson, use the following questions to help focus your discussion:

> How can we use what we know about graphing in two dimensions
> to help us graph in three dimensions?

> What does a solution to a three-variable equation represent?

6-16.   Consider the equation $5x + 8y + 10z = 40$.

    a.   Discuss with your team what you think the shape of the graph would be. Explain how you decided.

    b.   Is the point $(4, 5, -2)$ a solution to the equation $5x + 8y + 10z = 40$? Justify your answer.

    c.   Your team will be given a list of points to test in the equation. Plot each point that makes the equation true on the three-dimensional graphing tool your teacher has set up.

    d.   Now examine the solutions displayed on the graphing tool. With your team, discuss the questions below. Be ready to share your discoveries with the class.

        •   Are there any points that you suspect are solutions, but do not have a point showing on the graph?

        •   How many solutions do you think there are?

        •   Are there any points showing that you think are not solutions? Explain.

        •   What shape is formed by all of the solutions? That is, what is the shape of the graph of $5x + 8y + 10z = 40$?

6-17.   How can you graph an equation like $12x + 4y + 5z = 60$ in three dimensions? To come up with a strategy to graph a three-variable equation, look at the strategies you can use to graph a two-variable equation in two dimensions. For example, consider $5x + 8y = 40$.

a.   What is the shape of the graph of $5x + 8y = 40$? How can you tell?

b.   With your team, brainstorm all of the strategies you could use to graph $5x + 8y = 40$. Which strategy do you prefer? Why?

6-18.   Now you will work with your team to graph $12x + 4y + 5z = 60$.

a.   What do you think it will look like?

b.   Which of the strategies you used to graph a two-variable equation in problem 6-17 can be used to graph this three-variable equation? Work with your team to find a strategy and then graph $12x + 4y + 5z = 60$ on your isometric dot paper. Be prepared to share your strategy with the class.

6-19.   Use your new strategy to graph each of the following equations in three dimensions.

a. $13x + 4y + 5z = 260$ b. $12x - 9y + 108 = 0$

6-20.   Consider the graph of $x = 4$ for each of the following problems.

a.   Graph the solution to $x = 4$ in one dimension (on a number line).

b.   Graph the solutions to $x = 4$ in two dimensions (on the xy-plane).

c.   Graph the solutions to $x = 4$ in three dimensions (in the xyz-space).

Locating Points in Three Dimensions

When locating a point on a *number line*, a single number, x, is used.

The location of a point in a *plane* is given by two numbers, (x, y), called an ordered pair.

To locate a point in *space*, three numbers, (x, y, z), are used, which are called an **ordered triple**. The point $(2, 3, 1)$ is shown at right. The dotted lines help clarify which coordinate was graphed.

Review & Preview

6-21. For each of the following equations, find every point where its *three-dimensional* graph intersects one of the coordinate axes. That is, find the *x*-, *y*- and *z-intercepts*. Express your answer in (x, y, z) form.

   a. $6y + 15z = 60$ b. $3x + 4y + 2z = 24$

   c. $(x + 3)^2 + z^2 = 25$ d. $z = 6$

6-22. Answer each of the following questions. Illustrate your answers with a sketch.

   a.   What do you think the intersection of two planes looks like?

   b.   What do you think it means for two planes to be parallel?

   c.   What do you think it means for a line and a plane to be parallel?

6-23. Find an equation that will generate each graph.

a.

b.

c.

6-24. Is $y = \frac{1}{x}$ the parent of $y = \frac{1}{x^2+7}$? Explain your reasoning.

6-25. Solve each equation below for x.

a. $2x + x = b$

b. $2ax + 3ax = b$

c. $x + ax = b$

6-26. Mark claims to have created a sequence of three function machines that always gives him the same number he started with.

a. Test his machines. Do you think he is right?

b. Be sure to test negative numbers. What happens for negative numbers?

c. Mark wants to get his machines patented but has to prove that the set of machines will always do what he says it will, at least for positive numbers. Show Mark how to prove that his machines work for positive numbers by dropping in a variable (for example, n) and writing out each step the machines must take.

d. Why do the negative numbers come out positive?

6-27. Sketch the graph of $y = \log_5(x-2)$ and describe how the graph is transformed from the parent graph.

6-28. The table at right shows the total population of Mexico for the given years.

a. What was the average rate of change for the population from 1900 to 1950?

b. What was the average rate of change from 1960 to 2010?

c. When was the population growth rate higher?

Year	Population (millions)
1900	13.6
1910	15.2
1920	14.4
1930	16.6
1940	19.8
1950	26.3
1960	35.0
1970	50.7
1980	69.7
1990	87.8
2000	100.3
2010	113.7

6-29. Given $f(x) = -2x^2 - 4$ and $g(x) = 5x + 3$, calculate:

a. $g(-2)$ b. $f(-7)$ c. $f(g(-2))$ d. $f(g(1))$

6.1.3 What can I discover about 3-D systems?

· ·

Systems of Three-Variable Equations

You know a lot about systems of two-variable equations, their solutions, and their graphs. Today you will investigate systems of three-variable equations.

6-30.   THREE-DIMENSIONAL SYSTEM INVESTIGATION

Consider the following systems of equations:

System I	*System II*
$20x + 12y + 15z = 60$	$20x + 15y + 12z = 60$
$20x + 12y + 15z = 120$	$10x + 30y + 12z = 60$

Your Task: With your team, find out as much as you can about each of these systems of equations, their graphs, and their solutions. Be sure to record all of your work carefully and be prepared to share your summary statements with the class.

Discussion Points

What does the graph of a three-variable equation look like?

What does it mean to be a solution to a system of equations?

What does a solution to a three-variable system of equations look like on a graph?

Is there always a solution to a system of equations?

Further Guidance

6-31.   Using isometric dot paper, graph both equations in *System I* from problem 6-30 on a single three-dimensional coordinate system. Use different colors to help identify each graph.

a.   Describe the graph of the system in as much detail as you can.

b.   Looking at the graph, can you tell what the solution to this system is? Explain.

6-32. Using isometric dot paper, graph both equations in *System II* from problem 6-30 on a single three-dimensional coordinate system. Use different colors to help identify each graph.

    a. Describe the graph of the system in as much detail as you can.

    b. Looking at the graph, can you tell what the solution to this system is? Explain.

6-33. Now compare the graphs of the two systems. How are they similar? How are they different?

Further Guidance
section ends here.

6-34. Look closely at your graph of *System II*. Can you see the intersection of the two planes clearly? If not, make a new set of axes and graph the systems carefully.

    a. What does the intersection of two planes look like?

    b. Work with your team to find the coordinates of as many points as you can that lie in both planes. Show your work and describe your strategies. Be prepared to share your ideas with the class.

    c. Can you add a third equation to the system that will share the same intersection with the original two graphs?

6-35. On isometric dot paper, graph the system of equations at right. What shape is the intersection? Use color to show the intersection clearly on your graph.

$$10x + 6y + 5z = 30$$
$$6x + 15y + 5z = 30$$

6-36. Verify that $2^7 = 128$. Is it true that $\log 2^7 = \log 128$?

6-37. If $24 = y$, is it true that $\log 24 = \log y$? Justify your answer.

6-38.   Write the system of inequalities that would give the graph at right.

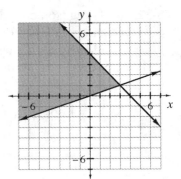

6-39.   Simplify each of the following expressions.

a. $\dfrac{2x^3+5x^2-3x}{4x^3-4x^2+x}$

b. $\dfrac{3x^2-5x-2}{2x^2-11x+15} \cdot \dfrac{2x^2-5x}{3x^3-5x^2-2x}$

6-40.   Solve $\sqrt{3x+1} - x = -3$ and check your solution.

a.   You should have gotten two values for x when you solved. Did you? If not, rework the problem.

b.   Did you check *both* solutions? What happened?

6-41.   Solve each of the following equations.

a. $(x+4)(2x-5)=0$

b. $(x+4)(x^2-5x+6)=0$

c. $3x(x+1)(2x-7)(3x+4)^2(x-13)(x+7)=0$

d.   Describe how to solve an equation made up of any number of factors all multiplied to equal zero.

6-42.   Determine if each of the following functions is odd, even, or neither.

a. $f(x)=3x^3+2$ b. $y=x^6+x^4$

6-43.   Solve for x, y, and z: $(2^x)(3^y)(5^z)=(2^3)(3^{x-2})(5^{2x-3y})$.

$6.1.4$ What is a solution in three dimensions?

Solving Systems of Three Equations with Three Unknowns

Today you will extend what you know about systems of equations to examine how to solve systems of equations with three variables. As you work with your team, look for connections to previous work. The focus questions below can help generate mathematical discussion.

What does a solution to a system in three variables mean?

What strategies can we use?

What does the intersection look like?

6-44. Review the strategies for solving systems that you already know as you solve the following two-variable system of equations. Use any method. Do not hesitate to change strategies if your first strategy seems cumbersome. If there is no solution, explain what that indicates about the graph of this system. Leave your solution in (x, y) form.

$$12x - 2y = 16$$
$$30x + 2y = 68$$

6-45. Solve the following three-variable system of equations by graphing it with your graphing tool or on isometric dot paper. Give your solution in (x, y, z) form. Then test your solution in the equations and describe your results.

$$2x + 3y + 3z = 6$$
$$6x - 3y + 4z = 12$$
$$2x - 3y + 2z = 6$$

6-46. FINDING AN EASIER WAY

As you saw in problem 6-45, using a graph to solve a system of three equations with three variables can lead to inconclusive results. What other strategies should be considered? Discuss this with your team and be prepared to share your ideas with the class.

6-47. Looking at the equations in problem 6-45, Elissa wanted to see if she could apply some of her solving techniques from two-variable equations to this three-variable system.

    a.   Elissa noticed that the first two equations could be combined to form the new equation $8x + 7z = 18$. How did she accomplish this? Explain.

    b.   Now that Elissa has an equation with only x and z, she needs to find another equation with only x and z to be able to solve the system. Choose a different pair of equations to combine and find a way to eliminate y so that the new equation only has x and z. Then solve the system to find x and z.

    c.   For which variable do you still need to solve? Work with your team to solve for this variable. Then write the solution as a point in (x, y, z) form.

    d.   Is your solution reasonable? Does it make sense? Does it agree with your graph?

6-48. Practice using your algebraic strategies by solving the systems below, if possible. If there is no solution or if the solution is different than you expected, use the graphing tool to help you figure out why.

    a. $x + y + 3z = 3$
          $2x + y + 6z = 2$
          $2x - y + 3z = -7$

    b. $20x + 12y + 15z = 60$
          $20x + 12y + 15z = 120$
          $10x + 20z = 30$

    c. $5x - 4y - 6z = -19$
          $-2x + 2y + z = 5$
          $3x - 6y - 5z = -16$

    d. $6x + 4y + z = 12$
          $6x + 4y + 2z = 12$
          $6x + 4y + 3z = 12$

6-49. Today you developed a way to solve a system of three equations with three variables. But what do the solutions of a system like those provided in problem 6-48 represent? Consider this as you answer the questions below with your graphing tool.

    a.   One of the systems in problem 6-48 had no solution. Graph this system with your graphing tool. Describe how the planes are positioned and why there is no common point on all three planes.

    b.   In what other ways could three planes be positioned so that there is no solution? Use paper or cardboard to help you communicate your ideas with others.

    c.   Graph the system in part (d) of problem 6-48 with your graphing tool and examine the result. How can you describe the intersection of these planes?

6-50. LEARNING LOG

In your Learning Log, describe your algebraic strategy to
solve a system of three equations with three variables.
Provide enough detail to allow you to repeat the process
when you refer to it later. Title this entry "Systems of Three
Equations with Three Variables" and include today's date.

MATH NOTES

METHODS AND **M**EANINGS

Graphing Planes in Three Dimensions

To graph a plane, it is easiest to use the intercepts to draw the
"trace lines" (the intersections of the plane with the xy-, xz-,
and yz-planes) that will represent the plane.

To find the intercepts, let two of the variables equal zero. Then solve to
find the intercept corresponding to the remaining variable.

For example, for $2x + 3y + 4z = 12$, the x-intercept is found by letting y
and z equal zero, which gives $2x = 12$. Therefore the x-intercept is
$(6, 0, 0)$. Similarly, the y-intercept is $(0, 4, 0)$, and the z-intercept is
$(0, 0, 3)$.

Drawing the line between two intercepts gives one
of the trace line in that coordinate plane. For
example, connecting the x- and y-intercepts, you
would get the equation $2x + 3y = 12$, which is the
trace line in the xy-plane when $z = 0$ in the equation
$2x + 3y + 4z = 12$. Connecting the x- and z-intercepts
gives the trace line in the xz-plane, etc.

Review & Preview

6-51. Use the algebraic strategies you developed in today's lesson
to solve the system of equations at right. Be sure to check
your solution.

$2x + y - 3z = -12$
$5x - y + z = 11$
$x + 3y - 2z = -13$

6-52.   Suppose that a two-bedroom house in Nashville is worth $110,000 and appreciates at a rate of 2.5% each year.

a.   How much will it be worth in 10 years?

b.   When will it be worth $200,000?

c.   In Homewood, houses are depreciating at a rate of 5% each year. If a house is worth $182,500 now, how much will it be worth two years from now?

6-53.   Solve $\sqrt{5x-1} = \sqrt{6+4x}$ and check your solution.

6-54.   If two quantities are equal, are their logarithms also equal? Consider the questions below.

a.   Is it true that 4^2 is equal to 2^4? Is this a special case, or is a^b equal to b^a for any values of a and b?

b.   Is $\log 4^2$ equal to $\log 2^4$? How can you be sure?

c.   Are the equations $x = 5$ and $\log x = \log 5$ equivalent? Justify your answer.

d.   Is the equation $\log 7 = \log x^2$ equivalent to the equation $7 = x^2$? How can you be sure?

6-55.   Use the ideas from problem 6-54 to help you solve the following equations.

a. $\log 10 = \log(2x - 3)$ b. $\log 25 = \log(4x^2 - 5x - 50)$

6-56.   Find an equation for each of the lines described below.

a.   The line with slope $\frac{1}{3}$ that goes through the point $(0, 5)$.

b.   The line parallel to $y = 2x - 5$ that goes through the point $(1, 7)$.

c.   The line perpendicular to $y = 2x - 5$ that goes through the point $(1, 7)$.

d.   The line that goes through the point $(0, 0)$ so that the tangent of the angle it makes with the x-axis is 2.

6-57.   Solve each equation below for y so that it can be entered into the graphing calculator.

a. $x^2 = x(2x - 4) + y$

b. $x = 3 + (y - 5)^2$

6-58.   Sketch the graph of each equation or inequality below.

a. $(x - 2)^2 + (y + 3)^2 = 9$

b. $(x - 2)^2 + (y + 3)^2 \geq 9$

6-59.   You are standing 60 feet away from a five-story building in Los Angeles, looking up at its rooftop. In the distance you can see the billboard on top of your hotel, but the building is completely obscured by the one in front of you. If your hotel is 32 stories tall and the average story is 10 feet high, how far away from your hotel are you?

6.1.5 How can I apply systems of equations?

Using Systems of Three Equations for Curve Fitting

In this lesson you will work with your team to find the equation of a quadratic function that passes through three specific points. You will be challenged to extend what you know about writing and solving a system of equations in two variables to solving a system of equations in three variables.

6-60.   In your work with parabolas, you have developed two forms for the general equation of a quadratic function: $y = ax^2 + bx + c$ and $y = a(x-h)^2 + k$. What information does each equation give you about the graph of a parabola? Be as detailed in your explanation as possible. When is each form most useful?

6-61.   Suppose the graph of a quadratic function passes through the points $(1, 0)$, $(2, 5)$, and $(3, 12)$. Sketch its graph. Then work with your team to develop an algebraic method to find the equation $y = ax^2 + bx + c$ of this specific quadratic function.

Discussion Points

What does the graph of any quadratic function look like?

What does it mean for the graph of $y = ax^2 + bx + c$
to pass through the point $(3, 12)$?

What solving method can we use to find a, b, and c?

How can we check our equation?

Would this method allow us to find
the equation of a quadratic using *any* three points?

Would this method work if we only had two points?

Further Guidance

6-62.   How many points does it take to determine the equation of a linear function $y = ax + b$? Discuss this with your team and include at least one sketch to support your answer.

Now think about the graph of a quadratic function $y = ax^2 + bx + c$. How many points do you think it would take to determine this graph? Why? Does there need to be any restriction on the points you use? Discuss these questions with your team and justify your answers before moving on to part (a).

a.   Suppose you wanted the graph of a quadratic function $y = ax^2 + bx + c$ to pass through the points $(1, 0)$, $(2, 5)$, and $(3, 12)$. How would these points be useful in finding the specific equation of this function? If your team has not already done so, include a sketch of the parabola going through these points to support your answer.

b.   It is often useful to label points with the variable they represent. For instance, for the point $(3, 12)$, which variable does the 3 represent? Which variable does the 12 represent?

c.   Using the general equation of a quadratic, $y = ax^2 + bx + c$, substitute the x- and y-values from your first point into the equation. Then do the same for the other two points to create three equations where the unknowns are a, b, and c.

d.   Now use the strategies you developed in Lesson 6.1.4 to solve the system of equations for a, b, and c.

e.   Use your results to write the equation of the quadratic function that passes through the points $(1, 0)$, $(2, 5)$, and $(3, 12)$. How can you check your answer? That is, how can you make sure your equation would actually go through the three points? Using the method your team decides on, check your equation.

——————   *Further Guidance*   ——————
                         section ends here.

6-63.   LEARNING LOG

In your Learning Log, summarize the method you used in
problem 6-61 (or problem 6-62) to find the equation
$y = ax^2 + bx + c$ of the quadratic function whose graph passes
through three given points. Title this entry "Finding the Equation of a Parabola
Given Three Points" and label it with today's date.

6-64.   Find the equation $y = ax^2 + bx + c$ of the function that passes through the three points given in parts (a) and (b) below. Be sure to check your answers.

a. $(3, 10), (5, 36)$, and $(-2, 15)$ b. $(2, 2), (-4, 5)$, and $(6, 0)$

6-65.   What happened in part (b) of problem 6-64? Why did this occur? (If you are not sure, plot the points on graph paper.)

6-66.   CPM engineers are considering developing a private space rocket. In a computer simulation, the rocket is approaching a star and is caught in its gravitational pull. When the rocket's engines are fired, the rocket will slow down, stop momentarily, and then pick up speed and move away from the star, avoiding its gravitational field. CPM engaged the rocket engines when it was 750 thousand miles from the star. After one full minute, the rocket was 635 thousand miles from the star. After two minutes, the ship was 530 thousand miles from the star.

a.   Name the three points given in the information above if x = the time since the engines were engaged and y = the distance (in thousands of miles) from the star.

b.   Based on the points in part (a), make a rough sketch of a graph that shows the distance reaching a minimum and then increasing again, over time. What kind of function could follow this pattern?

c.   Find the equation of a graph that fits the three points you found in part (a).

d.   If the ship comes within 50 thousand miles of the star, the shields will fail and the ship will burn up. Use your equation to determine whether the space ship has failed to escape the gravity of the star.

6-67.   Sickly Sid has contracted a serious infection and
has gone to the doctor for help. The doctor takes a
blood sample and finds 900 bacteria per cc (cubic
centimeter) and gives Sid a shot of a strong
antibiotic. The bacteria will continue to grow for a
period of time, reach a peak, and then decrease as
the medication succeeds in overcoming the
infection. After ten days, the infection has grown
to 1600 bacteria per cc. After 15 days it has grown
to 1875.

a.   Name three data points given in the problem statement.

b.   Make a rough sketch that will show the number of bacteria per cc over
time.

c.   Find the equation of the parabola that contains the three data points.

d.   Based on the equation, how long will it take until the bacteria are
eliminated?

e.   Based on the equation, how long had Sid been infected before he went to
the doctor?

6-68.   THE COMMUTER

Sensible Sally has a job that is 35 miles from her
home and needs to be at work by 8:15 a.m. She
wants to get as much sleep as she can, leave as late
as possible, and still get to work on time. Sally
discovered that if she leaves at 7:10, it takes her
40 minutes to get to work. If she leaves at 7:30, it
takes her 60 minutes to get work. If she leaves at
7:40, it takes her 50 minutes to get to work. Since her commute time increases
and then decreases, Sally decided to use a quadratic function to model her
commute.

a.   If x = the number of minutes after 7:00 that Sally leaves, and y = the
number of minutes it takes Sally to get to work, what three ordered pairs
can you determine from the problem?

b.   Use the three points from part (a) to find the equation of a parabola in
standard form that can be used to model Sally's commute.

c.   Will Sally make it to work on time if she leaves at 7:20?

6-69.   PAIRS PARABOLA CHALLENGE

Your challenge will be to work with a partner to create a parabola puzzle for another pair of students to solve. Follow the directions below to create a puzzle that will make them think and allow them to show off their algebra skills. When you are ready, you will trade puzzles with another pair and attempt to solve theirs.

a.   With your partner, decide on an equation for a parabola and then identify three points that lie on its graph. Keep track of how you came up with your equation and how you chose your points. Be ready to share strategies.

b.   Write the coordinates of the three points on an index card or small slip of paper to give to another pair of students. Be sure you keep a copy of your equation so you can check their work later.

c.   Trade points with another pair and work with your partner to solve their puzzle. When you are confident of your equation, check your work with the pair that wrote it.

6-70.   Make a conjecture about how you would find the equation of a cubic function that passes through a given set of points when graphed, $y = ax^3 + bx^2 + cx + d$. How many points do you think you would need to be given to be able to determine a unique equation? How could you extend the method you developed for solving a quadratic to solving a cubic?

Review & Preview

6-71.   Solve the system of equations at right and then check your solution in each equation. Be sure to keep your work well organized.

$$x - 2y + 3z = 8$$
$$2x + y + z = 6$$
$$x + y + 2z = 12$$

6-72.   Find the equation in $y = ax^2 + bx + c$ form of the parabola that passes through the points $(1, 5)$, $(3, 19)$, and $(-2, 29)$.

6-73.   This problem is a checkpoint for multiplying and dividing rational expressions.
It will be referred to as Checkpoint 6A.

Multiply or divide each pair of rational expressions. Simplify the result.

a. $\dfrac{x^2-16}{(x-4)^2} \cdot \dfrac{x^2-3x-18}{x^2-2x-24}$

b. $\dfrac{x^2-1}{x^2-6x-7} \div \dfrac{x^3+x^2-2x}{x-7}$

Check your answers by referring to the Checkpoint 6A materials located at the back of your book.

Ideally, at this point you are comfortable working with these types of problems and can solve them correctly. If you feel that you need more confidence when solving these types of problems, then review the Checkpoint 6A materials and try the practice problems provided. From this point on, you will be expected to do problems like these correctly and with confidence.

6-74.   Simplify each expression in parts (a) through (c) below. Then complete part (d).

a. $xy(\frac{1}{x}+\frac{1}{2y})$

b. $ab(\frac{2}{a}+\frac{4a}{b})$

c. $2x(3-\frac{1}{2x})$

d.   What expression would go in the box to make the equation
$\Box(\frac{2}{x}+\frac{7}{y})=2y+7x$ true?

6-75.   Change each of the following equations from logarithmic form to exponential form, or vice versa.

a. $y = \log_{12} x$

b. $x = \log_y 17$

c. $y = 1.75^{2x}$

d. $3y = x^7$

6-76.   Solve $\sqrt{3x-6} + 6 = 12$ and check your solution.

6-77.   The half-life of an isotope is 1000 years. A 50-gram sample of the isotope is sealed in a box.

a.   How much is left after 10,000 years?

b.   How long will it take to reduce to 1% of the original amount?

c.   How long will it take until all of the original sample of the isotope is gone?
Support your answer.

6-78.   Graph the following piecewise-defined function.

$$x > 0; \quad y = |x| + 3$$
$$x \le 0; \quad y = x^3 + 3$$

a.   Now shift the function down 3 units and to the left 2 units and draw the new graph on the same set of axes.

b.   Write the new equations for the shifted function.

6-79.   Rewrite each expression below as an exponential expression with a base of 2.

a.   16   b. $\frac{1}{8}$ c. $\sqrt{2}$ d. $\sqrt[3]{4}$

6-80.   Solve the system of equations at right and then check your solution in each equation. Be sure to keep your work well organized.

$$x + 2y - z = -1$$
$$2x - y + 3z = 13$$
$$x + y + 2z = 14$$

6-81.   Find an equation for the parabola that passes through the points $(-1, 10)$, $(0, 5)$, and $(2, 7)$.

6-82.   Change each of the following equations from logarithmic form to exponential form, or vice versa.

a. $a = \log_b 24$ b. $3x = \log_{2y} 7$

c. $3y = 2^{5x}$ d. $4p = (2q)^6$

6-83.   Add or subtract and simplify each of the following expressions. Justify that each step of your process makes sense.

a. $\dfrac{3x}{x^2+2x+1} + \dfrac{3}{x^2+2x+1}$ b. $\dfrac{3}{x-1} - \dfrac{2}{x-2}$

6-84. On their Team Test, Raymond, Sarah, Hannah, and Aidan were given $y = 4x^2 - 24x + 7$ to change into graphing form. Raymond noticed that the leading coefficient was a 4 and not a 1. His team agreed on a way to start rewriting, but then they worked in pairs and got two different solutions, shown below.

Raymond and Hannah

(1) $y = 4x^2 - 24x + 7$

(2) $y = 4(x^2 - 6x) + 7$

(3) $y = 4(x^2 - 6x + 3^2) + 7 - 36$

(4) $y = 4(x - 3)^2 - 29$

Aidan and Sarah

(1) $y = 4x^2 - 24x + 7$

(2) $y = 4(x^2 - 6x + 9) + 7 - 9$

(3) $y = 4(x - 3)^2 + 7 - 3^2$

(4) $y = 4(x - 3)^2 - 2$

Hannah says, *"Aidan and Sarah made a mistake in Step 3. Because of the factored 4 they really added 4(9) to complete the square, so they should subtract 36, not just 9."* Is Hannah correct? Justify your answer by showing whether the results are equivalent to the original equation.

6-85. Use the correct method from problem 6-84 to change each of the following equations to graphing form. Then, without graphing, find the vertex and equation of the line of symmetry for each.

a. $y = 2x^2 - 8x + 7$

b. $y = 5x^2 - 10x - 7$

6-86. Shift the graph of $y = \log(x)$ up 3 units and to the right 6 units. Graph both the original and the transformed functions on the same set of axes and write the equation for the transformed function.

6-87. Given $f(x) = 2x^2 - 4$ and $g(x) = 5x + 3$, find the value of each expression below.

a. $f(a)$

b. $f(3a)$

c. $f(a + b)$

d. $f(x + 7)$

e. $f(5x + 3)$

f. $g(f(x))$

6.2.1 How can I solve exponential equations?

Using Logarithms to Solve Exponential Equations

In Chapter 5, you learned what a logarithm was and several important facts about logs. In this lesson, you will learn about a property of logarithms that will be very useful for solving problems that involve exponents.

6-88.   **LOGARITHMS SO FAR**

There are three important log facts you have learned so far. Discuss these questions with your team to ensure everyone remembers these ideas. For each problem, make up an example to illustrate your ideas.

a.   What is a logarithm? How can log equations be converted into another form?

b.   What do you know about the logarithm key on your calculator?

c.   What does the graph of $y = \log(x)$ look like? Write a general equation for $y = \log(x)$.

6-89.   Marta was convinced that there had to be some way to graph $y = \log_2 x$ on her graphing calculator. She typed in $y = \log(2^x)$ and pressed $\boxed{\text{GRAPH}}$.

"It WORKED!" Marta yelled in triumph.

"Whaaaat?" said Celeste. *"I think $y = \log_2 x$ and $y = \log(2^x)$ are totally different, and I bet we can show it by converting both of them to exponential form."*

"Yeah, I think you're wrong, Marta," said Sophia. *"I think we can show that $y = \log_2 x$ and $y = \log(2^x)$ are totally different by looking at the graphs."*

a.   Show that the two equations are different by sketching the graph of $y = \log_2 x$. Then sketch what your graphing calculator shows to be the graph of $y = \log(2^x)$.

b.   Now show that $y = \log_2 x$ and $y = \log(2^x)$ are different by converting both of them to exponential form.

Core Connections Algebra 2

6-90.   The work you did in problem 6-89 is a **counterexample**, which shows that in general, the statement $\log_b x = \log(b^x)$ is *false*. For each of the following log statements, use the strategies from problem 6-89 to determine whether they are true or false, and justify your answer. Be ready to present your conclusions and justifications.

   a. $\log_5(25) \overset{?}{=} \log_{25}(5)$

   b. $\log(x^2) \overset{?}{=} (\log x)^2$

   c. $\log(7^x) \overset{?}{=} x \log(7)$

   d. $\log(2x) \overset{?}{=} \log_2 x$

6-91.   In the previous problem only *one* of the statements was true.

   a.   Use different numbers to make up four more statements that follow the same pattern as the one true statement, and test each one to see whether it appears to be true.

   b.   Use your results to complete the following statement, which is known as the **Power Property of Logarithms**: $\log(b^x) =$ _____ .

6-92.   Do you remember solving problems like $1.04^x = 2$ in your homework? What method(s) did you and your teammates use to find x? In tonight's homework there are several more of these problems. (You probably wish there were a more efficient way!)

6-93.   THERE MUST BE AN EASIER WAY

   It would certainly be helpful to have an easier method than guess and check to solve equations like $1.04^x = 2$. Complete parts (a) through (c) below to discover an easier way.

   a.   What makes the equation $1.04^x = 2$ so hard to solve?

   b.   Surprise! In the first part of this lesson, you already found a method for getting rid of inconvenient exponents! Talk with your team about how your results from problems 6-90 and 6-91 can help you rewrite the equation $1.04^x = 2$. Be prepared to share your ideas with the class.

   c.   Solve $1.04^x = 2$ using this new method. Be sure to check your answer.

6-94.   Solve the following equations. After checking your answer, round them to three decimal places.

   a. $5 = 2.25^x$

   b. $3.5^x = 10$

   c. $2(8^x) = 128$

   d. $2x^8 = 128$

6-95.   Complete the table at right and find its equation.

x	y
	1
	3
2	9
	27
4	
	243
6	
7	
8	

6-96.   Margee thinks she can use logs to solve $56 = x^8$, since logs seem to make exponents disappear. Unfortunately, Margee is wrong. Explain the difference between equations like $2 = 1.04^x$, in which you can use logs, and $56 = x^8$, in which it does not make sense to use logs.

6-97.   What values must x have so that $\log(x)$ is greater than 2? Justify your answer.

6-98.   At right is a graph of $y = \log_b x$. Describe the possible values for b.

6-99.   Consider the questions below.

a.   What can you multiply 8 by to get 1?

b.   What can you multiply x by to get 1?

c.   Using the rules of exponents, find a way to solve $m^8 = 40$. Remember that logarithms will not be useful here, but the exponent key on your calculator *will* be. (Obtain the answer as a decimal approximation using your calculator. Check your result by raising it to the 8th power.)

d.   Now solve $n^6 = 300$.

e.   Describe a method for solving $x^a = b$ for x with a calculator.

6-100.   Adam keeps getting negative exponents and fractional exponents confused. Help him by explaining the difference between $2^{1/2}$ and 2^{-1}.

6-101.   Solve each inequality and graph its solution on a number line.

   a. $|x| < 3$ b. $|2x+1| < 3$ c. $|2x+1| \geq 3$

6-102.   Consider the graph at right.

   a.   Is the graph a function? Explain.

   b.   Make a sketch of the inverse of this graph.
         Is the inverse a function? Justify your
         answer.

   c.   Must the inverse of a function be a function?
         Explain.

   d.   Describe what is characteristic about
         functions that do have inverse functions.

   e.   Could the inverse of a non-function be a function? Explain or give an
         example.

6-103.   Solve each system of equations below.

   a. $-4x = z - 2y + 12$ b. $3x + y - 2z = 6$
         $y + z = 12 - x$ $x + 2y + z = 7$
         $8x - 3y + 4z = 1$ $6x + 2y - 4z = 12$

   c.   What does the solution in part (b) tell you about the graphs?

6.2.2 How can I rewrite it?

Investigating the Properties of Logarithms

You already know the basic rules for working with exponents. Since logs are the inverses of exponential functions, they also have properties that are similar to the ones you already know. In this lesson, you will explore these properties.

6-104.   Marta now knows that if she wants to find $\log_2(30)$, she cannot just type $\log(2^{30})$ into her calculator, since her calculator's log key cannot directly calculate logs with base 2. But she still wants to be able to find what $\log_2(30)$ equals.

    a.   First, use your knowledge of logs and exponents to estimate $\log_2(30)$.

    b.   Now use what you learned in Lesson 6.2.1 to get a better estimate. Since you want to determine what $\log_2(30)$ equals, you can write $\log_2(30) = x$. When working with a log equation, it is often easier to first convert it to exponential form. Rewrite this equation in exponential form.

    c.   Use the methods you developed in class to solve this equation. Refer back to your work on problem 6-93 if you need help.

6-105.   Congratulations! You are smarter than your calculator. You have just evaluated a log with base 2, even though your calculator does not do that. Now you will practice some more.

    a.   First estimate an answer, then apply the method you have just developed to evaluate $\log_5(200)$.

    b.   Apply the process you used in part (a) to evaluate the expression $\log_a b = x$.

6-106.   Since logs and exponentials are inverses, the properties of exponents (which you already know) also apply to logs. The problems below will help you discover these new log properties.

    a.   Complete the two exponent rules below. In part (b), you will find the equivalent properties for logs.

$$x^a x^b = \underline{\hspace{2cm}} \quad \text{and} \quad \frac{x^b}{x^a} = \underline{\hspace{2cm}}$$

    b.   To help you find the equivalent log properties, use your calculator to solve for x in each problem below. Note that x is a whole number in parts (i) through (v). Look for patterns that would make your job easier and allow you to generalize in part (vi).

        $i.$ $\log(5) + \log(6) = \log(x)$ $ii.$ $\log(5) + \log(2) = \log(x)$

        $iii.$ $\log(5) + \log(5) = \log(x)$ $iv.$ $\log(10) + \log(100) = \log(x)$

        $v.$ $\log(9) + \log(11) = \log(x)$ $vi.$ $\log(a) + \log(b) = \log(\underline{\hspace{1cm}})$

    c.   What if the log expressions are being subtracted instead of added? Solve for x in each problem below. Note that x will not always be a whole number. Again, look for patterns that will allow you to generalize in part (vi).

        $i.$ $\log(20) - \log(5) = \log(x)$ $ii.$ $\log(30) - \log(3) = \log(x)$

        $iii.$ $\log(5) - \log(2) = \log(x)$ $iv.$ $\log(17) - \log(9) = \log(x)$

        $v.$ $\log(375) - \log(17) = \log(x)$ $vi.$ $\log(b) - \log(a) = \log(\underline{\hspace{1cm}})$

6-107.   LEARNING LOG

The two properties you found in problem 6-106 work for logs in *any* base, not just base 10. (You will officially prove this later.) You now know three different log properties and you have developed a process for solving log problems that are not in base 10. Write and explain each of these log properties in your Learning Log. Be sure to include examples, with at least one problem where you need to change to base 10. Title this entry "Logarithm Properties" and label it with today's date.

6-108.   LOG PROPERTY PUZZLES

Obtain the Lesson 6.2.2A Resource Page from your teacher or copy the table below. Use the log properties to fill in the missing parts. Be sure to remember that in every row, each expression is equivalent to every other expression.

Product Property		Quotient Property	
$\log_3 60 = \log_3 6 + \underline{} = \log_3 3 + \underline{}$		$= \log_3 120 - \underline{} = \log_3 240 - \underline{}$	
$\log_7 36 = =$		$= =$	
$= \log_6 9 + \log_6 2 =$		$= =$	
$= =$		$= \log_{25} 75 - \log_{25} 1.5 =$	
$= =$		$= \log 160 - \log 4 =$	

6-109.   Use the properties of logs to write each of the following expressions as a single logarithm, if possible.

a. $\log_{1/2}(4) + \log_{1/2}(2) - \log_{1/2}(5)$

b. $\log_2(M) + \log_3(N)$

c. $\log(k) + x\log(m)$

d. $\frac{1}{2}\log_5 x + 2\log_5(x+1)$

e. $\log(4) - \log(3) + \log(\pi) + 3\log(r)$

f. $\log(6) + 23$

6-110.   What values must x have so that $\log(x)$ has a negative value? Justify your answer.

6-111.   The fact that for any base m (when $m > 0$), $\log_m a + \log_m b = \log_m ab$ is called the **Product Property of Logarithms**. To prove that this property is true, follow the directions below.

a.   Since logarithms are the inverses of exponential functions, each of their properties can be derived from a similar property of exponents. Here, you are trying to prove that "logs turn products into sums." First, recall similar properties of exponents. If $a = m^x$ and $b = m^y$, write $a \cdot b$ as a power of m.

b.   Rewrite $a = m^x$, $b = m^y$, and your answer to part (a) in logarithmic form.

c.   In the third equation you wrote for part (b), substitute for x and y to obtain a log equation of base m that involves only the variables a and b.

d.   The property $\log_m a - \log_m b = \log_m \frac{a}{b}$ is called the **Quotient Property of Logarithms**. Use $a = m^x$ and $b = m^y$ to express $\frac{a}{b}$ as a power of m. Then use a similar process to rewrite each into log form and prove the Quotient Property of Logs.

6-112. The **Power Property of Logarithms**, which you learned in Lesson 6.2.1, is a little trickier to prove. A proof is given below. As you copy each step onto your paper, work with your team to make sense of what was done. Give a reason for each step.

To prove that $\log_m a^n = n \log_m a$,

Let $\quad \log_m a^n = p \quad$ and $\quad n \log_m a = q$

Convert to $m^p = a^n$

First rewrite as $\log_m a = \frac{q}{n}$ and then convert to $m^{q/n} = a$.

Using the two resulting equations, substitute for a and then simplify

$$m^p = (m^{q/n})^n$$
$$m^p = m^q$$

Therefore, $p = q$.

Remember that $p = \log_m a^n$ and $q = n \log_m a$, so $\log_m a^n = n \log_m a$, which was the goal of the proof.

METHODS AND MEANINGS

Logarithm Properties

The following definitions and properties hold true for all positive $m \neq 1$.

Definition of logs: $\quad \log_m(a) = n$ means $m^n = a$

Product Property: $\quad \log_m(a \cdot b) = \log_m(a) + \log_m(b)$

Quotient Property: $\quad \log_m(\frac{a}{b}) = \log_m(a) - \log_m(b)$

Power Property: $\quad \log_m(a^n) = n \cdot \log_m(a)$

Inverse relationship: $\quad \log_m(m)^n = n$ and $m^{\log_m(n)} = n$

MATH NOTES

6-113.   Solve each of the following equations to the nearest 0.001.

   a. $(5.825)^{(x-3)} = 120$ b. $18(1.2)^{(2x-1)} = 900$

6-114.   Simplify each expression below. If you are stuck, the ideas in problem 6-74 should be helpful.

   a. $\dfrac{x}{1 - \frac{1}{x}}$ b. $\dfrac{\frac{1}{a} + \frac{1}{b}}{\frac{1}{b} - a}$

6-115.   Use the definition of a logarithm to change $\log_2 7$ into a logarithmic expression of base 5.

6-116.   Sketch the graph of $y = \log_3(x + 4)$ and describe the transformation from its parent graph.

6-117.   Due to the worsened economy, merchants in downtown Hollywood cannot afford to replace their outdoor light bulbs when the bulbs burn out. On average, about thirteen percent of the light bulbs burn out every month. Assuming there are now about one million outside store lights in Hollywood, how long will it take until there are only 100,000 bulbs lit? Until there is only one bulb lit?

6-118.   Raymond, Hannah, Aidan, and Sarah were working together to change $y = 3x^2 - 15x - 5$ into graphing form. They started by rewriting it as $y = 3(x^2 - 5x) - 5$, when Raymond said, *"Will this one work? Look, the perfect square would have to be $(x - 2.5)^2$."*

After thinking about it for a while, Sarah said, *"That's OK. Negative 2.5 squared is 6.25, but because of the 3 we factored out, we are really adding 3(6.25) ."*

"Yes," Aidan added, *"So we have to subtract 18.75 to get an equivalent equation."*

Hannah summarized with the work shown at right.

$$y = 3x^2 - 15x - 5$$
$$y = 3(x^2 - 5x) - 5$$
$$y = 3(x - 2.5)^2 - 5 - 18.75$$
$$y = 3(x - 2.5)^2 - 23.75$$

What do you think? Did they rewrite the equation correctly? If so, find the vertex and the line of symmetry of the parabola. If not, explain their mistakes and show them how to do it correctly.

6-119. Use the ideas developed in problem 6-118 to change each of the following quadratic equations into graphing form. Identify the vertex and the line of symmetry for each one.

    a. $f(x) = 4x^2 - 12x + 6$ b. $g(x) = 2x^2 + 14x + 4$

6-120. Consider the function $y = 3(x + 2)^2 - 7$ as you complete parts (a) through (c) below.

    a.   How could you restrict the domain to show "half" of the graph?

    b.   Find the equation for the inverse function for your "half" graph.

    c.   What are the domain and range for the inverse function?

6-121. Add or subtract and simplify each of the following expressions. Justify that each step of your process makes sense.

    a. $\frac{3}{(x-4)(x+1)} + \frac{6}{x+1}$ b. $\frac{x+2}{x^2-9} - \frac{1}{x+3}$

6-122. Eniki has a sequence of numbers given by the formula $t(n) = 4(5^n)$.

    a.   What are the first three terms of Eniki's sequence?

    b.   Chelita thinks the number 312,500 is a term in Eniki's sequence. Is she correct? Justify your answer by either giving the term number or explaining why it is not in the sequence.

    c.   Elisa thinks the number 94,500 is a term in Eniki's sequence. Is she correct? Explain.

6.2.3 How can I find an exponential function?

Writing Equations of Exponential Functions

You have worked with exponential equations throughout this chapter. Today you will look at how you can find the equation for an exponential function using data.

6-123. DUE DATE

Brad's mother has just learned that she is pregnant! Brad is very excited that he will soon become a big brother. However, he wants to know when his new sibling will arrive and decides to do some research. On the Internet, he finds the following article:

Hormone Levels for Pregnant Women

When a woman becomes pregnant, the hormone HCG (human chorionic gonadotropin) is produced to enable the baby to develop.

During the first few weeks of pregnancy, the level of HCG hormone grows exponentially, starting with the day the embryo is implanted in the womb. However, the rate of growth varies with each pregnancy. Therefore, doctors cannot use just a single test to determine how long a woman has been pregnant. They must test the levels over time. Commonly, the HCG levels are measured two days apart to look for this rate of growth.

Brad's mother says she was tested for HCG during her last two doctor visits. On March 21, her HCG level was 200 mIU/ml (milli-international units per milliliter). Two days later, her HCG level was 392 mIU/ml.

a. Assuming that the model for HCG levels is of the form $y = ab^x$, find an equation that models the growth of HCG for Brad's mother's pregnancy.

b. Assuming that Brad's mother's level of HCG on the day of implantation was 5 mIU/ml, on what day did the baby most likely become implanted? How many days after implantation was his mother's first doctor visit?

c. Brad learned that a baby is born approximately 37 weeks after implantation. When can Brad expect his new sibling to be born?

Core Connections Algebra 2

6-124.   SOLVING STRATEGIES

In problem 6-123, you and your team developed a strategy to find the equation of an exponential equation of the form $y = ab^x$ when given two points on the curve.

a.   What different strategies were generated by the other teams in your class? If no one shares your solving method with the class, be sure to share yours. Take notes on the different strategies that are presented.

b.   Did any team use a system of exponential equations to solve for a and b? If not, examine this strategy as you answer the questions below.

   i.   The doctor visits provide two data points that can help you find an exponential model: $(21, 200)$ and $(23, 392)$. Use each of these points to substitute for x and y into $y = ab^x$. You should end up with two equations in terms of a and b.

   ii.   Consider the strategies you already have for solving systems of equations. Are any of those strategies useful for this problem? Discuss a way to solve your system from part (*i*) for a and b with your team. Be ready to share your method with the class.

6-125.   The context in problem 6-123 required you to assume that the exponential model had an asymptote at $y = 0$ to find the equation of the model. But what if the asymptote is not at the x-axis? Consider this situation below.

a.   Assume the graph of an exponential function passes through the points $(3, 12.5)$ and $(4, 11.25)$. Is the exponential function increasing or decreasing? Justify your answer.

b.   If the horizontal asymptote for this function is the line $y = 10$, make a sketch of its graph showing the horizontal asymptote.

c.   If this function has the equation $y = ab^x + c$, what would be the value of c? Use what you know about this function to find its equation. Verify that as x increases, the values of y get closer to $y = 10$.

d.   Find the y-intercept of the function. What is the connection between the y-intercept and the asymptote?

6-126.   Janice would like to have \$40,000 to help pay for college in 8 years. Currently, she has \$1000. What interest rate, when compounded yearly, would help her reach her goal?

   a.   What type of function would best model this situation? Explain how you know and write the general form of this function.

   b.   If y represents the amount of money and x represents the number of years after today, find an equation that models Janice's financial situation. What interest rate does she need to earn?

   c.   Janice's friend Sarah starts with \$7800 and wants to have \$18,400 twenty years from now. What interest rate does she need (compounded yearly)?

   d.   Is Janice's goal or Sarah's goal more realistic? Justify your response.

6-127.   Ryan has the chickenpox! He was told that the number of pockmarks on his body would grow exponentially until his body overcomes the illness. He found that he had 60 pockmarks on November 1, and by November 3 the number had grown to 135. To find out when the first pockmark appeared, he will need to find the exponential function that will model the number of pockmarks based on the day.

   a.   Ryan decides to find the exponential function that passes through the points $(3, 135)$ and $(1, 60)$. Use these points to write the equation of his function of the form $f(x) = ab^x$.

   b.   According to your model, what day did Ryan get his first chickenpox pockmark?

6-128.   Give an example of an equation that requires the use of logarithms to solve it.

6-129.   Write three different, but equivalent, expressions for each of the following logs. For example: $\log(7^{3/2})$ can be written as $\frac{3}{2}\log(7)$, $\frac{1}{2}\log(7^3)$, $3\log(\sqrt{7})$, etc.

   a. $\log(8^{2/3})$ b. $-2\log(5)$ c. $\log(na)^{bo}$

6-130.   Kendra just made a cup of hot chocolate that was too hot for her to drink. She set it aside so it could cool off. While she was waiting, her friend Lara called and Kendra forgot about her hot chocolate. Sketch a graph that shows the temperature of the hot chocolate since Kendra first set it aside. How cold will the hot chocolate get?

Core Connections Algebra 2

6-131. Find the equation of the parabola that passes through the points $(-2, 24)$, $(3, -1)$, and $(-1, 15)$.

6-132. Use $f(x) = 3 + \sqrt{2x - 1}$ to complete parts (a) through (e) below.

  a. What are the domain and range of $f(x)$?

  b. What is the inverse of $f(x)$? Call it $g(x)$.

  c. What are the domain and range of $g(x)$?

  d. Find an expression for $f(g(x))$.

  e. Find an expression for $g(f(x))$. What do you notice? Why does this happen?

6-133. Solve each of the following equations for x.

  a. $x^3 = 243$

  b. $3^x = 243$

6-134. Write the equation of each circle graphed below.

  a.

  b.

6-135. Add or subtract each expression below. Be sure to simplify.

  a. $\dfrac{x^2}{x-5} - \dfrac{25}{x-5}$

  b. $\dfrac{a^2}{a+5} + \dfrac{10a+25}{a+5}$

  c. $\dfrac{x^2}{x-y} - \dfrac{2xy-y^2}{x-y}$

  d. $\dfrac{x}{x+1} + \dfrac{1}{x-1}$

6-136. Find the inverse of each of the functions below. Write your answers in function notation.

  a. $p(x) = 3(x^3 + 6)$

  b. $k(x) = 3x^3 + 6$

  c. $h(x) = \dfrac{x+1}{x-1}$

  d. $j(x) = \dfrac{2}{3-x}$

6.2.4 Who killed Dr. Dedman?

An Application of Logarithms

Today you will put together everything that you have learned about logs and exponents to solve a murder mystery!

6-137.   THE CASE OF THE COOLING CORPSE

The coroner's office is kept at a cool 17°C. Agent 008 kept pacing back and forth trying to keep warm as he waited for any new information about his latest case. For more than three hours now, Dr. Dedman had been performing an autopsy on the Sideroad Slasher's latest victim, and Agent 008 could see that the temperature of the room and the deafening silence were beginning to irritate even Dr. Dedman. The Slasher had been creating more work than Dr. Dedman cared to investigate.

"Dr. Dedman, don't you need to take a break?" Agent 008 queried. *"You've been examining this body for hours! Even if there were any clues, you probably wouldn't see them at this point."*

"I don't know," Dr. Dedman replied, *"I just have this feeling something is not quite right. Somehow the Slasher slipped up with this one and left a clue. We just have to find it."*

"Well, I have to check in with headquarters," 008 stated. *"Do you mind if I step out for a couple of hours?"*

"No, that's fine," Dr. Dedman responded. *"Maybe I'll have something by the time you return."*

"Sure," 008 thought to himself. *"Someone always wants to be the hero and solve everything himself. The doctor just does not realize how big this case really is. The Slasher has left a trail of dead bodies through five states!"* Agent 008 left, closing the door quietly. As he walked down the hall, he could hear the doctor's voice describing the victim's gruesome appearance into the tape recorder fade away.

The hallway from the coroner's office to the elevator was long and dark. This was the only way to Dr. Dedman's office. Didn't this frighten most people? Well, it didn't seem to bother old Ajax Boraxo who was busy mopping the floor, thought 008.

Problem continues on next page →

6-137. *Problem continued from previous page.*

He stopped briefly to use the restroom and bumped into one of the deputy coroners, who asked, *"Dedman still at it?"*

"Sure is, Dr. Quincy. He's totally obsessed. He's certain there is a clue." As usual, when leaving the courthouse, 008 had to sign out.

"How's it going down there, Agent 008?" Sergeant Foust asked. Foust spent most of his shifts monitoring the front door, forcing all visitors to sign in while he recorded the time next to the signature. Agent 008 wondered if Foust longed for a more exciting aspect of law enforcement. He thought if he were doing Foust's job he would get a little stir-crazy sitting behind a desk most of the day. Why would someone become a cop to do this?

"Dr. Dedman is convinced he will find something soon. We'll see!" Agent 008 responded. He noticed the time: ten minutes before 2:00. Would he make it to headquarters before the chief left?

"Well, good luck!" Foust shouted as 008 headed out the door.

Some time later, Agent 008 sighed deeply as he returned to the coroner's office. Foust gave his usual greeting: *"Would the secret guest please sign in?"* he would say, handing a pen to 008 as he walked through the door. *"Sign in again,"* he thought to himself. *"Annoying!"* 5:05 PM. Agent 008 had not planned to be gone so long, but he had been caught up in what the staff at headquarters had discovered about that calculator he had found. For a moment he saw a positive point to having anyone who came in or out of the courthouse sign in: He knew by quickly scanning the list that Dr. Dedman had not left. In fact, the old guy must still be working on the case.

As he approached the coroner's office, he had a strange feeling that something was wrong. He could not hear or see Dr. Dedman. When he opened the door, the sight inside stopped him in his tracks. Evidently, Dr. Dedman was now the *newest* victim of the Slasher. But wait! The other body, the one the doctor had been working on, was gone! Immediately, the security desk with its annoying sign-in sheet came to mind. Yes, there were lots of names on that list, but if he could determine the time of Dr. Dedman's death, he might be able to scan the roster to find the murderer! Quickly, he grabbed the thermometer to measure the Doctor's body temperature. He turned around and hit the security buzzer. The bells were deafening. He knew the building would be sealed off instantly and security would be there within seconds.

"Oh no!" Foust cried as he rushed in, *"How could this happen? I spoke to the Doctor less than an hour ago!"*

As the security officers crowded into the room, Agent 008 explained what he knew, which was almost nothing. He had stopped long enough to check the doctor's body temperature: 27°C. That was 10°C below normal. Then he remembered: the tape recorder! Dr. Dedman had been taping his observations; that was standard procedure. They began looking everywhere.

Problem continues on next page →

6-137. *Problem continued from previous page.*

The Slasher must have realized that the doctor had been taping and taken the tape recorder as well. Exactly an hour had passed during the search, and Agent 008 noticed that the thermometer still remained in Dr. Dedman's side. The thermometer clearly read 24°C. Agent 008 knew he could now determine the time of death.

Coroner's Office – Please Sign In		
Name	**Time In**	**Time Out**
Lt. Borman	12:08	2:47
Alice Bingham	12:22	1:38
Chuck Miranda	12:30	2:45
Harold Ford	12:51	1:25
Ajax Boraxo	1:00	2:30
D.C. Quincy	1:10	2:45
Agent 008	1:30	1:50
Ronda Ripley	1:43	2:10
Jeff Dangerfield	2:08	2:48
Stacy Simmons	2:14	2:51
Brock Ortiz	2:20	2:43
Pierce Bronson	3:48	4:18
Max Sharp	3:52	5:00
Maren Ezaki	3:57	4:45
Caroline Cress	4:08	4:23
Milly Osborne	4:17	4:39
D.C. Quincy	4:26	4:50
Vinney Gumbatz	4:35	
Cory Delphene	4:48	4:57
Max Crutchfield	5:04	
Agent 008	5:05	
Security	5:12	

a. Make a sketch showing the relationship between body temperature and time. What type of function is it? Justify your answer.

b. Is there an asymptote for this relationship? If so, what does it represent? If not, explain why not.

c. Use your data and the general equation $y = km^x + b$ to find the equation that represents the temperature of the body at any certain time.

d. At approximately what time did Dr. Dedman die?

e. Who is the murderer?

6-138.   A rule-of-thumb used by car dealers is that the trade-in value of a car decreases
          by 20% of its value each year.

    a.   Explain how the phrase "decreases by 20% of its value each year" tells you
          that the trade-in value varies exponentially with time (i.e., can be
          represented by an exponential function).

    b.   Suppose the initial value of your car is $23,500. Write an equation
          expressing the trade-in value of your car as a function of the number of
          years from now.

    c.   How much will your car be
          worth in four years?

    d.   In how many years will the
          trade-in value of your car be
          $6000?

    e.   If your car is really 2.7 years old
          now, what was its trade-in value
          when it was new?

6-139.   Solve for x without using a calculator.

    a. $x = \log_{25}(5)$

    b. $\log_x(1) = 0$

    c. $23 = \log_{10}(x)$

6-140.   Using your calculator, solve the equations below.
          Round answers to the nearest 0.001.

    a. $x^6 = 125$ b. $x^{3.8} = 240$

    c. $x^{-4} = 100$ d. $(x+2)^3 = 65$

    e. $4(x-2)^{12.5} = 2486$

6-141.   If $f(x) = x^4$ and $g(x) = 3(x+2)$, find the value of each expression below.

a. $f(2)$ b. $g(2)$ c. $f(g(2))$ d. $g(f(2))$

e.   Are $f(x)$ and $g(x)$ inverses of each other? Justify your answer.

6-142.   Kirsta was working with the function
machine shown at right, but when she turned
her back, her little brother Caleb dropped in
a number. She didn't see what he dropped
in, but she did see what fell out: 9. What
operations must she perform on 9 to undo
what her machine did? Use this to find out
what Caleb dropped in.

$k(x) = \sqrt{x+5}$

6-143.   Write an equation for a machine that will undo
Kirsta's machine. Call it $c(x)$.

6-144.   What is the equation of the line of symmetry for the graph of $y = (x-17)^2$?
Justify your answer.

6-145.   This problem is a checkpoint for adding and subtracting rational expressions.
It will be referred to as Checkpoint 6B.

Add or subtract each pair of rational expressions. Simplify the result.

a. $\dfrac{4}{x^2+5x+6} + \dfrac{2x}{x+2}$ b. $\dfrac{3x^2+x}{(2x+1)^2} - \dfrac{3}{2x+1}$

Check your answers by referring to the Checkpoint 6B materials located at the
back of your book.

Ideally, at this point you are comfortable working with these types of problems
and can solve them correctly. If you feel that you need more confidence when
solving these types of problems, then review the Checkpoint 6B materials and
try the practice problems provided. From this point on, you will be expected to
do problems like these correctly and with confidence.

6-146.   Find $m\angle C$ in each triangle below.

a.

b.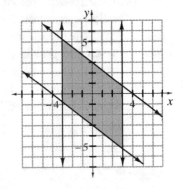

6-147.   Write a system of inequalities that could be
represented by the graph at right.

Chapter 6 Closure What have I learned?

Reflection and Synthesis

The activities below offer you a chance to
reflect about what you have learned during this
chapter. As you work, look for concepts that
you feel very comfortable with, ideas that you
would like to learn more about, and topics you
need more help with. Look for connections
between ideas as well as connections with
material you learned previously.

①   TEAM BRAINSTORM

What have you studied in this chapter? What ideas were important in what you
learned? With your team, brainstorm a list. Be as detailed as you can. To help
get you started, a list of Learning Log entries and Math Notes boxes are below.

What topics, ideas, and words that you learned *before* this chapter are connected
to the new ideas in this chapter? Again, be as detailed as you can.

Next consider the Standards for Mathematical Practice that follow
"③ PORTFOLIO". What Mathematical Practices did you use in this chapter?
When did you use them? Give specific examples.

How long can you make your list? Challenge yourselves. Be prepared to share
your team's ideas with the class.

Learning Log Entries

- Lesson 6.1.1 – Plotting Points in *xyz*-Space
- Lesson 6.1.4 – Systems of Three Equations with Three Variables
- Lesson 6.1.5 – Finding the Equation of a Parabola Given Three
  Points
- Lesson 6.2.2 – Logarithm Properties

Math Notes

- Lesson 6.1.2 – Locating Points in Three Dimensions
- Lesson 6.1.4 – Graphing Planes in Three Dimensions
- Lesson 6.2.2 – Logarithm Properties

② MAKING CONNECTIONS

Below is a list of the vocabulary used in this chapter. Make sure that you are familiar with all of these words and know what they mean. Refer to the glossary or index for any words that you do not yet understand.

3-D coordinate system	asymptote
isometric dot paper	logarithm
ordered triple	plane
Power Property of Logarithms	Product Property of Logarithms
Quotient Property of Logarithms	solution

Make a concept map showing all of the connections you can find among the key words and ideas listed above. To show a connection between two words, draw a line between them and explain the connection. A word can be connected to any other word as long as you can justify the connection.

While you are making your map, your team may think of related words or ideas that are not listed here. Be sure to include these ideas on your concept map.

PORTFOLIO: EVIDENCE OF MATHEMATICAL PROFICIENCY

This section gives you an opportunity to show growth
in your understanding of key mathematical ideas over
time as you complete this course.

Part 1: You may have done this problem before. You
have grown mathematically since then.
Explain everything that you know about
$y = x^2 - 4$ and $y = \sqrt{x+4}$. Be sure to include
everything you have learned since the last time you did this problem.

Part 2: Compare your responses to this "Growth Over Time" problem.
Consider each of the following questions as you write an evaluation of
your mathematical growth. If you only did the problem twice, then
answer accordingly.

- What new concepts did you include the second time you did the
  problem? In what ways was your response better than your first
  attempt?

- How was your final version different from the first two? What new
  ideas did you include?

- Did you omit anything in the final version that you used in one of the
  earlier versions? Why did you omit it?

- Is there anything you want to add to your current version? If so, add
  it and keep this version for future reference.

- Rate your three attempts by making three bars like the ones below and
  shading each bar (left to right) to represent how much you knew on
  each attempt.

Alternatively, your teacher may ask you to showcase your ability to use
logarithms to solve a problem involving an exponential function. Copy your
work from "The Case of the Cooling Corpse," problem 6-137, and enhance it if
needed.

Next consider the Standards for Mathematical Practice that follow. What
Mathematical Practices did you use in this chapter? When did you use them?
Give specific examples.

Your teacher may give you the Chapter 6 Closure Resource Page: Multiple
Representations of Logarithmic Functions Graphic Organizer page to work on.

BECOMING MATHEMATICALLY PROFICIENT
The Common Core State Standards for Mathematical Practice

This book focuses on helping you use some very specific Mathematical Practices. The Mathematical Practices describe ways in which mathematically proficient students engage with mathematics everyday.

Make sense of problems and persevere in solving them:

Making sense of problems and persevering in solving them means that you can solve problems that are full of different kinds of mathematics. These types of problems are not routine, simple, or typical. Instead, they combine lots of math ideas and everyday situations. You have to stick with challenging problems, try different strategies, use multiple representations, and use a different method to check your results.

Reason abstractly and quantitatively:

Throughout this course, everyday situations are used to introduce you to new math ideas. Seeing mathematical ideas within a context helps you make sense of the ideas. Once you learn about a math idea in a practical way, you can "**reason abstractly**" by thinking about the concept more generally, representing it with symbols, and manipulating the symbols. **Reasoning quantitatively** is using numbers and symbols to represent an everyday situation, taking into account the units involved, and considering the meaning of the quantities as you compute them.

Construct viable arguments and critique the reasoning of others:

To **construct a viable argument** is to present your solution steps in a logical sequence and to justify your steps with conclusions, relying on number sense, facts and definitions, and previously established results. You communicate clearly, consider the real-life context, and provide clarification when others ask. In this course, you regularly share information, opinions, and expertise with your study team. You **critique the reasoning of others** when you analyze the approach of others, build on each other's ideas, compare the effectiveness of two strategies, and decide what makes sense and under what conditions.

Model with mathematics:

When you **model with mathematics**, you take a complex situation and use mathematics to represent it, often by making assumptions and approximations to simplify the situation. Modeling allows you to analyze and describe the situation and to make predictions. For example, you model when you use multiple representations, including equations, tables, graphs, or diagrams to describe a situation. In situations involving the variability of data, you model when you describe the data with equations. Although a model may not be perfect, it can still be very useful for describing data and making predictions. When you interpret the results, you may need to go back and improve your model by revising your assumptions and approximations.

Use appropriate tools strategically:

To **use appropriate tools strategically** means that you analyze the task and decide which tools may help you model the situation or find a solution. Some of the tools available to you include diagrams, graph paper, calculators, computer software, databases, and websites. You understand the limitations of various tools. A result can be check or estimated by strategically choosing a different tool.

Attend to precision:

To **attend to precision** means that when solving problems, you need to pay close attention to the details. For example, you need to be aware of the units, or how many digits your answer requires, or how to choose a scale and label your graph. You may need to convert the units to be consistent. At times, you need to go back and check whether a numerical solution makes sense in the context of the problem.

You need to **attend to precision** when you communicate your ideas to others. Using the appropriate vocabulary and mathematical language can help make your ideas and reasoning more understandable to others.

Look for and make use of structure:

To **look for and make use of structure** is a guiding principle of this course. When you are involved in analyzing the structure and in the actual development of mathematical concepts, you gain a deeper, more conceptual understanding than when you are simply told what the structure is and how to do problems. You often use this practice to bring closure to an investigation.

There are many concepts that you learn by looking at the underlying structure of a mathematical idea and thinking about how it connects to other ideas you have already learned. For example, you understand the underlying structure of an equation such as $y = a(x-h)^2 + k$ which allows you to graph it without a table.

Look for and express regularity in repeated reasoning:

To **look for and express regularity in repeated reasoning** means that when you are investigating a new mathematical concept, you notice if calculations are repeated in a pattern. Then you look for a way to generalize the method for use in other situations, or you look for shortcuts. For example, the pattern of growth you notice in a geometric sequence results in being able to write a general exponential equation that highlights the growth and starting point.

④ **WHAT HAVE I LEARNED?**

Most of the problems in this section represent typical problems found in this chapter. They serve as a gauge for you. You can use them to determine which types of problems you can do well and which types of problems require further study and practice. Even if your teacher does not assign this section, it is a good idea to try these problems and find out for yourself what you know and what you still need to work on.

Solve each problem as completely as you can. The table at the end of the closure section has answers to these problems. It also tells you where you can find additional help and practice with problems like these.

CL 6-148. Graph in three dimensions.

    a. $(2, 3, 1)$ b. $(-2, 3, 0)$ c. $2x + y - z = 6$

CL 6-149. Determine the point of intersection of the three planes.

    a. $x + y + z = 3$ b. $x + y + 4z = 5$

        $2x - y + 2z = 6$ $-2x \quad +2z = 3$

        $3x + 2y - z = 13$ $3x + y - 2z = 0$

CL 6-150. The parabola $y = ax^2 + bx + c$ passes through the points $(2, 3), (-1, 6)$, and $(0, 3)$. Determine:

    a.   The equation of the parabola.

    b.   The vertex of the parabola.

    c.   The x-intercepts of the parabola.

CL 6-151. Solve each equation to the nearest thousandth (0.001).

    a. $2^x = 17$ b. $5x^3 = 75$

    c. $5(3^{x+1}) = 85$ d. $\log_3(x + 1) = -2$

CL 6-152.   A gallon of propane costs \$3.59. Inflation has caused prices to steadily increase 4% per year.

      a.   What did a gallon of propane cost ten years ago?

      b.   If this trend continues, how much longer will it be until it costs \$10?

CL 6-153.   Find the inverse of this equation: $y = 2 + \sqrt{2x - 4}$.

CL 6-154.   Use your Parent Graph Toolkit or make a table to graph $y = \log_2(x)$.

CL 6-155.   Use your answer to the previous problem to graph $y = 1 + \log_2(x - 3)$.
State the equation of the new asymptote and the new x-intercept.

CL 6-156.   Solve each of the following equations. Be sure to check your answers.

      a. $3|2x - 5| - 8 = -5$ b. $\sqrt{3x^2 + 11x} = 2$

CL 6-157.   Graph each of the following systems of inequalities.

      a. $y \geq 3(x - 2)^2 - 4$ b. $y > (x - 1)^2 - 5$
           $y > -2|x - 1| + 3$ $y > 3x - 5$
                                              $y \leq \frac{1}{2}(x - 1)^2 + 1$

CL 6-158.   Consider the function $f(x) = \sqrt{x + 3}$.

      a.   What are the domain and range of $f(x)$?

      b.   If $g(x) = x - 10$, what is $f(g(x))$?

      c.   What are the domain and range of $f(g(x))$?

      d.   Is $f(g(x)) = g(f(x))$? Justify why or why not.

CL 6-159.   Check your answers using the table at the end of this section. Which problems do you feel confident about? Which problems were hard? Have you worked on problems like these in previous math classes? Sort the problems into three groups: the ones you are confident you can do, the ones you need more practice with, and the ones you need further help to understand.

Answers and Support for Closure Activity #4
What Have I Learned?

Note: MN = Math Note, LL = Learning Log

Problem	Solutions	Need Help?	More Practice
CL 6-148.	a.	Lessons 6.1.1 and 6.1.2 MN: 6.1.2 and 6.1.4 LL: 6.1.1	Problems 6-6 and 6-19
	b.		
	c.		
CL 6-149.	a. $(4, 0, -1)$ b. $(-1, 4, 0.5)$	Lesson 6.1.4 LL: 6.1.4	Problems 6-48, 6-51, 6-71, 6-80, and 6-103
CL 6-150.	a. $y = x^2 - 2x + 3$ b. $(1, 2)$ c. No x-intercepts	Lesson 6.1.5 LL: 6.1.5	Problems 6-64, 6-67, 6-68, 6-69, 6-72, 6-81, and 6-131
CL 6-151.	a. $x = 4.087$ b. $x = 2.466$ c. $x = 1.579$ d. $x = -0.889$	Lessons 6.2.1 and 6.2.2	Problems 6-11, 6-94, 6-113, 6-133, and 6-140
CL 6-152.	a. $2.43 b. 26.1 years	Lessons A.3.2 and B.2.3	Problems 6-15, 6-52, 6-117, and 6-138
CL 6-153.	$y = \frac{(x-2)^2}{2} + 2$	Lessons 5.1.1 and 5.1.3 LL: 5.1.1	Problems 6-102, 6-120, 6-132, and 6-136

Problem	Solutions	Need Help?	More Practice
CL 6-154.		Lessons 5.2.2 and 5.2.3 LL: 5.2.3	Problems 5-68, 5-69, and 5-94
CL 6-155.	Asymptote: $x = 3$ Intercept: $(3.5, 0)$	Lesson 5.2.4	Problems 5-94 and 5-118
CL 6-156.	a. $x = 2, 3$ b. $x = \frac{1}{3}, -4$	Lessons 4.1.2 and 4.1.3 LL: 4.1.1 and 4.1.4	Problems 4-22, 4-23, 6-40, 6-53, and 6-76
CL 6-157.	a. b.	Lesson 4.2.1 MN: 4.2.3 and 4.2.4 LL: 4.2.1	Problems 5-13, 5-67, 6-33, 6-58, and 6-147
CL 6-158.	a. domain: $x \geq -3$, range: $y \geq 0$ b. $f(g(x)) = \sqrt{x - 7}$ c. domain: $x \geq 7$, range: $y \geq 0$ d. no, $g(f(x)) = \sqrt{x + 3} - 10$ and $\sqrt{x + 3} - 10 \neq \sqrt{x - 7}$	Lesson 5.1.3 MN: 5.1.3 LL: 5.2.5	Problems 6-87, 6-132, and 6-141

Chapter 7 Trigonometric Functions

This chapter begins with an experiment that will generate a new curve. You will then explore the relationship between right-triangle trigonometry and this new curve. You will be introduced to a new representation that is useful for the study of trigonometric functions: a unit circle. You will also learn how to use radians instead of degrees to describe angles.

In the second section of this chapter, you will transform trigonometric functions and find general equations for them. You will also learn about a new property that is characteristic of trigonometric functions called a period. Then you will write equations for the curve that you generated in the experiment at the beginning of the chapter.

Guiding Question

Mathematically proficient students look for and make use of structure.

As you work through this chapter, ask yourself:

How can I use what I know about right-triangle trigonometry to describe functions determined by rotations about a circle?

Chapter Outline

Section 7.1 In this section, you will use your understanding of the trigonometric ratios in right triangles to build an understanding of three new functions. You will recognize and create multiple representations of the functions $y = \sin\theta$ and $y = \cos\theta$. You will discover relationships between a unit circle and a graph of a trigonometric function. You will also learn to use a new unit, radians, to measure arcs and angles.

Section 7.2 In this section, you will apply your expertise with transforming parent graphs to graph functions of the family whose parents are $y = \sin x$ and $y = \cos x$. You will develop general equations for periodic or trigonometric functions. You will also learn about a property particular to these types of functions called a period.

7.1.1 What cyclic relationships can I model?

Introduction to Cyclic Models

In this chapter, you will learn about a new family of functions that are very useful for describing relationships that are **cyclic** (that is, they have repeating cycles), like the height of the ocean as the tides fluctuate between high and low or the distance of a swinging pendulum from its center point.

7-1.   EMERGENCY!

Nurse Nina rushes through the hospital with one hand on her clipboard and the other pulling a portable blood stand. The bags of blood swinging from the stand are needed in the emergency room *'stat'* for three patients in severe need. She is so intent on delivering the blood in time that she does not notice that one of the bags has a small hole in it and is dripping on the floor behind her. As she reaches the emergency room, she is horrified to see a small pool of blood beginning to form on the floor. Looking down the corridor from where she came, she sees the trail of blood that dripped and notices that it forms a very interesting pattern.

What shape do you think the trail of blood created?

Your Task: Use the materials and instructions provided by your teacher to re-create the pattern that the nurse saw on the hallway floor behind her. Make as many observations as you can about the shape you see and how that shape relates to what was happening to the bag of blood. Be sure to keep track of all the details. Be prepared to explain your observations to the class. Note: Complete directions for conducting this experiment are on the next page.

Directions for the Pendulum Experiment (Problem 7-1)

Find a space in the classroom where there is room to work. You may need to move your table or desks out of the way.

Set up your pendulum by attaching your bag of liquid to a meter stick using string, as shown at right.

Assign the following tasks:

- One student holds the meter stick from which the pendulum swings.

- One student holds the bag, releases it when ready, and then stops it when it reaches the end of the paper.

- Two students hold the butcher paper, one at each end, and slide it *at a constant rate* underneath the swinging pendulum. Be sure to slide the paper parallel to the meter stick and perpendicular to the swing of the pendulum, as shown in the diagram at right.

Tips for a successful experiment:

- The student holding the meter stick should hold the places where the string attaches. Otherwise, the string has a tendency to slide toward the center of the meter stick.

- Use as much of the string as you can so that your pendulum is as long as possible.

- When you are ready, have your teacher cut a *very* small hole in the corner of the bag. The student holding the bag should pinch this hole closed until the pendulum begins swinging.

- Be sure to slide the butcher paper under the pendulum *at a constant rate*.

- As you pull the bag up to start the pendulum swinging, hold it taut from the bottom corner so that the bag remains in line with the string (see diagram at right).

- Have an extra bag ready to place the dripping bag into when the experiment is complete.

7-2.   Now make predictions about the new curve that you created in problem 7-1.

    a.   With your team, design your own curve similar to the one already created. Decide exactly how you want it to look. How long do you want each cycle? How tall do you want it to be? Where do you want it to be on your paper? Where do you want it to start? Once you have decided on your new curve, make a sketch of it on your paper.

    b.   Predict how you could conduct an experiment to get exactly the curve you have described. How fast should you move the paper? Where would you start it? How high would you start your pendulum? Be prepared to share your predictions and their justifications with the class.

7-3.   Draw a sketch of one of the shapes the class created with the drips from the swinging pendulum in problem 7-1.

    a.   Sketch what the shape would look like if the bag were pulled out farther before it was let go.

    b.   Sketch what the shape would look like if the paper underneath the pendulum traveled faster.

7-4.   Karin was working on graphing the function $f(x) = \frac{2}{x-3}$. She made a table (shown below), but she is not sure how to graph the values in the table. Show Karin how to make her graph and tell her everything you know about her function.

x	−3	−2	−1	0	1	2	3	4	5	6	7	8	9
$f(x)$	$-\frac{1}{3}$	$-\frac{2}{5}$	$-\frac{1}{2}$	$-\frac{2}{3}$	−1	−2	*	2	1	$\frac{2}{3}$	$\frac{1}{2}$	$\frac{2}{5}$	$\frac{1}{3}$

*undefined

7-5.   In each of the following triangles, find the length of the side labeled x.

a.

28 feet

b.

150 cm

c.

47 meters

7-6.   Copy the triangles at right and label the missing side lengths.

7-7.   Find the equation of the parabola that passes through the points $(0, 0)$, $(3, 9)$, and $(6, 0)$.

7-8.   Solve and check your solution: $2\sqrt{21 - x} - \sqrt{3x - 6} = 5$.

7-9.   Consider the function $y = x^2 + 5x + 7$.

a.   Complete the square to find the vertex.

b.   Find the y-intercept.

c.   Use the vertex, the y-intercept, and the symmetry of parabolas to find a third point and sketch the graph.

7-10.   Find the x- and y-intercepts of $y - 7 = 3^{(x+4)}$.

7-11.   Change $x^2 - 2x + y^2 - 29 = 0$ to graphing form, sketch the graph, and label the important points.

7.1.2 How can I graph it?

Graphing the Sine Function

Today you will use what you know about right-triangle relationships and graphing functions to investigate a new function.

7-12.   *"HURRY!!! Let's get there before the line gets too long!"* shouts Antonio to his best friend René as they race to get on *The Screamer*, the newest attraction at the local amusement park.

"It's only been open for one day, and already everyone is saying it's the scariest ride at the park!" exclaims Antonio. *"I hear they really had to rush to get it done in time for summer."*

Antonio whistles as he screeches to a halt in front of the huge sign that says, *"Welcome to The Screamer, the Scariest Ride on Earth."* The picture below it shows an enormous wheel that represents *The Screamer*, with its radius of 100 feet. Half of the wheel is below ground level, in a very dark, murky pit with water at the bottom. As *The Screamer* rotates at dizzying speeds, riders fly up into the air before plunging downward through blasts of freezing air, hair-raising screams, and sticky spider webs into the pit where they splash through the dark, eerie water on their way back above ground.

René and Antonio wait impatiently to get on the ride, watching passengers load and unload. New passengers get on and strap themselves in as others emerge from the pit looking queasy. The ride rotates 15° to load and unload the next set of riders. As René straps himself in, he remembers Antonio's ominous words: *"I hear they really had to rush to get it done in time for summer."*

Sure enough, just as the ride plunges René and Antonio into the greasy water, they hear the piercing scream of metal twisting. Sparks fly and the pit fills with smoke as the ride grinds to a halt. To escape, all of the passengers must climb vertically to ground level from wherever they got stuck, either up from the pit or down from dizzying heights.

Problem continues on next page →

7-12. *Problem continued from previous page.*

notch to turn

Your Task: Find a function that describes the distance each passenger must climb in order to escape from the broken ride, *The Screamer*.

To help you gather data, your teacher will provide you with materials to build a model of this situation. Layer your transparency circle on top of your cardboard circle and insert a toothpick to act as an axle. Then slide the circles into the slit in your cardboard box, as shown in the diagram at right.

a. Use the transparent one-unit ruler to measure the escape heights on the model for at least 16 different possible seat positions. The seat could be in the pit, high in the air, or right at ground level. Remember that this position depends on the angle of the ride's rotation when it broke down. The radius of the model wheel will be referred to as one unit. That is, a model height of one unit corresponds to an actual height of 100 feet on the ride, so an actual height of 80 feet on the ride will be represented by a measured height of 0.8 units on the model. Record your data in a table like the one shown below. Leave room for additional columns.

Degree of Rotation from 0° (Platform)	Measured Height $0 \le y \le 1$	Actual Height Above (or Below) Platform	

b. Graph your data on a large graph.

c. Suppose you were asked to add 20 more data points to your table. What shortcuts could you use to reduce the amount of work?

7-13.   The function that models the situation in problem 7-12 is a new parent function. To help you figure out what it is, sketch the right triangle shown in the diagram at right.

   a.   With your team, write an equation and use it to calculate the height of the triangle. Does the calculated escape height seem reasonable when compared to the data you collected in problem 7-12?

   b.   Write an equation representing the escape height $h(\theta)$ for *any* passenger, that is, for any angle of rotation of *The Screamer*. Note that the symbol θ is the angle represented by the Greek letter "theta."

   c.   Enter the data from the first two columns of your table into your graphing calculator. Adjust the viewing window so you can see all of the data. Then graph $h(\theta)$ on top of the data. How well does $h(\theta)$ fit your data?

   d.   Adjust the viewing window so that you can see more of the graph of $h(\theta)$. Describe the behavior of the graph as θ gets larger. Does this make sense? Why or why not?

   e.   Use the 'table' function of your calculator to find the values that it calculated for $h(\theta)$. Add another column to your table from problem 7-12, label it with the equation you found for $h(\theta)$, and enter these values, rounding off to the nearest hundredth. How do the calculated values compare with your measured ones?

7-14.   René and Antonio finally make it home from the amusement park unhurt, but in need of a shower. As soon as they have cleaned up, they go over to a friend's house to share their scary experience on *The Screamer*. They draw a picture of the Ferris wheel and five of the seats, located at 15°, 30°, 45°, 60°, and 75° (shown at right and on the Lesson 7.1.2D Resource Page provided by your teacher).

   a.   Label each triangle with its *calculated* height. You can use your data from problem 7-12. If you do not have data for all of these angles, return to the 'table' function on your calculator. Plot these heights at their angle location on the coordinate system to the right of the circle. You will be plotting points in the form (x = angle in degrees, y = height).

   b.   Draw five new triangles that are congruent to the first five, but that are located in the second quadrant. Label these with their angle measures (from 0°) and heights. Use the angle measures and heights to plot five new points on the graph that correspond to these five new points on the circle.

Problem continues on next page →

7-14.   *Problem continued from previous page.*

   c.   Continue this process by drawing triangles in the third and fourth
         quadrants. You should have a total of twenty triangles drawn and twenty
         points plotted. Then label the points where the circle intersects the *x*- and
         y-axes with their angle measures and heights and then add points for them
         to the graph as well. Sketch a smooth curve through the points.

   d.   With your team, discuss all of the relationships you can find among the
         points on the circle and between your unit circle and the graph. Be
         prepared to share your ideas with the class.

METHODS AND MEANINGS

Special Right-Triangle Relationships

As you may recall from geometry, there are
certain right triangles whose sides have
special relationships that make certain
calculations easier. One such triangle is half of
an equilateral triangle and is known as a
30° – 60° – 90° triangle, named after the degree
measures of its angles.

The other special triangle is half of a square
and is known as the **45° – 45° – 90° triangle**.
Both triangles and the relationships between
their side lengths are shown at right.

Review & Preview

7-15.   Copy the triangles at right.

   a.   Label the missing sides with their *exact*
         lengths. That is, leave your answers in
         radical form.

   b.   The 30° – 60° – 90° triangle is sometimes called a half-equilateral triangle.
         Draw a picture to illustrate this, and explain how that fact can be used to
         help label the missing sides in part (a).

7-16. Find the measure of angle A in the diagram at right.

7-17. Find the x- and y-intercepts of the quadratic function $y = 2x^2 + x - 10$.

7-18. Evaluate each expression without using a calculator or changing the form of the expression.

a. $\log(1)$

b. $\log(10^3)$

c. $10^{\log(4)}$

d. $10^{3\log(4)}$

7-19. Complete the table of values for $f(x) = \frac{x^2 + 4x - 5}{x - 1}$.

x	-2	-1	0	1	2	3
y						

a. Graph the points in the table. What kind of function does it appear to be? Why is it not correct to connect all of the dots?

b. Look for a simple pattern for the values in the table. What appears to be the relationship between x and y? Calculate $f(0.9)$ and $f(1.1)$ and add the points to your graph. Is there an asymptote at $x = 1$? If you are unsure, calculate $f(0.99)$ and $f(1.01)$ as well.

c. Simplify the formula for $f(x)$. What do you think the complete graph looks like?

7-20. In 1998, Terre Haute, Indiana had a population of 72,000 people. In 2000, the population had dropped to 70,379. City officials expect the population to level off eventually at 60,000.

a. What kind of function would best model the population over time?

b. Write an equation that would model the changing population over time.

7-21. A semi-circular tunnel is 26 feet high at its highest point. A road 48 feet wide is centered under the tunnel. Bruce needs to move a house on a trailer through the tunnel. The load is 22 feet wide and 24 feet high. Will he make it? Use a diagram to help justify your reasoning completely.

7-22. Find the value of x.

a.

b.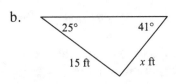

7-23. Solve the system of equations shown at right.

$$x + y + z = 40$$
$$y = x - 5$$
$$x = 2z$$

7-24. What is the domain of the entire graph of $h(\theta) = \sin\theta$? Justify your reasoning.

7-25. Antonio's friend Jessica was also on *The Screamer* when it broke. Her seat was 65 feet above the ground. What was her seat's angle of rotation? Is there more than one possibility?

7-26. Hilda was working on her homework. She completed the square to change $y = 3x^2 - 24x + 55$ to graphing form in order to identify the vertex of the parabola. She did the work at right and identified the vertex to be $(4, 39)$. When she got back to class and checked her answers, she discovered that the vertex she found is incorrect, but she cannot find her mistake. Examine Hilda's work and explain to her what she did wrong. Then show her how to complete the square correctly and identify the vertex.

$$y = 3x^2 - 24x + 55$$
$$y = 3(x^2 - 8x) + 55$$
$$y = 3(x^2 - 8x + 16) + 55 - 16$$
$$y = 3(x - 4)^2 + 39$$

7-27. Mr. Keis wrote the following problem on the board and told his class, "*No calculators please. Simplify. You have sixty seconds!*"

$$\left(\frac{13^{12}}{14^{23}}\right)\left(\frac{27^3}{13^{11}}\right)\left(\frac{2^{10}}{27^4}\right)\left(\frac{14^{22}}{13}\right)\left(\frac{27}{2^9}\right)$$

Time yourself and simplify the expression. Did you meet the challenge?

7-28. Graph the system at right.

$$1 + x - y \geq 3x - 2y - 4$$
$$y < 2x^2 + 1$$

7-29.   Use your knowledge of shifting parent graphs to graph each equation below.

      a. $y = -2(x-3)^2 + 4$ b. $y = \frac{1}{2}(x+2)^3 - 3$

      c. $y = 2|x-5|$ d. $y = \sqrt{x-2} - 3$

7-30.   Find the x- and y-intercepts for the quadratic equation $y + 3 = 8x^2 - 10x$.

7-31.   A function $W(x)$ is sketched at right.

      a.   Make your own copy of the graph, and then sketch the graph of the inverse of $W(x)$.

      b.   Is the inverse a function? Explain.

7-32.   Mary has an antique marble collection containing 40 marbles. She has five more red marbles than blue and twice as many red as green marbles. Write a system of equations to find the number of each color of marble.

7.1.3 How are circles and sine graphs connected?

Unit Circle ↔ Graph

Throughout this course, you have used multiple representations (table, graph, equation, and situation) to solve problems, investigate functions, and justify conclusions. In Lesson 7.1.2 you found that a unit circle is one representation of a sine function. Today you will investigate the connections between the unit circle and its graph, as you build a deeper understanding of the sine function.

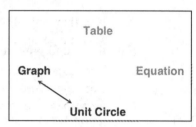

7-33. Draw a circle on your paper. Then draw a triangle that could represent René and Antonio's position on the wheel when *The Screamer* came to a sudden stop. Be sure to choose a different angle position from any of those you drew in problem 7-14.

a. Label the triangle with its height and its angle measure (from 0°).

b. Did any other riders have to climb the same distance to get to safety (up *or* down) as René and Antonio did? If so, draw the corresponding triangles and label them completely.

c. What is the relationship between these triangles? Work with your team to generalize a method for finding all of the other corresponding angles when you are given just one angle.

7-34.   In problem 7-33, you used a unit circle to find the height of a seat on *The Screamer*. Could you use your graph of $y = \sin\theta$ instead to find the height?

   a.   Use the Lesson 7.1.3 Resource Page (also called a sine calculator) provided by your teacher to find the height of a seat that has rotated $130°$ from the starting platform.

   b.   Are there any other seats at exactly the same height? If so, indicate them on your resource page.

   c.   How can you use the symmetry of the graph to calculate which angles correspond to seats with the same height? Discuss this with your team and be prepared to share your strategies with the class.

   d.   For each of the following angles, use the sine calculator from the resource page to find the height at that angle and to find another angle with the same height. Then sketch a small unit circle, draw in each pair of angles, and label the heights.

   i. $80°$ *ii.* $200°$ *iii.* $310°$

7-35.   LEARNING LOG

With your team, discuss the ways in which a unit circle and the graph of $s(\theta) = \sin\theta$ are connected. Be prepared to share your ideas with the class. Then record your ideas in a Learning Log. Use diagrams, arrows, and other math tools to help demonstrate your ideas. Label this entry "Unit Circle $\leftrightarrow$ Graph for $s(\theta) = \sin\theta$" and label it with today's date.

7-36.   Sketch a graph of the first two cycles of $s(\theta) = \sin\theta$. Then label your graph to show the following positions of a passenger on *The Screamer*.

   a.   The passenger gets on initially.

   b.   The passenger reaches the bottom of the water pit.

   c.   The passenger is halfway between the highest point of *The Screamer* and the ground level.

7-37.   Each of the points on the graph at right represents the position of a rider on *The Screamer*. Draw a diagram of each rider's position on a unit circle and describe where the rider is located.

7-38.   While trying to measure the height of a tree, Julie noticed that a 3.5-foot post had a 4.25-foot shadow. If the tree's shadow is 100 feet long, how tall is the tree?

7-39.   Given that $\log 2 \approx 0.3010$, $\log 3 \approx 0.4771$ and $\log 5 \approx 0.6990$, calculate each of the following logarithms without using a calculator.

a. $\log 6$ b. $\log 15$ c. $\log 9$ d. $\log 50$

7-40.   Find the *x*- and *y*-intercepts of the quadratic function $y = 3x^2 + 6x + 1$.

7-41.   Write the quadratic function in problem 7-40 in graphing form and sketch its graph.

7-42.   Solve $|x+5| = |x| - 5$ by graphing. Express your solution algebraically.

7-43.   Solve $\log_2 x = 2^x$ using any method.

7-44.   Maria Elena is collecting college pennants. She has five fewer pennants from Washington campuses than from California campuses and twice as many pennants from California campuses as from Pennsylvania campuses. She has 40 pennants in her collection. Write a system of equations to find the number of Pennants from each state.

7.1.4 How can I graph cosine?

Graphing and Interpreting the Cosine Function

In this lesson, you will use your knowledge of right triangles again—this time to develop your understanding of another trigonometric function.

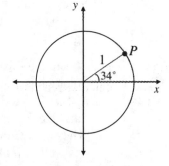

7-45.   Work with your team to find the coordinates of point *P* on the unit circle shown at right. Is there more than one way to find point *P*? Be prepared to share your strategies with the class.

7-46.   Now generalize what you found in problem 7-45 to write the coordinates of point *Q* on the unit circle shown at left.

7-47.   What can a sine value tell you about a point on a circle? What about a cosine value?

7-48.   If you know the sine of an angle in a unit circle, can you find its cosine? How? Work with your team to find a strategy and be prepared to share it with the class.

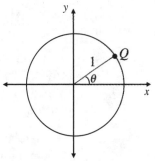

7-49.   An angle θ on the unit circle has a cosine of $\frac{3}{4}$.

   a.   Find the exact coordinates of point *Q* by using the Pythagorean Theorem.

   b.   What is the value of $\sin \theta$?

   c.   Using what you determined in problems 7-47 and 7-48, how could you rewrite the Pythagorean Theorem using trigonometric functions for the lengths of the sides? When written like this, the Pythagorean Theorem is called the **Pythagorean Identity**.

7-50.   Obtain a copy of the Lesson 7.1.4A Resource Page from your teacher. You
        will use the same process to graph the cosine function as you did to graph the
        sine function, but you need to use the base of the triangle instead of the height.

   a.   Label the length of the base of each triangle in the unit circle. Plot these
        lengths at their angle location on the coordinate system to the right of the
        circle. You will be plotting points in the form (x = angle in degrees,
        y = base).

   b.   Draw five new triangles that are congruent to the first five, but that are
        located in the second quadrant. Label the angle measure (from 0°) and
        the base for each triangle. Add five new corresponding points to the
        graph.

   c.   Continue this process by drawing triangles in the third and fourth
        quadrants. You should have a total of twenty triangles drawn and twenty
        points plotted. Then find the four points where the circle crosses the axes
        and label them with both their angle measures and their horizontal
        distances from the origin. Add points for these to the graph on the right
        as well. Finally, sketch a smooth curve through the points.

   d.   Compare this graph to the sine graph you got from graphing heights in
        problem 7-14. How are the two graphs similar? How are they different?

7-51.   Remember the scary Ferris wheel, *The Screamer*?
        LaRasha does! She was riding *The Screamer*,
        sitting 27 horizontal feet away from the central
        support pole, when the ride stopped. What was her
        seat's angle of rotation? Is there more than one
        possibility? Justify your answer using as many
        representations as you can.

7-52.   UNIT CIRCLE ↔ GRAPH

        In problem 7-51, did you use a graph of $y = \cos\theta$ to find lengths of bases of
        triangles?

   a.   Use the Lesson 7.1.4B Resource Page (a cosine-calculator graph)
        provided by your teacher to find the length of the base of a triangle
        formed by a seat on *The Screamer* that had rotated 130° from the starting
        platform.

   b.   Are there any other triangles with the same base? If so, mark their
        corresponding points on your cosine calculator.

   c.   How can you use the symmetry of the cosine-calculator graph to calculate
        the angle location of seats on *The Screamer* that have the same base? Is
        your method different than the one you used to find the heights?

Core Connections Algebra 2

7-53.   Use the Pythagorean Identity to find the exact coordinates of a point on the unit circle that has $\sin\theta = \frac{1}{4}$.

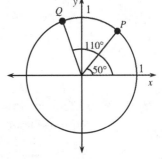

7-54.   Find the coordinates of points P and Q on the unit circle at right.

7-55.   The measure of $\angle ROS$ in $\triangle ROS$ below is $60°$.

a.   The curved arrow represents the rotation of $\overline{OR}$, beginning from the positive x-axis. Through how many degrees has $\overline{OR}$ rotated?

b.   If $OR = 1$, what are the *exact* lengths of OS and SR?

c.   What are the *exact* coordinates of point R?

7-56.   What angle in the first quadrant could you reference to help you find the sine and cosine of each of the following angles?

a. $330°$ b. $120°$ c. $113°$ d. $203°$

7-57.   Solve $\left(\frac{1}{8}\right)^{(2x-3)} = \left(\frac{1}{2}\right)^{(x+2)}$ for x.

7-58.   Sketch a graph of each equation below.

a. $y = -2(x-2)^2 + 3$ b. $y = (x-1)^3 + 3$

7-59.   Solve $3^x + 5 = x^2 - 5$ using any method.

7-60.   Rip-Off Rentals charges $25 per day plus 50¢ per mile to rent a mid-sized car. Your teacher will rent you his or her family sedan and charge you only 3¢ if you drive one mile, 6¢ if you drive two miles, 12¢ if you drive three, 24¢ for four, and so on.

    a.   Write an equation that will give you the cost to rent each car.

    b.   If you plan to rent the car for a two-day road trip, which is the better deal if you drive 10 miles? 20 miles? 100 miles?

7-61.   Refer back to your solutions from problems 7-23, 7-32, and 7-44. Explain how these problems are related.

7-62.   Shinna was riding *The Screamer* when it broke down. Her seat was 53 horizontal feet from the central support pole. What was her seat's angle of rotation? How can you tell?

7-63.   Sketch a unit circle. In your circle, sketch in an angle that has:

    a.   A positive cosine and a negative sine.

    b.   A sine of –1.

    c.   A negative cosine and a negative sine.

    d.   A cosine of about –0.9 and a sine of about 0.4.

    e.   Could an angle have a sine equal to 0.9 and cosine equal to 0.8? Give an angle or explain why not.

7-64.   A 70° angle is drawn for you in the unit circle at right.

    a.   Approximate the coordinates of point R.

    b.   How could you represent the *exact* coordinates of point R?

    c.   Show that the Pythagorean Identity works for this angle.

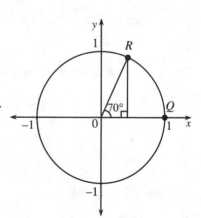

7-65.   Daniel sketched the graphs at right for $y = \sin\theta$ and $y = \cos\theta$.

Unfortunately, he forgot to label the graphs, and now he cannot remember which graph goes with which equation. Explain to Daniel how he can tell (and remember!) which graph is $y = \sin\theta$ and which is $y = \cos\theta$.

7-66.   Consider the system of equations $y = \cos x$ and $y = -1$.

a.   Is it possible to solve this system by substitution? By the Elimination Method? By graphing?

b.   List at least five possible solutions.

c.   Consider the list of solutions you wrote in part (b) as a sequence and write an equation to represent *all* possible solutions.

7-67.   This problem is a checkpoint for finding the *x*- and *y*-intercepts of a quadratic function. It will be referred to as Checkpoint 7A.

Find the *x*- and *y*-intercepts for the graph of $y = x^2 + 4x - 17$ without using a graphing calculator.

Check your answers by referring to the Checkpoint 7A materials located at the back of your book.

Ideally, at this point you are comfortable working with these types of problems and can solve them correctly. If you feel that you need more confidence when solving these types of problems, then review the Checkpoint 7A materials and try the practice problems provided. From this point on, you will be expected to do problems like these correctly and with confidence.

7-68.   Solve each equation.

a. $\frac{3}{x+1} = \frac{4}{x}$

b. $\frac{3}{x+1} + \frac{4}{x} = 2$

c. $\frac{3}{x+2} + 5 = \frac{3}{x+2}$

d.   Explain why part (c) has no solution.

7-69.   A $5' \times 4' \times 3'$ box is made for the purpose of storage. What is the longest pole that can fit inside the box?

7-70.   While working on their homework on sequences, Davis was suddenly stumped!

"This problem doesn't make sense!" he exclaimed. Tess was working on her homework as well.

"What's the problem?" she asked.

"This problem is about a SEQUENCE, $t(n) = 9n - 2$, but it is asking whether or not it is a function. How can a sequence be a function?"

"Well of course a sequence is a function!" said Tess.

Who is right? Should Davis be confused, or is Tess correct? What is the difference between a sequence and a function? Explain completely.

7.1.5 How else can I measure angles?

Defining a Radian

Whose idea was it to measure angles in degrees? And why are there 360° in a full turn? This decision actually dates back almost 4000 years! Degrees were created by the Babylonians, an ancient people who lived in the region that is now Iraq. The Babylonians also based their number system, called a sexigesimal system, on sixty.

Although you are familiar with measuring angles in degrees, this is not the only way to measure angles, nor is it necessarily the most useful. Today you will learn a different unit for measuring angles called a **radian**. Using radians instead of degrees is actually the standard across mathematics! When you take calculus, you will learn why radians are used in math more often than degrees.

7-71.   What word are you reminded of when you hear the word radian? Discuss this with your team and make a conjecture about how this might relate to a way to measure angles. Be prepared to share your ideas with the class.

7-72.   HOW TO MAKE A RADIAN

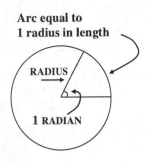

Imagine wrapping the radius of a circle around the
circle. The angle formed at the center of the circle that
corresponds to the arc that is one radius long has a
measure of exactly one **radian**.

Your teacher will provide each member of your team
with a different-sized circular object and some scissors.

a.   Trace your circular object onto a sheet of paper and carefully
      cut out the circle. Fold the paper circle in half and then in
      half again so that it is in the shape of a quarter circle, as in the
      diagram at right. How can you see the radius of your circular
      object in this new folded shape?

b.   Place your circular object onto another sheet of paper and trace it again,
      only this time leave the circular object in place. Roll (or wrap) a straight
      edge of your folded circle around your circular object and mark one radius
      length on the traced circle. Then mark another radius length that begins
      where the first one ended. Continue marking radius lengths until you have
      gone around the entire circle.

c.   Remove the circular object from your paper. On your traced circle,
      connect each radius mark to the center, creating central angles. Each angle
      you see, formed by an arc with a length of one radius, measures
      one **radian**. Label each of the radius lengths and each angle that measures
      one full radian. Write a short description of how you constructed an angle
      with measure one radian.

7-73.   Assume the radius of a circle is one unit.

a.   What is the area of the circle? What is its circumference?

b.   How many radii would it take to wrap completely around the circle?
      Express your answer as a decimal approximation *and* as an exact value.

c.   Does the size of the circle matter? That is, does the number of radii it
      takes to wrap around the circle change as the radius of the circle gets larger
      or smaller? Why does this make sense?

d.   Exactly how many radians are in 360°? In 90°?

7-74. LEARNING LOG

How is a radian related to a radius? Explain your
understanding of this relationship in your Learning Log.
Use diagrams to support your explanation. Title this entry
"Radians" and label it with today's date.

7-75. Parts (a) through (g) below describe angles. Draw each angle on its own unit
circle.

a. 1 degree   b. 1 radian   c. π radians   d. $\frac{\pi}{2}$ radians

e. $\frac{\pi}{4}$ radians   f. $\frac{\pi}{3}$ radians   g. $\frac{\pi}{6}$ radians

7-76. Find your sine-calculator (the Lesson 7.1.3 Resource Page). Use your new
understanding of radians to convert the units on the θ axis from degrees to
radians. Be prepared to share your conversion strategies with the class.

METHODS AND MEANINGS

MATH NOTES

Radians

A **radian** is defined as an angular
measure such that an arc length of one
radius on a circle of radius one
produces an angle with measure one
radian. It can also be thought of as the
ratio of an arc length to the radius of
the corresponding circle.

The circumference of any complete circle is $2\pi r$ units, so the
corresponding radian measure is $\frac{2\pi r}{r} = 2\pi$. Thus, there are
2π radians in a complete circle.

7-77. Your scientific or graphing calculator can function in both degrees and radians. See if you can determine how to put your calculator in radian mode and then how to switch it back to degree mode. On most scientific calculators, a small "DEG" or "RAD" shows on the screen to let you know in which mode you are working.

a. With your calculator in degree mode, find sin 60° and record your answer. Then switch to radian mode and find $\sin \frac{\pi}{3}$. Did you get the same answer? Explain why your answers should be the same or different.

b. Find $\sin \frac{\pi}{4}$. Which angles, measured in degrees, would have the same sine as $\sin \frac{\pi}{4}$?

7-78. Calculate each of the following values. Express your answers both exactly and as decimal approximations.

a. $\sin(\frac{\pi}{4})$

b. $\sin(\frac{2\pi}{3})$

7-79. Show how the Zero Product Property can be used to solve each of the following equations.

a. $x(2x-1)(x-3)=0$

b. $2x^3 + x^2 - 3x = 0$

7-80. Solve each of the following equations.

a. $5^x = 72$

b. $2^{3x} = 7$

c. $3^{(2x+4)} = 17$

7-81. Greg was working on his homework. He completed the square to change $y = 2x^2 - 6x + 2$ to graphing form and identify the vertex of the parabola. He did the work at right and identified the vertex to be $(\frac{3}{2}, -\frac{1}{4})$.

$y = 2x^2 - 6x + 2$

$y = 2(x^2 - 3x) + 2$

$y = 2(x^2 - 3x + \frac{9}{4}) + 2 - \frac{9}{4}$

$y = 2(x - \frac{3}{2})^2 - \frac{1}{4}$

When he got back to class and checked his answers, he discovered that his vertex was wrong, but he cannot find his mistake. Examine Greg's work and explain to him where the mistake occurred. Then show him how to correct the mistake and state the vertex.

7-82.   Change each of the following equations to graphing form and then, without graphing, identify the vertex and axis of symmetry for each.

   a. $y = 3x^2 - 18x + 26$

   b. $y = 3x^2 - 4x - 11$

7-83.   Solve each of the following equations for x.

   a. $171 = 3(5^x)$

   b. $171y = 3(x^5)$

7-84.   Sketch a graph of $x^2 + y^2 = 100$.

   a.   Is it a function?

   b.   What are its domain and range?

   c.   Draw a central angle that measures $\frac{2\pi}{3}$ radians. If you remove this wedge of the circle, how much area remains?

7-85.   Find the equation for the inverse of the function $f(x) = 2\sqrt{\frac{(x-3)}{4}} + 1$. Sketch the graph of both the original and the inverse.

7.1.6   What do I know about a unit circle?

Building a Unit Circle

In this lesson, you will further develop your understanding of the unit circle and how useful it can be. By the end of the lesson, you should be able to answer the questions below.

> What can the unit circle help me understand about an angle?

> What does my information about angles in the first quadrant tell me about angles in other quadrants?

7-86.   There are some angles for which you know the *exact values* of sine and cosine. In other words, you can find the exact sine and cosine without using a calculator. Work with your team to find as many such angles (expressed in radians) as you can.

7-87.   Now you will build a unit circle. Obtain the Lesson 7.1.6 Resource Page from your teacher. There are points shown at $\frac{\pi}{12}, \frac{\pi}{6}, \frac{\pi}{4}, \frac{\pi}{3}, \frac{5\pi}{12}, \frac{7\pi}{12}, \frac{2\pi}{3}, \frac{3\pi}{4}, \frac{5\pi}{6}$, and $\frac{11\pi}{12}$ units along the circle, starting from the positive *x*-axis.

   a.   Find and label the exact coordinates, in (x,y) form, for three of the points shown in the *first quadrant*.

   b.   Mark *all* other points in the unit circle for which you can find *exact* coordinates. Not all of them are shown. Label each of these points with its angle of rotation (in radians) and its coordinates.

   c.   If you have not done so already, label each angle with its corresponding radian measure.

7-88. Draw a new unit circle, label a point that corresponds to a rotation of $\frac{\pi}{12}$, and put your calculator in radian mode.

   a. What are the coordinates of this point, correct to two decimal places?

   b. Use the information you found in part (a) to determine each of the following values: (Hint: Drawing each angle on the unit circle will be very helpful.)

   i. $\sin(-\frac{\pi}{12})$ ii. $\cos\frac{13\pi}{12}$ iii. Challenge: $\cos\frac{7\pi}{12}$

7-89. For angle α in the first quadrant, $\cos\alpha = \frac{8}{17}$. Use that information to find each of the following values without using a calculator. Be prepared to share your strategies with the class.

   a. $\sin\alpha$ b. $\sin(\pi + \alpha)$ c. $\cos(2\pi - \alpha)$

ᗰETHODS AND ᗰEANINGS

Reference Angle

For every angle of rotation, there is an angle in the first quadrant ($0 \le \theta \le 90°$) whose cosine and sine have the same absolute values as the cosine and sine of the original angle. This first-quadrant angle is called the **reference angle**.

For example, the angles 51°, 129°, 231°, and 309° (pictured at right) all share the reference angle of 51°.

7-90.   Calculate the value of each expression below. Give an exact measurement, if possible. Each measure is given in radians.

   a. $\sin(4)$

   b. $\sin(\frac{4\pi}{3})$

7-91.   Find the exact values of the angles that are solutions to the equation $\sin(\theta) = 0.5$. Express your solutions in radians.

7-92.   You have seen that you can calculate values of the sine function using right triangles formed by a radius of the unit circle. Values of θ that result in $30° - 60° - 90°$ or $45° - 45° - 90°$ triangles are used frequently on exercises and tests because their sine and cosine values can be found exactly, without using a calculator. You should learn to recognize these values quickly and easily. The same is true for values of $\cos\theta$ and $\sin\theta$ that correspond to the x- and y-intercepts of the unit circle.

   The central angles that correspond to these "special" values of x are 30°, 45°, 60°, 90°, 120°, 135°, 150°, 180°, 210°, 225°, 240°, 270°, 300°, 315°, and 330°. What these angles have in common is that they are all multiples of 30° or 45°, and some of them are also multiples of 60° or 90°.

   Copy and complete a table like the one below for all special angles between 0° and 360°.

Degrees	0	30	45	60	90	120		
Radians	0	$\frac{\pi}{6}$						

7-93.   Draw a picture of an angle that measures 6 radians.

   a.   Approximately how many degrees is this?

   b.   Using only your picture, estimate the sine of 6 radians.

7-94.   Evaluate each expression without using a calculator or changing the form of the expression.

   a. $\log(10)$

   b. $\log(\sqrt{10})$

   c. $\log(0)$

   d. $10^{(2/3)\log(27)}$

7-95.   What interest rate (compounded annually) would you need to earn in order to double your investment in 15 years?

7-96.   Angle A is an obtuse angle with a sine of $\frac{3}{10}$. What is the tangent of angle A?

7-97.   Find the inverse functions for the functions given below.

   a. $f(x) = \sqrt[3]{4x - 1}$

   b. $g(x) = \log_7 x$

7-98.   Solve each of the following equations.

   a. $2(x-1)^2 = 18$

   b. $2^x + 3 = 10$

7.1.7 What is tangent?

The Tangent Function

In the past several lessons, you have used your understanding of the sine and cosine ratios to develop and interpret the functions $s(\theta) = \sin\theta$ and $c(\theta) = \cos\theta$. In this lesson, you will expand your understanding by exploring the tangent ratio and graphing the function $t(\theta) = \tan\theta$.

7-99. Jamal was working on his homework when he had a brilliant realization. He was drawing a triangle in a unit circle to estimate the sine of $\frac{\pi}{10}$, when he realized that this triangle is the same kind of triangle that he draws when he wants to find the slope of a line.

   a. How could you express the slope of the radius in terms of sine and cosine?

   b. Is there any other way you can use a trigonometric ratio to represent the slope? Discuss this with your team.

7-100. THE TANGENT FUNCTION

   Obtain the Lesson 7.1.7 Resource Page from your teacher. Use your knowledge of sine, cosine, and tangent to create a graph of the tangent function. Conduct a full investigation of the tangent function. Be prepared to share your summary statements with the class.

Discussion Points

Does every angle have a tangent value?

How is the tangent graph similar to or different from the sine and cosine graphs?

Why does the tangent graph have asymptotes?

Further Guidance

7-101. For each angle in the first quadrant of the unit circle on your resource page, determine the sine and cosine.

a. Use your knowledge of tangent to complete a table like the one below. Start with the exact values for the sine and cosine.

θ	$\sin\theta$	$\cos\theta$	$\tan\theta$ (exact)	$\tan\theta$ (approximate to nearest 0.01)
$\frac{\pi}{6}$	$\frac{1}{2}$	$\frac{\sqrt{3}}{2}$	$\frac{1}{\sqrt{3}}$	
$\frac{\pi}{4}$	$\frac{\sqrt{2}}{2}$	$\frac{\sqrt{2}}{2}$		
$\frac{\pi}{3}$	$\frac{\sqrt{3}}{2}$	$\frac{1}{2}$		

b. Plot the tangent values on the graph to the right of the unit circle.

c. Draw five new triangles that are congruent to the first five, but that are located in the second quadrant. Add values for these new angles to your table and your graph.

d. Continue this process by drawing triangles in the third and fourth quadrants. You should have a total of twenty triangles drawn and twenty angle values on your graph. If you have not done so already, add data to your table and points to your graph corresponding to the intercepts of the unit circle.

7-102. Investigate the tangent graph by analyzing the following questions:

a. Describe the domain and range of the tangent function.

b. Describe any special points or asymptotes.

c. Does it have symmetry? Describe any symmetry you see in the graph.

d. How is the graph of $t(\theta)=\tan\theta$ different from the graphs of $s(\theta)=\sin\theta$ and $c(\theta)=\cos\theta$?

Further Guidance
section ends here.

7-103. Draw a new unit circle and label a point that corresponds to a rotation of $\frac{\pi}{6}$ radians.

a. What are the coordinates of this point? Use exact values.

b. Use this information to find each of the following values without a calculator. (Hint: Drawing each angle on the unit circle will be very helpful.)

  i: $\tan\left(\frac{7\pi}{6}\right)$ ii: $\cos\left(\frac{13\pi}{6}\right)$ iii: $\tan\left(\frac{2\pi}{3}\right)$

Sine, Cosine, and Tangent

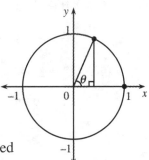

For any real number θ, the **sine of θ**, denoted $\sin \theta$, is the y-coordinate of the point on the unit circle reached by a rotation of θ radians from **standard position** (counter-clockwise starting from the positive x-axis).

The **cosine of θ**, denoted $\cos \theta$, is the x-coordinate of the point on the unit circle reached by a rotation of θ radians from standard position.

The **tangent of θ**, denoted by $\tan \theta$, is the slope of the terminal ray of an angle (the radius) formed by a rotation of θ radians in standard position.

The **Pythagorean Identity**, $\sin^2 \theta + \cos^2 \theta = 1$, describes the relationship between the side lengths of a right triangle formed in a unit circle with the radius as the hypotenuse.

MATH NOTES

7-104. What central angle, measured in degrees, corresponds to a distance around the unit circle of $\frac{7\pi}{3}$?

a. What other angles will take you to the same point on the circle?

b. Make a sketch of the unit circle showing the resulting right triangle.

c. Find $\sin\left(\frac{7\pi}{3}\right)$, $\cos\left(\frac{7\pi}{3}\right)$, and $\tan\left(\frac{7\pi}{3}\right)$ exactly.

7-105. Evaluate each of the following trig expressions without using a calculator.

a. $\sin(180°)$ b. $\sin(360°)$ c. $\sin(-90°)$

d. $\sin(510°)$ e. $\cos(90°)$ f. $\tan(-90°)$

7-106.   How do you convert from degrees to radians and from radians to degrees? Explain and justify your method completely. Add some examples to your Toolkit.

7-107.   Convert each of the following angle measures. Give exact answers.

a. $\frac{7\pi}{6}$ radians to degrees

b. $\frac{5\pi}{3}$ radians to degrees

c.   45 degrees to radians

d.   100° to radians

e.   810° to radians

f. $\frac{7\pi}{2}$ radians to degrees

7-108.   Sketch a graph of $f(x) = \frac{1}{2}(x+1)^3$. Then sketch its inverse and write the equation of the inverse.

7-109.   Rewrite $f(x) = 2x^2 - 16x + 34$ in graphing form.

7-110.   For angle θ in the third quadrant, $\cos\theta = -\frac{12}{13}$. Use this information to find each of the following values without using a calculator.

a. $\sin\theta$

b. $\tan\theta$

7-111.   Given that $\log_x 2 = a$, $\log_x 5 = b$, and $\log_x 7 = c$, write expressions using $a, b,$ and/or c for each log expression below.

a. $\log_x 10$

b. $\log_x 49$

c. $\log_x 50$

d. $\log_x 56$

7-112.   The temperature of a pizza after it has been delivered depends on how long it has been sitting on the family-room table.

a.   Sketch a reasonable graph of this situation. Be sure to label the axes.

b.   Should your graph have an asymptote? Why or why not?

7.2.1 How can I transform a sine graph?

Transformations of $y = \sin x$

In Chapter 2, you developed expertise in investigating functions and transforming parent graphs. In this section, you will investigate families of trigonometric functions and their transformations. By the end of this section, you will be able to graph any sine or cosine equation and write the equation of any sine or cosine graph.

7-113.   As you have seen with many functions in this and other courses, x is generally used to represent an input and y is used to represent the corresponding output. By this convention, trigonometric functions should be written $y = \sin x$, $y = \cos x$, and $y = \tan x$. But beware! Something funny is happening.

With your team, examine the unit circle and the three graphs below. What do x and y represent in the unit circle? What do they represent in each of the graphs? Discuss this with your team and be prepared to share your ideas with the class.

a.

b.

c.

d.

7-114.   With your team, you will apply your knowledge about transforming graphs of functions to transform the graphs of $y = \sin x$ and $y = \cos x$ and find their general equations.

Your Task: As a team, investigate $y = \sin x$ and $y = \cos x$ completely. You should make graphs, find the domain and range, and label any important points or asymptotes. Then make a sketch and write an equation to demonstrate each transformation of the sine or cosine function you can find. Finally, find a general equation for a sine and a cosine function. Be prepared to share your summary statements with the class.

Discussion Points

What can we change in a cyclic graph?

Which points are important to label?

How can we apply the transformations we use with other functions?

Are there any new transformations that are special to the sine function?

Further Guidance

7-115.   Sketch a graph of at least one cycle of $y = \sin x$. Label the intercepts. Then work with your team to complete parts (a) through (c) below.

a.   Write an equation for each part below and sketch a graph of a function that has a parent graph of $y = \sin x$, but is:

   i. Shifted 3 units up.   *ii*.   Reflected across the *x*-axis.

   iii. Shifted 2 units to the right.   *iv*.   Vertically stretched.

b.   Which points are most important to label in a periodic function? Why?

c.   Write a general equation for the family of functions with a parent graph of $y = \sin x$.

=========   *Further Guidance*   =========
               section ends here.

7-116.   Imagine the graph $y = \sin x$ shifted up one unit.

   a.   Sketch what it would look like.

   b.   What do you have to change in the equation $y = \sin x$ to move the graph *up* one unit? Write the new equation.

   c.   What are the intercepts of your new equation? Label them with their coordinates on the graph.

   d.   When you listed intercepts in part (c), did you list more than one x-intercept? Should you have?

7-117.   The graph at right was made by shifting the first cycle of $y = \sin x$ to the left.

   a.   How many units to the left was it shifted?

   b.   Figure out how to change the equation of $y = \sin x$ so that the graph of the new equation will look like the one in part (a). If you do not have a graphing calculator at home, sketch the graph and check your answer when you get to class.

7-118.   Which of the situations below (if any) is best modeled by a sinusoidal function? Explain your reasoning.

   a.   The number of students in each year's graduating class.

   b.   Your hunger level throughout the day.

   c.   The high-tide level at a point along the coast.

7-119.   The CPM Amusement Park has decided to imitate *The Screamer* but wants to make it even better. Their ride will consist of a circular track with a radius of 100 feet, and the center of the circle will be 50 feet under ground. Passengers will board at the highest point, so they will begin with a blood-curdling drop. Write a function that relates the angle traveled *from the starting point* to the height of the rider above or below the ground.

7-120.   Should $y = \sin x$ and $y = \cos x$ both be parent graphs, or is one the parent of the other? Give reasons for your decision.

7-121.   Find the equation of the exponential function of the form $y = ab^x$ that passes through each of the following pairs of points.

a. $(1, 18)$ and $(4, 3888)$ b. $(-2, -8)$ and $(3, -0.25)$

7-122.   Solve each of the following equations. Be sure to check your solutions.

a. $\frac{3}{x} + \frac{2}{x+1} = 5$

b. $x^2 + 6x + 9 = 2x^2 + 3x + 5$

c. $8 - \sqrt{9 - 2x} = x + 3$

7-123.   Evaluate each of the following expressions exactly.

a. $\tan \frac{2\pi}{3}$ b. $\tan \frac{7\pi}{6}$

7-124.   David Longshot is known for his long golf drives. Today he hit the ball 250 yards and estimated that the ball reached a maximum height of 15 yards. Find a quadratic equation that would model the path of the golf ball.

7.2.2 What is missing?

One More Parameter for a Cyclic Function

In this lesson, you will study one more transformation that is unique to cyclic functions. You will also extend your understanding of these functions to include those with input values that do not correspond to angles.

7-125.   Does the general equation $y = a\sin(x-h)+k$ allow for every possible transformation of the graph of $y = \sin x$? Are there any transformations possible *other than* the ones produced by varying values of a, h, and k? Look back at the graphs you made for the swinging bag of blood in the first lesson of this chapter. Discuss this with your team and be prepared to share your conjectures with the class.

7-126.   THE RADAR SCREEN

Brianna is an air traffic controller. Every day she watches the radar line (like a radius of a circle) go around her screen time after time. On one particularly slow travel day, Brianna noticed that it takes 2 seconds for the radar line to travel through an angle of $\frac{\pi}{6}$ radians. She decided to make a graph in which the *input* is time and the *output* is the distance from the outward end of the radar line to the horizontal axis.

Your Task: Following the input and output specifications above, make a table and graph for Brianna's radar.

Discussion Points

How can we calculate the outputs?

How is this graph different from other similar graphs we have made?

How long does it take to complete one full cycle on the radar screen? How can we see that on the graph?

7-127.   Now that you have seen that it is possible to have a sine graph with a cycle
         length other than 2π, work with your team to make conjectures about how you
         could change your general equation to allow for this new transformation.

    a.   In the general equation $y = a\sin(x - h) + k$, the quantities a, h,
         and k are called **parameters**. Where could a new parameter
         fit into the equation?

    b.   Use your graphing calculator to test the result of putting this new
         parameter into your general equation. Once you have found the place for
         the new parameter, investigate how it works. What happens when it gets
         larger? What happens when it gets smaller?

    c.   Write a general equation for a sine function that includes the new
         parameter you discovered.

7-128.   Another word for cycle length is **period**. Which of the following have a period
         of 2π? Which do not? How can you tell? If the period is not 2π, what is it?

    a.

    b.   A pendulum takes 3 seconds to
         complete one cycle.

    c. $y = \sin\theta$

    d.   A radar line takes 1 second to
         travel through 1 radian.

7-129.   Find an equation for each graph below.

a.

b.

c.

d.

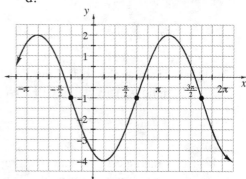

7-130.   Claudia graphed $y = \cos\theta$ and $y = \cos(\theta + 360°)$ on the same set of axes. She did not see any difference in their graphs at all. Why not?

7-131. This problem is a checkpoint for completing the square to find the vertex of a parabola. It will be referred to as Checkpoint 7B.

Complete the square to change the equation $y = 2x^2 - 4x + 5$ into graphing form. Identify the vertex of the parabola and sketch the graph.

Check your answers by referring to the Checkpoint 7B materials located at the back of your book.

Ideally, at this point you are comfortable working with these types of problems and can solve them correctly. If you feel that you need more confidence when solving these types of problems, then review the Checkpoint 7B materials and try the practice problems provided. From this point on, you will be expected to do problems like these correctly and with confidence.

7-132. Find the x- and y-intercepts of the graphs of each of the following equations.

a. $y = 2x^3 - 10x^2 - x$

b. $y + 2 = \log_3(x - 1)$

7-133. The average cost of movie tickets is $9.50. If the cost is increasing 4% per year, in how many years will the cost double?

7-134. Change each equation to graphing form. For each equation, find the domain and range and determine if it is a function.

a. $y = -2x^2 - x + 13$

b. $y = -3x^2 - 6x + 12$

7-135. Too Tall Thomas has put Rodney's book bag on the snack-shack roof. Rodney goes to borrow a ladder from the school custodian. The tallest ladder available is 10 feet long and the roof is 9 feet from the ground. Rodney places the ladder's tip at the edge of the roof. The ladder is unsafe if the angle it makes with the ground is more than 60°. Is this a safe situation? Justify your conclusion.

7-136.   Deniz's computer is infected with a virus that will erase information from her hard drive. It will erase information quickly at first, but as time goes on, the rate at which information is erased will decrease. In t minutes after the virus starts erasing information, $5{,}000{,}000(\frac{1}{2})^t$ bytes of information remain on the hard drive.

   a.   Before the virus starts erasing, how many bytes of information are on Deniz's hard drive?

   b.   After how many minutes will there be 1000 bytes of information left on the drive?

   c.   When will the hard drive be completely erased?

7-137.   Graph $f(x) = |x - 6| - 4$.

   a.   Explain how you can graph this without making an $x \to y$ table, but using parent graphs.

   b.   Graph $g(x) = ||x - 6| - 4|$. Explain how you can graph $g(x)$ without making an $x \to y$ table by using your earlier graph.

7.2.3   What is the period of a function?

Period of a Cyclic Function

In Lesson 7.2.2, you found a place for a new parameter in the general form of a trigonometric equation and discovered that it must have something to do with the period. By the end of this lesson, you will have the tools you need to find the equation for any sine or cosine graph and will be able to graph any sine or cosine equation. In other words, you will learn the graph $\leftrightarrow$ equation connection. The following questions can help your team stay focused on the purpose of this lesson.

| Table |
| Graph $\longleftrightarrow$ Equation |
| Unit Circle or Situation |

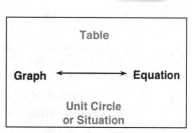

How can we write the equation for any sine or cosine graph?

How can we graph any sine or cosine function?

7-138.   Find the period for each of the following situations:

   a.   The input is the angle θ in the unit circle and the output is the cosine of θ.

   b.   The input is time and the output is the average daily temperature in New York.

   c.   The input is the distance Nurse Nina has traveled along the hallway and the output is the distance of bloody drips from the midline of the hallway.

7-139.   Make sure your graphing calculator is in radian mode.

   a.   Set the domain and range of the viewing window so that you would see just one complete cycle of $y = \sin x$. What is the domain for one cycle? What is the range?

   b.   Graph $y = \sin x$, $y = \sin(0.5x)$, $y = \sin(2x)$, $y = \sin(3x)$, and $y = \sin(5x)$. Make a sketch and answer the following questions for each equation.

       i.   How many cycles of each graph appear on the screen?

       ii.   The **midline** is the horizontal axis that goes through the center of the graph. What is the equation for the midline of these graphs?

       iii. What is the **amplitude** (height above the midline) of each graph?

       iv.   What is the period (cycle length) of each graph?

       v.   Is each equation a function?

   c.   Make a conjecture about the graph of $y = \sin(bx)$ with respect to each of the questions (*i*) through (*v*) above. If you cannot make a conjecture yet, try more examples.

   d.   Create at least three of your own examples to check your conjectures. Be sure to include sketches of your graphs.

   e.   What is the relationship between the period of a sine graph and the value of *b* in its equation?

7-140.   Refer to the graph you made by swinging a pendulum in Lesson 7.1.1. Decide where to draw *x*- and *y*-axes and find the equation of your graph. Is there more than one possible equation? Be prepared to share your strategies with the class.

Core Connections Algebra 2

7-141.   *Without* using a graphing calculator, describe each of the
         following functions by stating the amplitude, period, horizontal
         shift, and midline (vertical shift). Using this information, sketch
         the graph of each function. *After* you have completed each
         graph, check your sketch with a graphing calculator and correct
         and explain any errors.

a. $y = \sin 2(x - \frac{\pi}{6})$ b. $y = 3 + \sin(\frac{1}{3}x)$

c. $y = 3\sin(4x)$ d. $y = \sin\frac{1}{2}(x + 1)$

e. $y = -\sin 3(x - \frac{\pi}{3})$ f. $y = -1 + \sin(2x - \frac{\pi}{2})$

7-142.   Farah and Thu were working on writing the
         equation of a sine function for the graph at right.
         They figured out that the amplitude is 3, the
         horizontal shift is $\frac{\pi}{4}$ and the midline is $y = -2$.
         They can see that the period is π, but they
         disagree on the equation. Farah has written
         $f(x) = 3\sin 2(x - \frac{\pi}{4}) - 2$ and Thu has written
         $f(x) = 3\sin(2x - \frac{\pi}{4}) - 2$.

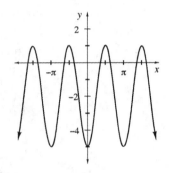

a.   Whose equation is correct? How can you be sure?

b.   Graph the incorrect equation and explain how it is different from the
     original graph.

7-143.   Look back at the general equation you wrote for the family of sine functions in
         problem 7-114. Now that you have learned how the period affects the equation,
         work with your team to add a new parameter (call it b) that allows your general
         equation to account for any transformation of the sine function, including
         changes in the length of each cycle. Be prepared to share your general equation
         with the class.

7-144.   Use what you learned in class to complete parts (a) through (c) below.

   a.   Describe what the graph of $y = 3\sin(\frac{1}{2}x)$ will look like compared to the graph of $y = \sin x$.

   b.   Sketch both graphs on the same set of axes.

   c.   Explain the similarities and differences between the two graphs.

7-145.   What is the period of $y = \sin(2\pi x)$? How do you know?

7-146.   Colleen and Jolleen both used their calculators to find $\sin 30°$. Colleen got $\sin 30° = -0.9880316241$, but Jolleen got $\sin 30° = 0.5$. Is one of their calculators broken, or is something else going on? Why did they get different answers?

7-147.   Ceirin's teacher promised a quiz for the next day, so Ceirin called Adel to review what they had done in class. *"Suppose I have $y = \sin 2x$,"* said Ceirin, *"what will its graph look like?"*

"It will be horizontally compressed by a factor of 2," replied Adel, *"so the period must be π."*

"Okay, now let's say I want to shift it one unit to the right. Do I just subtract 1 from x, like always?"

"I think so," said Adel, *"but let's check on the graphing calculator."* They proceeded to check on their calculators. After a few moments they both spoke at the same time.

"Rats," said Ceirin, *"it isn't right."*

"Cool," said Adel, *"it works."*

When they arrived at school the next morning, they compared the equations they had put in their graphing calculators while they talked on the phone. One had $y = \sin 2x - 1$, while the other had $y = \sin 2(x - 1)$.

Which equation was correct? Did they both subtract 1 from x? Explain. Describe the rule for shifting a graph one unit to the right in a way that avoids this confusion.

7-148.   George was solving the equation $(2x-1)(x+3)=4$ and he got the solutions $x=\frac{1}{2}$ and $x=-3$. Jeffrey came along and said, *"You made a big mistake! You set each factor equal to zero, but it's not equal to zero, it's equal to 4. So you have to set each factor equal to 4 and then solve."* Who is correct? Show George and Jeffrey how to solve this equation. To be sure that you are correct, check your solutions.

7-149.   Compute the value of each expression without using a calculator.

    a. $\log(8)+\log(125)$ b. $\log_{25}(125)$

    c. $\frac{1}{2}\log(25)+\log(20)$ d. $7^{\log_7(12)}$

7-150.   An exponential function $y=km^x+b$ passes through $(3,7.5)$ and $(4,6.25)$. It also has an asymptote at $y=5$.

    a.   Find the equation of the function.

    b.   If the equation also passes through $(8,w)$, what is the value of w?

7-151.   Consider the equation $f(x)=3(x+4)^2-8$.

    a.   Find an equation of a function $g(x)$ such that $f(x)$ and $g(x)$ intersect in only one point.

    b.   Find an equation of a function $h(x)$ such that $f(x)$ and $h(x)$ intersect in no points.

7.2.4 What are the connections?

Graph ↔ Equation

In the past few lessons, you have been developing the understanding necessary to graph a cyclic equation without making a table and to write an equation from a cyclic graph. In today's lesson, you will strengthen your understanding of the connections between a cyclic equation and its graph. By the end of this lesson, you will be able to answer the following questions:

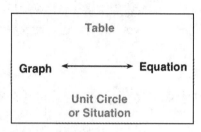

Does it matter if we use sine or cosine?

What do we need to know to make a complete graph or write an equation?

7-152.   What do you need to know about the sine or cosine functions to graph them or write their equations? Talk with your team and write a list of all of the attributes of a sine or cosine function that you need to know to write an equation and graph it.

7-153.   CREATE-A-CURVE

Split your team into pairs. With your partner, you will create your own sine or cosine function, write its equation, and draw its graph. Be sure to keep your equation and graph a secret! Start by choosing whether you will work with a sine or a cosine function.

a.   Half the distance from the highest point to the lowest point is called the **amplitude**. You can also think of amplitude as the vertical stretch. What is the amplitude of your function?

b.   How far to the left or right of the *y*-axis will your graph begin? In other words, what will be the **horizontal shift** of your function?

c.   How much above or below the *x*-axis will the center of your graph be? In other words, what will be the **midline** of your function?

d.   What will the **period** of your function be?

e.   What will the **orientation** of your graph in relation to $y = \sin x$ or $y = \cos x$ be? Is it the same or is it flipped?

f.   Now that you have decided on all of the attributes for your function, write its equation.

7-154. Copy the equation for your curve from problem 7-153 on a clean sheet of paper. Trade papers with another pair of students.

    a. Sketch a graph of the equation you received from the other pair of students.

    b. When you are finished with your graph, give it back to the other pair so they can check the accuracy of your graph.

7-155. When you look at a graph and prepare to write an equation for it, do you think it matters if you choose sine or cosine? Which do you think will work best?

With your team, find *at least four* different equations for the graph at right. Be prepared to share your equations with the class.

    a. Did it matter if you choose sine or cosine?

    b. Which of your equations do you prefer? Why?

7-156. Brenna's mom, Mrs. Herstone, is watching Brenna playing at the park. Some children are pushing Brenna around the merry-go-round. Mrs. Herstone decides to take some data, so she started her stopwatch. At 0.5 seconds Brenna is farthest from Mrs. Herstone, 26 feet away. When the stopwatch reads 4.2 seconds, Brenna is closest at 12 feet away. Find a cyclic equation that models the distance Brenna is from Mrs. Herstone over time if the merry-go-round is spinning at a constant rate.

7-157.   LEARNING LOG

In your Learning Log, write your ideas about the target
questions for this lesson: *Does it matter if I use sine or
cosine? What do I need to know to make a complete graph
or write an equation?* Title this entry "Cyclic Equations
and Graphs" and label it with today's date.

METHODS AND MEANINGS

General Equation for Sine Functions

The general equation for the **sine function** is $y = a\sin[b(x - h)] + k$.

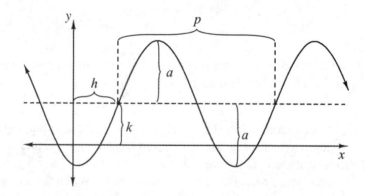

The **amplitude** (half of the distance between the highest and the lowest
points) is **a**.

The **period** is the length of one cycle. It is labeled **p** on the graph.

The number of cycles in 2π is **b**.

The **horizontal shift** is **h**.

The **vertical shift** is **k**. The **midline** is $y = k$.

7-158. Susan knew how to shift $y = \sin x$ to get the graph at right, but she wondered if it would be possible to get the same graph by shifting $y = \cos x$.

    a. Is it possible to write a cosine function for this graph?

    b. If you think it is possible, find an equation that does it. If you think it is impossible, explain why.

    c. Adlai said, *"I can get that graph without shifting to the right or left."* What equation did he write?

7-159. In the function $y = 4\sin(6x)$, how many cycles of sine are there from 0 to 2π? How long is each cycle (i.e., what is the period)?

7-160. Write the equation of a sinusoidal function that has an amplitude of 7 and a period of 8π. Sketch its graph.

7-161. Recall the strategies you developed for converting degrees to radians. How could you reverse that? Convert each of the following angle measures. Be sure to show all of your work.

    a. π radians to degrees   b. 3π radians to degrees

    c. 30 degrees to radians   d. $\frac{\pi}{4}$ radians to degrees

    e. 225 degrees to radians   f. $\frac{3\pi}{2}$ radians to degrees

7-162. Find the exact value for each of the following trig expressions. For parts (g) and (h), solve the equations and assume that $0 \le \theta \le 2\pi$.

    a. $\cos\left(\frac{3\pi}{4}\right) =$ b. $\tan\left(\frac{4\pi}{3}\right) =$

    c. $\sin\left(\frac{11\pi}{6}\right) =$ d. $\sin\left(\frac{3\pi}{4}\right) =$

    e. $\tan\left(\frac{5\pi}{4}\right) =$ f. $\tan\left(\frac{17\pi}{6}\right) =$

    g. $\tan(\theta) = 1$ h. $\tan(\theta) = -1$

7-163.   Solve this system of equations: $5x - 4y - 6z = -19$
$$-2x + 2y + z = 5$$
$$3x - 6y - 5z = -16$$

7-164.   Use the Zero Product Property to solve each equation in parts (a) and (b) below.

a. $x(2x + 1)(3x - 5) = 0$ b. $(x - 3)(x - 2) = 12$

c.   Write an equation and show how you can use the Zero Product Property to solve it.

7-165.   Find a quadratic equation whose graph has each of the following characteristics:

a.   No x-intercepts and a negative y-intercept.

b.   One x-intercept and a positive y-intercept.

c.   Two x-intercepts and a negative y-intercept.

7-166.   A two-bedroom house in Seattle was worth \$400,000 in 2005. If it appreciates at a rate of 3.5% each year:

a.   How much will it be worth in 2015?

b.   When will it be worth \$800,000?

c.   In Jacksonville, houses are depreciating at 2% per year. If a house is worth \$200,000 now, how much value will it have lost in 10 years?

Chapter 7 Closure What have I learned?

Reflection and Synthesis

The activities below offer you a chance to reflect about what you have learned during this chapter. As you work, look for concepts that you feel very comfortable with, ideas that you would like to learn more about, and topics you need more help with. Look for connections between ideas as well as connections with material you learned previously.

TEAM BRAINSTORM

What have you studied in this chapter? What ideas were important in what you learned? With your team, brainstorm a list. Be as detailed as you can. To help get you started, a list of Learning Log entries and Math Notes boxes are below.

What topics, ideas, and words that you learned *before* this chapter are connected to the new ideas in this chapter? Again, be as detailed as you can.

How long can you make your list? Challenge yourselves. Be prepared to share your team's ideas with the class.

Learning Log Entries
- Lesson 7.1.3 – Unit Circle $\leftrightarrow$ Graph for $s(\theta) = \sin\theta$
- Lesson 7.1.5 – Radians
- Lesson 7.2.4 – Cyclic Equations and Graphs

Math Notes
- Lesson 7.1.2 – Special Right Triangle Relationships
- Lesson 7.1.5 – Radians
- Lesson 7.1.6 – Reference Angle
- Lesson 7.1.7 – Sine, Cosine, and Tangent
- Lesson 7.2.4 – General Equation for Sine Functions

② MAKING CONNECTIONS

Below is a list of the vocabulary used in this chapter. Make sure that you are familiar with all of these words and know what they mean. Refer to the glossary or index for any words that you do not yet understand.

amplitude	angle	cosine
cyclic function	horizontal shift	midline
orientation	parameter	period
radian	reference angle	sine
special right triangles	tangent	theta (θ)
trigonometric functions	unit circle	vertical shift

Make a concept map showing all of the connections you can find among the key words and ideas listed above. To show a connection between two words, draw a line between them and explain the connection. A word can be connected to any other word as long as you can justify the connection.

While you are making your map, your team may think of related words or ideas that are not listed here. Be sure to include these ideas on your concept map.

③   PORTFOLIO: EVIDENCE OF MATHEMATICAL PROFICIENCY

This section gives you an opportunity to show growth in
your understanding of key mathematical ideas over time
as you complete this course.

Part 1: You may have done this problem before. You
have grown mathematically since then. Explain
everything that you know about $f(x) = 2^x - 3$. Be
sure to include everything you have learned since
the last time you did this problem.

Part 2: Compare your responses to this "Growth Over Time" problem. Write
an evaluation of your growth based on your responses. Consider each
of the following questions as you write your answer. If you only did the
problem twice, then answer accordingly.

- What new concepts did you include the second time you did the
  problem? In what ways was your response better than your first
  attempt?

- How was your final version different from the first two? What new
  ideas did you include?

- Did you omit anything in the final version that you used in one of the
  earlier versions? Why did you omit it?

- Rate your three attempts by making three bars like the ones below
  and shading each bar (left to right) to represent how much you knew
  on each attempt.

First Attempt:	
Second	
Final Attempt:	

- Is there anything you want to add to your current version? If so, add
  it and keep this version for future reference.

Include a copy of the unit circle you built in Lesson 7.1.6 in your portfolio.
Make enhancements as necessary.

Your teacher may give you the Chapter 7 Closure Resource Page:
Trigonometric Functions and the Unit Circle Graphic Organizer page to
work on.

④ WHAT HAVE I LEARNED?

Most of the problems in this section represent typical problems found in this chapter. They serve as a gauge for you. You can use them to determine which types of problems you can do well and which types of problems require further study and practice. Even if your teacher does not assign this section, it is a good idea to try these problems and find out for yourself what you know and what you still need to work on.

Solve each problem as completely as you can. The table at the end of the closure section has answers to these problems. It also tells you where you can find additional help and practice with problems like these.

CL 7-167. Describe how you can tell the difference between the graphs of $y = \sin x$ and $y = \cos x$. Be sure to justify your ideas.

CL 7-168. Convert the following angles to radians.

a. 225°   b. 75°   c. −15°   d. 330°

CL 7-169. Sketch each of the following angles in its own unit circle.

a. An angle that has a positive cosine and a negative sine.

b. All angles that have a sine of 0.5.

c. An angle that measures $\frac{4\pi}{3}$ radians. Find its exact sine.

d. An angle with a negative cosine and a positive tangent.

CL 7-170. Without using a calculator, give the exact value of each expression.

a. $\sin 60°$ b. $\cos 180°$ c. $\tan 225°$

d. $\sin \frac{\pi}{4}$ e. $\cos \frac{2\pi}{3}$ f. $\tan \frac{3\pi}{2}$

CL 7-171.   If an angle between 0 and 2π radians has a sine of –0.5, what is its cosine? How do you know?

CL 7-172.   Find the exact values of x and y in the drawings below.

a.

b.

CL 7-173.   Rewrite each equation below in graphing form and sketch its graph. Then state the domain and range and whether or not it is a function.

a. $y = 3x^2 - 30x + 73$

b. $x^2 + y^2 - 6x + 4y + 4 = 0$

CL 7-174.   Solve each equation to the nearest thousandth.

a. $2 \cdot 3^x = 40.8$

b. $3x^4 = 27$

c. $\log_5(2x+1) = 3$

d. $\log(x) + \log(2x) = 5$

CL 7-175.   Find an equation for an exponential function that passes through the points $(1, 22), (3, 20.125)$, and has a horizontal asymptote at $y = 20$.

CL 7-176.   Check your answers using the table at the end of this section. Which problems do you feel confident about? Which problems were hard? Have you worked on problems like these in previous chapters math classes? Sort the problems into three groups: the ones you are confident you can do, the ones you need more practice with, and the ones you need further help to understand.

Answers and Support for Closure Activity #4
What Have I Learned?

Note: MN = Math Note, LL = Learning Log

Problem	Solutions	Need Help?	More Practice
CL 7-167.	The graph of $y = \cos x$ has a y-intercept of 1 because $\cos 0 = 1$ and the base of the triangle at 0 degrees in the unit circle is 1 unit long. The graph of $y = \sin x$ has a y-intercept of 0 because $\sin 0 = 0$ and the height of the triangle at 0 degrees in the unit circle is 0 units.	Lessons 7.1.2, 7.1.3, and 7.1.4 MN: 7.1.7 LL: 7.2.4	Problems 7-14, 7-36, 7-47, 7-48, 7-50, 7-51, 7-54, 7-62, 7-63, 7-65, and 7-114
CL 7-168.	a. $\frac{5\pi}{4}$　　b. $\frac{5\pi}{12}$ c. $-\frac{\pi}{12}$　　d. $\frac{11\pi}{6}$	Lesson 7.1.5	Problems 7-77, 7-92, 7-106, 7-107, and 7-161
CL 7-169.	a. 　b. c. 　$\sin \frac{4\pi}{3} = -\frac{\sqrt{3}}{2}$ d.	Lessons 7.1.3 and 7.1.6 MN: 7.1.5	Problems 7-63, 7-75, and 7-104
CL 7-170.	a. $\frac{\sqrt{3}}{2}$　　b. -1 c. 1　　　d. $\frac{\sqrt{2}}{2}$ e. $-\frac{1}{2}$　　f. undefined	Lessons 7.1.5 and 7.1.6	Problems 7-78, 7-90, 7-104, 7-105, 7-123, and 7-162
CL 7-171.	$\frac{\sqrt{3}}{2}$ or $-\frac{\sqrt{3}}{2}$; If the sine is negative, the angle must lie in the 3rd or 4th quadrant and 0.5 is one leg of a 30°-60°-90° triangle.	Lessons 7.1.3, 7.1.4, and 7.1.6 MN: 7.1.7	Problem 7-34, 7-52, 7-63, 7-77, and 7-104

Problem	Solutions	Need Help?	More Practice
CL 7-172.	a. $x = 5\sqrt{2}$, $y = 5\sqrt{2}$ b. $x = 60°$, $y = 30°$	MN: 7.1.2	Problems 7-6 and 7-15
CL 7-173.	a. $y = 3(x-5)^2 - 2$, $-\infty < x < \infty$, $y \geq -2$; it is a function. b. $(x-3)^2 + (y+2)^2 = 9$, $0 \leq x \leq 6$, $-5 \leq y \leq 1$; it is not a function.	Lessons 2.1.3, 2.1.4, and 2.2.3 Checkpoint 7B MN: 2.1.4 and 2.2.3	Problems 7-41, 7-109, 7-131, and 7-134
CL 7-174.	a. $x \approx 2.745$ b. $x \approx 1.732$ c. $x = 62$ d. $x \approx 223.607$	Lessons 6.2.1 and 6.2.2	Problems 7-18, 7-39, 7-83 part (a), 7-94, and 7-149
CL 7-175.	$y = 8(\frac{1}{4})^x + 20$	Lesson 6.2.3	Problems 7-20 and 7-136

Chapter 8

In this chapter you will expand your knowledge of families of functions to include polynomial functions. As you investigate the equation ↔ graph connection for polynomials, you will learn how to search for factors (which can help you find x-intercepts) and how to use division to find additional factors.

When you investigate the graphs of polynomials and systems involving polynomials, you will see many that appear not to intersect. As you investigate these systems further, you will learn about imaginary and complex numbers.

In the last section of the chapter, you will apply your knowledge of polynomials to model some of the attractions at a county fair.

Guiding Question

Mathematically proficient students reason abstractly and quantitatively.

As you work through this chapter, ask yourself:

How can the degree of a polynomial help me determine the nature of its graph or a possible equation?

Chapter Outline

Section 8.1 You will investigate polynomial functions and learn how to sketch graphs of them without using a graphing calculator. You will also learn how to find polynomial equations from their graphs.

Section 8.2 Here you will solve equations you could not solve earlier by expanding the set of numbers you use. You will be introduced to a number system called *complex numbers*. You will learn what imaginary and complex numbers are, their properties, and how they are used to represent solutions when graphs do not intersect.

Section 8.3 In this section, you will learn how to divide polynomials by applying your knowledge of area models and factoring. You will solve equations using polynomial division to factor polynomials.

8.1.1 How can I describe the graph?

Sketching Graphs of Polynomial Functions

In previous courses and chapters, you learned how to graph many types of functions, including lines and parabolas. Today you will work with your team to apply what you know to more complicated **polynomial** equations. Just as quadratic polynomial equations can be written in standard or factored form, other polynomial equations can be written in standard or factored form. For example, $y = x^4 - 4x^3 - 3x^2 + 10x + 8$ is in standard form, but it can be written in factored form as $y = (x+1)^2(x-2)(x-4)$.

During this lesson, you will develop techniques for sketching the graph of a polynomial function from its equation, and you will justify why those techniques work.

8-1. The Mathamericaland Carnival Company has decided to build a new roller coaster to use at this year's county fair. The new coaster will have a very special feature: part of the ride will be underground. The designers will use polynomial functions to describe different pieces of the track. Part of the design is shown at right. Your task is to guess a possible equation to represent the track and test it on your graphing calculator. To help get an idea of what to try, start by checking the graphs of the equations given below. Think about how the graphs are the same and how they are different.

$$y = x(x-2)$$
$$y = (x-2)^2$$
$$y = x(x-2)(x-3)$$

Your Task: Use the information you found by graphing the above equations to help you make guesses about the equation that would produce the graph of the roller coaster. Once you have found a graph that has a shape close to this one, try zooming in or changing the viewing window on your graphing calculator to see the details better. Keep track of what you tried and the equations you find that fit most accurately.

8-2.   POLYNOMIAL FUNCTION INVESTIGATION

In this investigation, you will determine which information in a polynomial equation can help you sketch its graph.

Your Task: With your team, create summary statements explaining the relationship between a polynomial equation and its graph. To accomplish this task, first divide up the equations listed below so each team member is responsible for two or three of them. Make a complete graph of each of your functions. Whenever possible, start by making a sketch of your graph without using your graphing calculator. Then, as a team, share your observations including your responses to the Discussion Points. Choose two or three equations that can be used to represent all of your findings. You can choose them from the list below, or you can create new ones as a team.

The form of your presentation to the class can be on a poster, a display to be projected onto the board or as a PowerPoint™ presentation. Whichever format your teacher decides, make sure you include complete graphs and summary statements that are well justified.

$P_1(x) = (x-2)(x+5)^2$ $P_2(x) = 2(x-2)(x+2)(x-3)$

$P_3(x) = x^4 - 21x^2 + 20x$ $P_4(x) = (x+3)^2(x+1)(x-1)(x-5)$

$P_5(x) = -0.1x(x+4)^3$ $P_6(x) = x^4 - 9x^2$

$P_7(x) = 0.2x(x+1)(x-3)(x+4)$ $P_8(x) = x^4 - 4x^3 - 3x^2 + 10x + 8$

Discussion Points

What can we predict from looking at the equation of a polynomial?
Why does this make sense?

Which form of a polynomial equation is most useful for making a graph?
What information does it give?

How can we use the equation to help predict what a useful window might be?

Which examples are most helpful in finding the connections between the equation and the graph?

How does changing the exponent on one of the factors change the graph?

Further Guidance

8-3. As a team, examine the first polynomial $P_1(x) = (x-2)(x+5)^2$.

    a. To which family of functions does it belong? How do you know? Based on its equation, sketch the shape of its graph.

    b. Now use your graphing calculator to graph $P_1(x)$. Label the x-intercepts. How are the x-intercepts related to the equation? "Reading" from left to right along the x-axis, describe the graph before the first x-intercept, between x-intercepts, and after the last x-intercept.

8-4. Continuing your work as a team, examine the equation $P_2(x) = 2(x-2)(x+2)(x-3)$.

    a. How many distinct (different) linear factors are there? How many x-intercepts would you predict it would have on its graph? Draw the graph and label the x-intercepts. How is this graph similar to or different from the graph of $P_1(x)$?

    b. Does the constant factor of 2 have any effect on the x-intercepts? On the shape of the graph? On the y-intercept? How would the graph change if the constant factor of 2 were changed to -2?

8-5. What is different about $P_3(x) = x^4 - 21x^2 + 20x$? What x-intercept(s) can you determine from the equation, before graphing with the calculator? Explain how you know. Use the graph to figure out exactly what the other intercepts are. Explain how you can prove that your answers are exact.

8-6. With your team, divide up the work to investigate $P_4(x)$ through $P_8(x)$ and continue your investigation, referring back to the "Your Task" statement and the discussion points in problem 8-2.

         ———— *Further Guidance* ————
               section ends here.

8-7. LEARNING LOG

Based on what your team learned and on the class discussion that followed, record a list of useful strategies for graphing polynomial functions. Use as many of the new vocabulary words as you can and write down the ones you are not sure of yet. You will add to and refine this list over the next several lessons. Title this entry "Graphing Polynomials" and label it with today's date.

METHODS AND **M**EANINGS

Polynomials, Degree, Coefficients

Refer to the Math Notes box in Lesson 3.1.3 for an explanation of a **polynomial** in one variable.

Polynomials with one variable (often x) are usually arranged with powers of x in order, starting with the highest, left to right.

The highest power of the variable in a polynomial of one variable is called the **degree** of the polynomial. The numbers that multiply each term are called **coefficients**. See the examples below.

Example 1: $f(x) = 7x^5 + 2.5x^3 - \frac{1}{2}x + 7$ is a polynomial function of degree 5 with coefficients $7, 0, 2.5, 0, -\frac{1}{2}$, and 7. Note that the last term, 7, is called the **constant term** but represents the variable expression $7x^0$, since $x^0 = 1$.

Example 2: $y = 2(x+2)(x+5)$ is a polynomial in factored form with degree 2 because it can be written in standard form as $y = 2x^2 + 14x + 20$. It has coefficients 2, 14, and 20.

8-8. For each equation below, make tables that include x-values from –2 to 2 and draw each graph.

    a. $y = (x-1)^2(x+1)$

    b. $y = (x-1)^2(x+1)^2$

    c. $y = x^3 - 4x$

    d.   What are the parent functions for these equations?

8-9.   **Polynomials** are expressions that can be written as a sum of terms of the form:

$$(\text{any number}) \cdot x^{(\text{whole number})}$$

Which of the following equations are polynomial equations? For those that are not polynomials, explain why not. Check the Lesson 8.1.1 Math Notes box for further details about polynomials.

a. $f(x) = 8x^5 + x^2 + 6.5x^4 + 6$ b. $y = \frac{3}{5}x^6 + 19x^2$

c. $y = 2^x + 8$ d. $f(x) = 9 + \sqrt{x} - 3$

e. $P(x) = 7(x-3)(x+5)^2$ f. $y = x^2 + \frac{1}{x^2+5}$

g.   Write an equation for a new polynomial function and then write an equation for a new function that is not a polynomial.

8-10.   Describe the possible numbers of intersections for each of the following pairs of graphs. Sketch a graph for each possibility. For example, a circle could intersect a line twice, once, or not at all. Your solution to each part should include all of the possibilities and a sketched example of each one.

a.   Two different lines.   b.   A line and a parabola.

c.   Two different parabolas.   d.   A parabola and a circle.

8-11.   Solve the following system: $y = x^2 - 5$
                                                              $y = x + 1$

8-12.   A table can be used as a useful tool for finding some inverse functions. When the function has only one x in it, the function can be described with a sequence of operations, each applied to the previous result. Consider the following table for $f(x) = 2\sqrt{x-1} + 3$.

	1st	2nd	3rd	4th
What f does to x:	subtracts 1	$\sqrt{\ }$	multiplies by 2	adds 3

Since the inverse must undo these operations, in the opposite order, the table for $f^{-1}(x)$ would look like the one below.

	1st	2nd	3rd	4th
What does f^{-1} to x:	subtracts 3	divides by 2	$(\ )^2$	adds 1

a.   Copy and complete the following table for $g^{-1}(x)$ if $g(x) = \frac{1}{3}(x+1)^2 - 2$

	1st	2nd	3rd	4th
What g does to x:	adds 1	$(\ )^2$	divides by 3	subtracts 2
What g^{-1} does to x:			$\sqrt{\ }$	

b.   Write the equations for $f^{-1}(x)$ and $g^{-1}(x)$.

8-13.   Describe the difference between the graphs of $y = x^3 - x$ and $y = x^3 - x + 5$.

8-14.   Sketch the graph of each equation below.

a. $y = \sin(2\pi x)$ b. $y = 3\sin(\pi x)$ c. $y = 2\sin(2\pi x) + 1$

8-15.   An arithmetic sequence starts out $-23, -19, -15 \ldots$

a.   What is the equation?

b.   How many times must the generator be applied so that the result is greater than 10,000?

8-16.   Without a calculator, find two solutions $0° \le \theta < 360°$ that make each of the following equations true.

a. $\cos\theta = \frac{1}{2}$ b. $\tan\theta = -1$ c. $\sin\theta = \frac{\sqrt{3}}{2}$ d. $\cos\theta = -\frac{\sqrt{3}}{2}$

8-17.   Which of the following equations are polynomial functions? For each one that is not, justify why not.

    a. $y = 3x^2 + 2x^2 + x$ b. $y = (x-1)^2(x-2)^2$

    c. $y = x^2 + 2^x$ d. $y = 3x - 1$

    e. $y = (x-2)^2 - 1$ f. $y^2 = (x-2)^2 - 1$

    g. $y = \frac{1}{x^2} + \frac{1}{x} + \frac{1}{2}$ h. $y = \frac{1}{2}x + \frac{1}{3}$

    i. $y = x$ j. $y = -7$

8-18.   Samantha thinks that the equation $(x-4)^2 + (y-3)^2 = 25$ is equivalent to the equation $(x-4) + (y-3) = 5$. Is she correct? Are the two equations equivalent? Explain how you know. If they are not equivalent, explain Samantha's mistake.

8-19.   Find the **roots** (the solutions when $y = 0$) of each of the following polynomial functions.

    a. $y = x^2 - 6x + 8$ b. $f(x) = x^2 - 6x + 9$ c. $y = x^3 - 4x$

8-20.   Sketch a graph of $y = x^2 - 7$.

    a.   How many roots does this graph have?

    b.   What are the roots of the function?

8-21.   Solve $x^2 + 2x - 5 = 0$.

    a.   How many x-intercepts does $y = x^2 + 2x - 5$ have?

    b.   Approximately where does the graph of $y = x^2 + 2x - 5$ cross the x-axis?

8-22.   Graph the inequality $x^2 + y^2 \le 25$, and then describe its graph in words.

8-23. Find x if $2^{p(x)} = 4$ and $p(x) = x^2 - 4x - 3$.

8-24. Start with the graph of $y = 3^x$, then write new equations that will shift the graph as described below.

a. Down 4 units.   b. Right 7 units.

8-25. THE COUNTY FAIR FERRIS WHEEL

Consider this picture of a Ferris wheel. The wheel
has a 60-foot diameter and is drawn on a set of
axes with the Ferris wheel's hub (center) at the
origin. Use a table like the one below and draw a
graph that relates the angle (in standard position)
of the spoke leading to your seat to the
approximate height of the top of your seat above
or below the height of the central hub. The table
below starts at –90°, your starting position before you ride around the wheel.

x (angle)	–90°	–45°	0°	45°	90°	135°	180°	....	270°
y (height)	–30'								

a. The wheel goes around (counter-clockwise) several times during a ride. How could you reflect this fact in your graph? Update your graph.

b. What is the maximum distance above or below the center that the top of your seat attains during the ride?

c. Find an equation to fit the County Fair Ferris wheel ride.

8.1.2 How can I predict the graph?

More Graphs of Polynomials

Today you will use what you learned in the Polynomial Function Investigation in Lesson 8.1.1 to respond to some questions. Thinking about how to answer these questions should help you clarify and expand on some of your ideas as well as help you learn how to use the polynomial vocabulary.

8-26.   As directed by your teacher, use your finger to trace an approximate graph of polynomial functions in the air. Alternatively, you may sketch each of the polynomial functions below quickly on paper. Just sketch the graph without the x- and y-axes.

    a. $P(x) = (x+10)(x+7)(x-12)$

    b. $Q(x) = (x+6)(x+3)(x-5)(x-8)$

    c. $R(x) = -(x+4)(x+2)(x-6)(x-10)$

    d. $W(x) = (x+7)^2(x-7)^2$

    e. $S(x) = (x+6)(x+3)(x-5)(x-8)(x-12)$

8-27.   Look back at the work you did in Lesson 8.1.1 problem 8-2, Polynomial Function Investigation. Then answer the following questions.

    a.   What is the maximum number of roots a polynomial of degree 3 can have? Sketch an example.

    b.   What do you think is the maximum number of roots a polynomial of degree n can have?

    c.   Can a polynomial of degree n have fewer than n roots? Under what conditions?

8-28. For each polynomial function shown below, state the minimum degree its equation could have.

i. *ii.* *iii.* *iv.*

a. Which of the graphs above show that as the *x*-values get very large, the *y*-values continue to get larger and larger?

b. How would you describe the other graphs for very large *x*-values?

c. When the *y*-values of a graph get very large as the *x*-values get large, the graph has **positive orientation**. When the *y*-values of a graph get very small as the *x*-values get large, the graph has **negative orientation**. How is each of the above graphs oriented?

8-29. For each graph in problem 8-28, you decided what the minimum degree of its equation could be. Under what circumstances could graphs that look the same as these have polynomial equations of a *higher* degree?

Consider the graphs of $y = (x-1)^2$ and $y = (x-1)^4$.

a. How are these graphs similar? How are they different?

b. Could the equation for graph (*ii*) from the previous problem be degree 4?

c. Could it have degree 5? Explain.

d. How is the graph of $y = x^3$ similar to or different from the graph of $y = x^5$?

e. How do the shapes of graphs of $y = (x-2)^3$ and $y = (x+1)^5$ with repeated factors differ from the shapes of graphs of equations that have three or five factors that are different from one another?

8-30. In the first example from the Polynomial Function Investigation, $P_1(x) = (x-2)(x+5)^2$, $(x+5)^2$ is a factor. This squared factor produces what is called a **double root** of the function.

a. What effect does this have on the graph?

b. Check your equations for a **triple root**. What effect does a triple root have on the graph?

8-31.   You can use a number line to represent the *x*-values for which a polynomial
         graph is above or below the *x*-axis. The bold parts of each number line below
         show where the output values of a polynomial function are positive. That is,
         where the graph is above the *x*-axis. The open circles show locations of the
         x-intercepts or roots of the function. Where there is no shading, the value of the
         function is negative. Sketch a possible graph to fit each number line, and then
         write a possible equation. Each number line represents the *x*-axis for a different
         polynomial.

a.   b.

c.   d.

8-32.   What can you say about the graphs of polynomial functions with an even degree
         compared to the graphs of polynomial functions with an odd degree? Use
         graphs from the Polynomial Functions Investigation (and maybe some others) to
         justify your response.

8-33.   Choose three of the polynomials you graphed in the Polynomial Functions
         Investigation (problem 8-2) and create number lines for their graphs similar to
         the ones in problem 8-31.

$P_1(x) = (x - 2)(x + 5)^2$ $P_2(x) = 2(x - 2)(x + 2)(x - 3)$

$P_3(x) = x^4 - 21x^2 + 20x$ $P_4(x) = (x + 3)^2(x + 1)(x - 1)(x - 5)$

$P_5(x) = -0.1x(x + 4)^3$ $P_6(x) = x^4 - 9x^2$

$P_7(x) = 0.2x(x + 1)(x - 3)(x + 4)$ $P_8(x) = x^4 - 4x^3 - 3x^2 + 10x + 8$

8-34.   Create a new number-line description (like the ones in problem 8-31) and then
         trade with a partner. (Each team member should create a different number line.)
         After you have traded, find a possible graph and equation for a polynomial
         function to fit the description you have received. Then justify your results to
         your team and check your team members' results.

8-35.   Without using a calculator, sketch rough graphs of the following functions.

a. $P(x) = -x(x + 1)(x - 3)$

b. $P(x) = (x - 1)^2(x + 2)(x - 4)$

c. $P(x) = (x + 2)^3(x - 4)$

METHODS AND MEANINGS

Roots and Zeros

The **roots** of a polynomial function, $p(x)$, are the **solutions** of the equation $p(x) = 0$. Another name for the roots of a function is **zeros of the function** because at each root, the value of the function is zero. The real roots (or zeros) of a function have the same value as the x-values of the x-intercepts of its graph because the x-intercepts are the points where the y-value of the function is zero.

Sometimes roots can be found by factoring and solving for $p(x) = 0$.

In the Parabola Lab investigation (Lesson 2.1.2), you discovered how to make a parabola "sit" on the x-axis (the polynomial has one root), and you looked at ways of making parabolas intersect the x-axis in two specific places (two roots).

Review & Preview

8-36.   Where does the graph $y = (x+3)^2 - 5$ cross the x-axis?

8-37.   If you were to graph the function $f(x) = (x-74)^2(x+29)$, where would the graph intersect the x-axis?

8-38.   For each pair of intercepts given below, write an equation for a quadratic function in standard form.

    a. $(-3,0)$ and $(2,0)$ b. $(-3,0)$ and $(\frac{1}{2},0)$

8-39.   What is the degree of each polynomial function below?

    a. $P(x) = 0.08x^2 + 28x$ b. $y = 8x^2 - \frac{1}{7}x^5 + 9$

    c. $f(x) = 5(x+3)(x-2)(x+7)$ d. $y = (x-3)^2(x+1)(x^3+1)$

8-40.   Consider the following types of graphs. Which graphs are polynomial functions? Explain your reasoning.

   a.   Parabolas   b.   Exponentials

   c.   Cubics   d.   Lines

   e.   Circles

8-41.   Graph each system below and shade the solution region.

   a. $y \geq x^2 - 4$ b. $y < 2x + 5$
        $y < -3x + 1$ $y \geq |x + 1|$

8-42.   A circle with its center on the line $y = 3x$ in the 1st quadrant is tangent to the y-axis.

   a.   If the radius is 2, what is the equation of the circle?

   b.   If the radius is 3, what is the equation of the circle?

8-43.   Sketch the graph of each function below on the same set of axes.

   a. $y = 2^x$ b. $y = 2^x + 5$ c. $y = 2^x - 5$

8-44.   For each equation, find two solutions $0° \leq \theta < 360°$, which make the equation true. You should not need a calculator.

   a. $\sin \theta = \frac{1}{2}$ b. $\tan \theta = \sqrt{3}$

   c. $\cos \theta = \frac{\sqrt{3}}{2}$ d. $\sin \theta = -\frac{\sqrt{2}}{2}$

8.1.3 How can I find the equation?

Stretch Factors for Polynomial Functions

In Lesson 8.1.2 you found possible equations for the graphs of polynomial functions based on their *x*-intercepts. Many of the sketches you used did not even include the scale on the *y*-axis. In this lesson, you will focus on figuring out equations that represent *all* of the points on the graphs.

8-45. Find reasonable equations for each of the following polynomial functions. Without using a graphing calculator, how can you check the accuracy of your equations? Were each of your equations accurate? If not, why do you think your equation(s) were not accurate?

a.

b.

c.

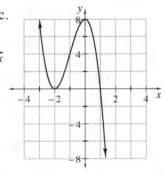

8-46. What is the difference between the graphs of the functions $y = x^2(x-3)(x+1)$ and $y = 3x^2(x-3)(x+1)$?

Core Connections Algebra 2

8-47. ARE THE INTERCEPTS ENOUGH?

Melvin wrote the equation
$y = (x + 3)(x + 1)(x - 2)^2$ to represent the graph at right.

a. Explain how you can decide whether the equation represents the graph. What can you do to the equation to make it a better fit for the graph? What equation would fit better?

b. Before you figured it out, you could have written the polynomial for this graph as $P(x) = a(x + 3)(x + 1)(x - 2)^2$. What if you did not have a graphing calculator, but you were told that the graph goes through the point (1, 16)? How could you use that information to determine the exact equation? Once you have decided on a method with your team, try it. How can you test the accuracy of your equation?

8-48. THE COUNTY FAIR COASTER RIDE

Now that you have more expertise with polynomial equations and their graphs, the Mathamericaland Carnival Company has hired your team to find the *exact* equation to represent its roller-coaster track.

The numbers along the *x*-axis are in hundreds of feet. At 250 feet from the starting point, the track will be 20 feet below the surface. This gives the point $(2.5, -0.2)$.

a. What degree polynomial represents the portion of the roller coaster represented by the graph at right?

b. What are the roots?

c. Find an exact equation for the polynomial that will generate the curve of the track.

d. What is the deepest point of the roller coaster's tunnel?

8-49.   Some polynomials have a stretch factor, just like the *a* in parabolas and other parent functions. Write an exact equation, including the stretch factor, for each graph below.

a.

b.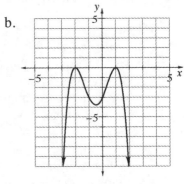

8-50.   Write a polynomial equation for a function with a graph that bounces off the *x*-axis at $(-1,0)$, crosses it at $(4,0)$, and goes through the point $(-2,-18)$.

8-51.   Armando came up with the equation $y = 3(x+1)^4(x-4)$ for problem 8-50. Does his equation fit all of the given criteria? Why or why not? Is it the same as the equation you came up with?

8-52.   What if problem 8-50 also had said that the graph went through the point $(1,-36)$? Is there still more than one possible equation? Explain.

8-53.   What information about the graph of a polynomial function is necessary to determine exactly one correct equation? Discuss this with your team.

METHODS AND MEANINGS

Notation for Polynomials

MATH NOTES

The **general equation** of a second-degree (quadratic) polynomial is often written in the form $f(x) = ax^2 + bx + c$, and the general equation of a third-degree (cubic) polynomial is often written in the form $f(x) = ax^3 + bx^2 + cx + d$.

For a polynomial with an undetermined degree n, it is unknown how many letters will be needed for the coefficients. Instead of using a, b, c, d, e, etc., mathematicians use only the letter a, and they used subscripts, as shown below.

$$f(x) = (a_n)x^n + (a_{n-1})x^{(n-1)} + \ldots + (a_1)x^1 + a_0$$

This general polynomial has degree n and coefficients $a_n, a_{n-1}, \ldots, a_1, a_0$.

For example, for $7x^4 - 5x^3 + 3x^2 + 7x + 8$, the degree is 4. In this specific case, a_n is a_4 and $a_4 = 7$, a_{n-1} is $a_3 = -5$, a_{n-2} is $a_2 = 3$, $a_1 = 7$, and $a_0 = 8$.

Review & Preview

8-54. What is the stretch factor for the equation of the graph in part (c) of problem 8-45? Write the exact equation of the function.

8-55. For each of the following polynomial expressions, find the degree, list the coefficients, and then label them a_0 through a_n. Refer to the example in the Math Notes box above about polynomial notation.

a. $6x^4 - 3x^3 + 5x^2 + x + 8$ b. $-5x^3 + 10x^2 + 8$ c. $-x^2 + x$

d. $x(x-3)(x-5)$ e. x f. 10

8-56. Write a polynomial equation for a graph that passes through the point $(-1, 60)$ and has three x-intercepts: $(-4, 0)$, $(1, 0)$, and $(3, 0)$.

8-57.   The *x*-intercepts of a quadratic polynomial are given below. Find a possible
         quadratic equation in standard form.

   a. $x = \frac{3}{4}, x = -2$ b. $x = -\sqrt{5}, x = \sqrt{5}$

8-58.   Solve the equation $\sqrt{5 - 2x} + 7 = 4$ and check your solution.

8-59.   Find the center and radius of each circle below.

   a. $(y - 7)^2 = 25 - (x - 3)^2$ b. $x^2 + y^2 + 10y = -9$

   c. $x^2 + y^2 + 18x - 8y + 47 = 0$ d. $y^2 + (x - 3)^2 = 1$

8-60.   Without using a calculator, find the solution to each equation.

   a. $2^x = 17$ b. $\log_3(x + 1) = 5$

   c. $\log_3(3^x) = 4$ d. $4^{\log_4(x)} = 7$

8-61.   Solve each absolute value inequality.

   a. $|2x + 1| < 5$ b. $2|3x - 2| \geq 10$

8-62.   Write a possible equation for the graph
         at right.

Core Connections Algebra 2

8.2.1 What are imaginary numbers?

Introducing Imaginary Numbers

In the past, you have not been able to solve some quadratic equations like $x^2 + 4 = 0$ and $x^2 + 1 = 0$, because there are no real numbers you can square to get a negative answer. To solve this issue, mathematicians created a new, expanded number system based on one new number. However, this was not the first time mathematicians had invented new numbers! To read about other such inventions, refer to the Historical Note that follows problem 8-63.

In this lesson, you will learn about imaginary numbers and how you can use them to solve equations you were previously unable to solve.

8-63. Consider the equation $x^2 = 2$.

a. How do you "undo" squaring a number?

b. When you solve $x^2 = 2$, how many solutions should you get?

c. How many x-intercepts does the graph of $y = x^2 - 2$ have?

d. Solve the equation $x^2 = 2$. Write your solutions both as radicals and as decimal approximations.

Historical Note: Irrational Numbers

In Ancient Greece, people believed that all numbers could be written as fractions of whole numbers (what are now called **rational numbers**). Many individuals realized later that some numbers could not be written as fractions (such as $\sqrt{2}$), and these individuals challenged the accepted beliefs. Some of the people who challenged the beliefs were exiled or outright killed over these challenges!

The Greeks knew that for a one-unit square, the length of the diagonal, squared, yielded 2. When it was shown that no rational number could do that, the existence of what are called **irrational numbers** was accepted and symbols like $\sqrt{2}$ were invented to represent them.

The problem $x^2 = 3$ also has no rational solutions; fractions can never work exactly. The rational (i.e., decimal) solutions that calculators and computers provide are only approximations; the exact answer can only be represented in radical form, namely, $\pm\sqrt{3}$.

8-64.   Mathematicians throughout history have resisted the idea that some equations may not be solvable. Still, it makes sense that $x^2 + 1 = 0$ cannot be solved because the graph of $y = x^2 + 1$ has no x-intercepts. What happens when you try to solve $x^2 + 1 = 0$?

Historical Note: Imaginary Numbers

In some ways, each person's math education parallels the history of mathematical discovery. When you were much younger, if you were asked, *"How many times does 3 go into 8?"* or *"What is 8 divided by 3?"* You might have said, *"3 doesn't go into 8."* Then you learned about numbers other than whole numbers, and the question had an answer. Later, if you were asked, *"What number squared makes 5?"* you might have said, *"No number squared makes 5."* Then you learned about numbers other than rational numbers, and you could answer that question.

Similarly, until about 500 years ago, the answer to the question, *"What number squared makes –1?"* was, *"No number squared makes –1."* Then something remarkable happened. An Italian mathematician named Bombelli used a formula for finding the roots of third-degree polynomials. Within the formula was a square root, and when he applied the formula to a particular equation, the number under the square root came out negative. Instead of giving up, he had a brilliant idea. He had already figured out that the equation had a solution, so he decided to see what would happen if he pretended that there *was* a number he could square to make a negative. Remarkably, he was able to continue the calculation, and eventually the "imaginary" number disappeared from the solution. More importantly, the resulting answer worked; it solved his original equation. This led to the acceptance of these so-called **imaginary numbers**. The name stuck, and mathematicians became convinced that all quadratic equations do have solutions. Of course, in some situations you will only be interested in real number solutions (that is, solutions not having an imaginary part).

8-65.   In the 1500s, an Italian mathematician named Rafael Bombelli invented the imaginary number $\sqrt{-1}$, which is now called i. $\sqrt{-1} = i$ implies that $i^2 = -1$. After this invention, it became possible to find solutions for $x^2 + 1 = 0$; they are i and $-i$. The value of $\sqrt{-16} = \sqrt{16(-1)} = \sqrt{16i^2} = 4i$. Use the definition of i to rewrite each of the following expressions.

a. $\sqrt{-4}$ b. $(2i)(3i)$ c. $(2i)^2(-5i)$ d. $\sqrt{-25}$

8-66.   Graph the function $y = x^2 - 4x + 5$.

    a.   Does the graph cross the x-axis? Should the equation $x^2 - 4x + 5 = 0$ have real solutions?

    b.   Use the Quadratic Formula to solve $x^2 - 4x + 5 = 0$. Use your new understanding of imaginary numbers to simplify your results as much as possible.

    c.   A real number plus (or minus) a multiple of i, like each of the solutions to $x^2 - 4x + 5 = 0$, is called a **complex number**. Check one of your solutions from part (b) by substituting it into the equation for x and simplifying the result.

8-67.   When a graph crosses the x-axis, the x-intercepts are often referred to as the **real roots** of the equation that results when $y = 0$. You have seen that solutions to equations can be real or complex, so it follows that roots can also be real or complex. Compare and contrast what happens with the graphs and equations for the three cases in parts (a) through (c) below.

    a.   Sketch the graph of $y = (x + 3)^2 - 4$. What are the roots?

    b.   Sketch the graph of $y = (x + 3)^2$. What are the roots?

    c.   Sketch the graph of $y = (x + 3)^2 + 4$. Can you find the roots by looking at the graph? Why or why not? Find the roots by solving $(x + 3)^2 + 4 = 0$.

    d.   Make general statements about the relationship between graphs of parabolas and the kinds of roots their equations have.

8-68.   Consider the equations $y = x^2$ and $y = 2x - 5$.

    a.   On one set of axes, sketch the graphs and label the intersection.

    b.   Use algebra to solve the system of equations.

    c.   Discuss your results with your team. What could these solutions mean?

8-69.   Do the graphs of $y = \frac{1}{x}$ and $y = -x + 1$ intersect? What kind of algebraic solutions will this system have? Verify your answer by solving the system.

METHODS AND MEANINGS

Imaginary and Complex Numbers

MATH NOTES

The imaginary number i is defined as the square root of -1, so $i = \sqrt{-1}$. Therefore $i^2 = -1$, and the two solutions of the equation $x^2 + 1 = 0$ are $x = i$ and $x = -i$.

In general, i follows the rules of real number arithmetic. The sum of two imaginary numbers is imaginary (unless it is 0). Multiplying the imaginary number i by every possible real number would yield the set of all the imaginary numbers.

The set of numbers that solve equations of the form $x^2 = $ (a negative real number) is called the set of **imaginary numbers**. Imaginary numbers are not positive, negative, or zero. The collection (set) of positive and negative numbers (integers, rational numbers (fractions), and irrational numbers), are referred to as the **real numbers**.

The sum of a real number (other than zero) and an imaginary number, such as $2 + i$, is generally neither real nor imaginary. Numbers such as these, which can be written in the form $a + bi$, where a and b are real numbers, are called **complex numbers**. Each complex number has a real component, a, and an imaginary component, bi. The real numbers are considered to be complex numbers with $b = 0$, and the imaginary numbers are complex numbers with $a = 0$.

Review & Preview

8-70.   Write each of the following expressions in the form $a + bi$.

   a. $-18 - \sqrt{-25}$ b. $\frac{2 \pm \sqrt{-16}}{2}$ c. $5 + \sqrt{-6}$

8-71.   Explain why $i^3 = -i$. What does i^4 equal?

8-72.   If $f(x) = x^2 + 7x - 9$, calculate the values in parts (a) through (c) below.

   a. $f(-3)$ b. $f(i)$ c. $f(-3 + i)$

8-73.   Is $5 + 2i$ a solution to $x^2 - 10x = -29$? How can you be sure?

8-74.   Solve $16^{(x+2)} = 8^x$.

8-75.   Is $(x - 5)^2$ equivalent to $(5 - x)^2$? Explain why or why not.

8-76.   Calculate the value of each expression below.

     a. $\sqrt{-49}$ b. $\sqrt{-2}$ c. $(4i)^2$ d. $(3i)^3$

8-77.   Find the inverse functions below.

     a.   If $f(x) = 2x - 3$, then what does $f^{-1}(x)$ equal?

     b.   If $h(x) = (x - 3)^2 + 2$, then what does $h^{-1}(x)$ equal?

8-78.   Solve each equation.

     a. $5.2(3.75)^x = 100$ b. $4 + 3x^4 = 81$

8.2.2 What are complex roots?

Complex Roots

In this lesson, you will solve equations as well as reverse your thinking to investigate the relationship between the complex solutions to a quadratic equation and the equation from which these solutions came.

8-79. Find the roots of each of the following quadratic functions by solving for x when $y = 0$. Does the graph of either of these functions intersect the x-axis?

    a. $y = (x+5)^2 + 9$ b. $y = x^2 - 4x + 9$

8-80. What do you notice about the complex solutions in problem 8-79? Describe any patterns you see. Discuss these patterns with your team and write all of your observations.

8-81. In parts (a) through (d) below, look for patterns as you calculate the sum and the product for each pair of complex numbers. Use what you find to answer parts (e) through (g).

    a. $2 + i,\ 2 - i$ b. $3 - 5i,\ 3 + 5i$

    c. $-4 + i,\ -4 - i$ d. $1 + i\sqrt{3}, 1 - i\sqrt{3}$

    e.   What complex number can you multiply $3 + 2i$ by to get a real number?

    f.   What happens when you multiply $(-4 + 5i)(-4 + 3i)$?

    g.   What complex number can you multiply $a + bi$ by to get a real number?

8-82.   WHAT EQUATION HAS THESE SOLUTIONS?

Each of the four pairs of complex numbers in problem 8-81 could be the roots of a quadratic function.

Your Task: With your team, create a quadratic equation for each pair of complex numbers in parts (a) through (d) of problem 8-81 such that those numbers are the roots. Discuss the methods you use for writing the equations and write summary statements describing your methods.

Discussion Points

How can we reverse the process of solving?

How can we use what we know about factors and zeros?

How are the solutions related to the standard form of the equation?

Further Guidance

8-83.   Problem 8-81 made Mariposa curious about sums and products. She decided to solve the equation $x^2 - 6x + 25 = 0$ and look at the sums and products of its solutions. What patterns can you help her find that might give her ideas about the equation once she knows the solutions?

8-84.   Austin had another idea. He knew that if 3 and –5 were solutions of a quadratic equation then $(x - 3)$ and $(x + 5)$ would be factors that could be multiplied to get a quadratic polynomial. How could his idea be used with the pairs of complex solutions in problem 8-81? Choose one pair and show how to use your idea.

8-85.   Melvin had still another idea. "Why not just let $x = -4 \pm i$ and work backwards?" He asked. Would his idea work?

—————   *Further Guidance*   —————
section ends here.

8-86.   For each pair of numbers below, find a quadratic equation that has these numbers as solutions.

a. $\frac{3}{4}$ and –5

b. $3i$ and $-3i$

c. $5 + 2i$ and $5 - 2i$

d. $-3 + \sqrt{2}$ and $-3 - \sqrt{2}$

METHODS AND **M**EANINGS

MATH NOTES

The Discriminant and Complex Conjugates

With the introduction of complex numbers, the use of the terms **roots** and **zeros** of polynomials expands to include complex numbers that are solutions of the equations when $p(x) = 0$.

For any quadratic equation $ax^2 + bx + c = 0$, you can determine whether the roots are real or complex by examining the part of the quadratic formula that is under the square-root sign. The value of $b^2 - 4ac$ is known as the **discriminant**. The roots are real when $b^2 - 4ac \geq 0$ and complex when $b^2 - 4ac < 0$.

For example, in the equation $2x^2 - 3x + 5 = 0$, $b^2 - 4ac = (-3)^2 - 4(2)(5) = -31 < 0$, so the equation has two complex roots and the parabola $y = 2x^2 - 3x + 5$ does not intersect the x-axis.

Complex roots of quadratic equations with real coefficients will have the form $a - bi$ and $a + bi$, which are called **complex conjugates**. The sum and product of two complex conjugates are always real numbers.

For example, the conjugate for the complex number $-5 + 3i$, is $-5 - 3i$. $(-5 + 3i) + (-5 - 3i) = -10$ and $(-5 + 3i)(-5 - 3i) = 25 - 9i^2 = 34$.

Review & Preview

8-87.   For each of the following sets of numbers, find the equation of a function that has these numbers as roots.

a. $-3 + i$ and $-3 - i$

b. $5 + \sqrt{3}$ and $5 - \sqrt{3}$

c. $-2, \sqrt{7}$, and $-\sqrt{7}$

d. $4, -3 + i$, and $-3 - i$

8-88.   Raul claims that he has a shortcut for deciding what kind of roots a function has. Jolene thinks that a shortcut is not possible. She says you just have to solve the quadratic equation to find out. They are working on $y = x^2 - 5x - 14$.

Jolene says, *"See, I just start out by trying to factor. This one can be factored $(x - 7)(x + 2) = 0$, so the equation will have two real solutions and the function will have two real roots."*

"But what if it can't be factored?" Raul asked. *"What about $x^2 + 2x + 2 = 0$?"*

"That's easy! I just use the Quadratic Formula," says Jolene. *"And I get... let's see... negative two plus or minus the square root of... two squared... that's 4... minus... eight..."*

"Wait!" Raul interrupted. *"Right there, see, you don't have to finish. 2^2 minus $4 \cdot 2$, that gives you -4. That's all you need to know. You'll be taking the square root of a negative number so you will get a complex result."*

"Oh, I see," said Jolene. *"I only have to consider part of the solution, the inside of the square root."*

Use Raul's method to tell whether each of the following functions has real or complex roots without completely solving the equation. Note: Raul's method is also summarized in the Math Notes box for this lesson.

a. $y = 2x^2 + 5x + 4$

b. $y = 2x^2 + 5x - 3$

8-89.   Sketch the graphs and find the area of the intersection of the inequalities below.

$$y > |x + 3|$$
$$y \le 5$$

8-90.   Consider this geometric sequence: $i^0, i^1, i^2, i^3, i^4, i^5, ..., i^{15}$.

a.   You know that $i^0 = 1$, $i^1 = i$, and $i^2 = -1$. Calculate the result for each term up to i^{15}, and describe the pattern.

b.   Use the pattern you found in part (a) to calculate i^{16}, i^{25}, i^{39}, and i^{100}.

c.   What is i^{4n}, where n is a positive whole number?

d.   Based on your answer to part (c), simplify i^{4n+1}, i^{4n+2}, and i^{4n+3}.

e.   Calculate i^{396}, i^{397}, i^{398}, and i^{399}.

8-91.   Use the pattern from the previous problem to help you to evaluate the following
         expressions.

   a. i^{592} b. i^{797} c. $i^{10,648,202}$

8-92.   Describe how you would evaluate i^n where n could be any integer.

8-93.   Show how to solve the equations below *without* using your
         calculator. You will have radicals or logarithms in your answers.

   a. $3^x = 17$ b. $x^3 = 17$

8-94.   Match each equation with the appropriate graph. Do this without
         using a graphing calculator.

   a. $y = \sin(x + \frac{\pi}{2})$ b. $y = \sin(2x)$ c. $y = 2\sin(\frac{x}{2})$

   d. $y = \sin(x) - 3$ e. $y = -\sin[2(x - \frac{\pi}{8})]$

8-95.   The La Quebrada Cliff Divers perform shows for the public by jumping into the sea off the cliffs at Acapulco, Mexico. The height (in feet) of a diver at a certain time (in seconds) is given by $h = -16t^2 + 16t + 400$.

   a.   Use the vertex and y-intercept to make a sketch that represents the dive. What form of the quadratic function helps you determine the y-intercept efficiently? What form helps you determine the vertex easily?

   b.   At what height did the diver start his jump? What is the maximum height he achieved?

8-96.   Consider the graph at right.

   a.   What is the parent for this function?

   b.   What is the equation of the vertical asymptote?

   c.   Write a possible equation for this graph.

8.2.3 Where are the complex numbers?

More Complex Numbers and Equations

If the number line is filled with real numbers, how can imaginary and complex numbers be represented geometrically? In this lesson, you will learn a way to graph complex numbers and interpret the graphical meaning of complex solutions.

8-97.   Avi and Tran were trying to figure out how they could represent complex numbers geometrically. Avi decided to make a number line horizontal like the x-axis to represent the real part as well as a vertical line like the y-axis to represent the imaginary part.

a.   Draw a set of axes and label them as Avi described.

b.   How could Avi and Tran graph a point to represent the complex number $3 + 4i$? Be prepared to share your strategies with the class.

c.   Use the method from part (b) to plot points to represent the six numbers below.

   i. $2 + 5i$ ii. $6 - i$ iii. $-5 - 3i$

   iv. 4 v. $7i$ vi. $-4 + 2i$

8-98.   On a new set of **complex axes** (like those drawn by Avi and Tran in problem 8-97), locate points representing all of the following complex numbers.

a. $3 + 4i$, $3 - 4i$, $-3 + 4i$, and $-3 - 4i$.

b.   The four complex numbers represented by $\pm 4 \pm 3i$.

c. 5, -5, $5i$, and $-5i$

d.   What do you notice about your graph? How far from $(0, 0)$ is each point?

8-99. On the real number line, the distance from 0 to a point on the line is defined as the absolute value of the number. Similarly, in the **complex plane** (the plane defined by a set of complex axes), the **absolute value** of a complex number is its distance from zero or the origin $(0,0)$. In the previous problem, the absolute value of all of those complex numbers was 5. For each of the following questions, a sketch in the complex plane will help in visualizing the result.

a. What is the absolute value of $-8 + 6i$?

b. What is the absolute value of $7 - 2i$?

c. What is $|4 + i|$?

d. What is the absolute value of $a + bi$?

8-100. Based on the following graphs, how many *real* roots does each polynomial function have?

a.

b.

Graphs (a) and (b) above have been vertically shifted to create graphs (c) and (d) shown below. How many *real* roots does each of these new polynomial functions have?

c.

d.

The polynomials in parts (c) and (d) do not have fewer roots. Polynomial (c) still has *two* roots, but now the roots are complex. Polynomial (d) has *three* roots: two are complex, and only one is real.

8-101.   Recall that a polynomial function with degree n crosses the x-axis at most n times. For instance, $y = (x+1)^2$ intersects the x-axis once, while $y = x^2 + 1$ does not intersect it at all. The function $y = x^2 - 1$ intersects it twice. These graphs are shown below.

$y = (x+1)^2$ $y = x^2 + 1$ $y = x^2 - 1$

a.   The graph of a third-degree equation might intersect the x-axis one, two, or three times. Make sketches of all these possibilities.

b.   Can a third-degree equation have zero real roots? Explain why or why not.

8-102.   Now consider the graph of $y = x^3 - 3x^2 + 3x - 2$.

a.   How many real solutions could $x^3 - 3x^2 + 3x - 2 = 0$ have?

b.   Check to verify that $x^3 - 3x^2 + 3x - 2 = (x-2)(x^2 - x + 1)$.

c.   Find all of the solutions of $x^3 - 3x^2 + 3x - 2 = 0$.

d.   How many x-intercepts does $y = x^3 - 3x^2 + 3x - 2$ have? How many real roots and how many non-real roots (complex)?

8-103.   Sketch the graph of $f(x) = x^2 + 4$ and solve the equation $x^2 + 4 = 0$ to find its roots.

     a.   Describe the parabola. Be sure to include the vertex and the equation of its axis of symmetry.

     b.   With a partner, obtain a copy of the Lesson 8.2.3 Resource Page from your teacher, and follow the directions below to make a 3-D model that will show the location of the complex roots in a complex plane that is perpendicular to the real plane in which you drew the graph of the parabola.

          i.   Fold the paper on the line marked **bi** and **–bi**. This is a "mountain" fold, so the printing is on the outside.

          ii.   Cut the paper exactly along the dotted line. Do not cut beyond the dotted portion.

          iii.   Now make "valley" folds on the two lines parallel to the first fold.

          iv.   Hold the two ends of the paper and push them toward the center so the center pops up, and then fold the top and bottom of the paper back on the line marked "center."

You should have a three-dimensional coordinate system with the xy-plane facing you and the i-axis coming out toward you. The equation $f(x) = x^2 + 4$ should be in the lower right corner. Now locate the roots of the function on your 3-D model.

METHODS AND MEANINGS

MATH NOTES

Graphing Complex Numbers

To represent complex numbers, an imaginary axis and a real axis are needed. Real numbers are on the horizontal axis and imaginary numbers are on the vertical axis, as shown in the examples below. This representation is called the **complex plane**.

In the complex plane, $a + bi$ is located at the point (a, b). The number $2 + 3i$ is located at the point $(2, 3)$. The number i or $0 + 1i$ is located at $(0, 1)$. The number -2 or $-2 + 0i$ is located at $(-2, 0)$.

The **absolute value** of a complex number is its distance from the origin. To find the absolute value, calculate the distance from $(0, 0)$ to (a, b):

$$|a + bi| = \sqrt{a^2 + b^2}$$

Examples:

$$|-2 + 3i| = \sqrt{(-2)^2 + 3^2} = \sqrt{13}$$

$$|-1 - i| = \sqrt{(-1)^2 + (-1)^2} = \sqrt{2}$$

$$|5i| = 5$$

8-104. In parts (a) through (d) below, for each polynomial function $f(x)$, the graph of $f(x)$ is shown. Based on this information, state the numbers of linear and quadratic factors the factored form of its equation should have and how many real and complex (non-real) solutions $f(x) = 0$ might have. (Assume a polynomial function of the lowest possible degree for each one.)

Example: $f(x)$ at right will have three linear factors, therefore three real roots and no complex roots.

a.

b.

c.

d.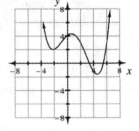

8-105. Make a sketch of a graph $p(x)$ so that $p(x) = 0$ would have the indicated number and type of solutions.

   a.   5 real solutions   b.   3 real and 2 complex

   c.   4 complex   d.   4 complex and 2 real

   e.   For parts (a) through (d), what is the lowest degree each function could have?

8-106.	Consider the function $y = x^3 - 9x$.

    a.	What are the roots of the function? (Factoring will help!)

    b.	Sketch a graph of the function.

8-107.	Make rough sketches of the graphs of each of the following polynomial functions. Be sure to label the x- and y- intercepts.

    a.	$y = x(2x + 5)(2x - 7)$ b.	$y = (15 - 2x)^2(x + 3)$

8-108.	Graph $y \geq |x + 2| - 3$ and $y \leq 2$ on the same set of axes.

8-109.	Fireworks for the annual Fourth of July show are launched straight up from a steel platform. The launch of the entire show is computer controlled. The height of a particular firework in meters off ground level is given by $h = -4.9t^2 + 49t + 11.27$, where time, t, is in seconds.

    a.	What was the height of the platform? What is the maximum height the firework reached? How many seconds until it hit the ground?

    b.	Rewrite the equation in factored form. Why might factored form of the equation be useful?

8-110.	You are given the equation $5x^2 + bx + 20 = 0$. For what values of b does this equation have real solutions?

8-111.	Show that each of the following equations is true.

    a.	$(i - 3)^2 = 8 - 6i$ b.	$(2i - 1)(3i + 1) = -7 - i$

    c.	$(3 - 2i)(2i + 3) = 13$

8-112.	Consider the functions $y = \frac{1}{2}$ and $y = \frac{16}{x^2 - 4}$. Find the coordinates where the graphs of the functions intersect.

8.3.1 How can I divide polynomials?

Polynomial Division

When you graphed polynomial functions in the first section of this chapter, you learned that the factored form of a polynomial is very useful for finding the roots of the function or the x-intercepts of the graph. But what happens when you do not have the factored form and you need to find all of the roots? You will investigate the answer to this question in this lesson.

8-113.   Andre needs to find the exact roots of the function $f(x) = x^3 + 2x^2 - 7x - 2$. When he uses his graphing calculator, he can see that one of the x-intercepts is 2, but there are two other intercepts that he cannot identify exactly.

Andre remembers that he learned how to multiply binomials and other polynomials using area models. He figures that since division is the inverse (or undo) operation for multiplication, he should be able to reverse the multiplication process to divide. As he thinks about that idea, he comes across the following news article.

Polydoku Craze Sweeping Nation!

(CPM) – Math enthusiasts around the nation have entered a new puzzle craze involving the multiplication of polynomials. The goal of the game, which enthusiasts have named Polydoku, is to fill in squares so that the multiplication of two polynomials will be completed.

	1	2	3	4	5
A	$\times$	$2x^3$	$-x^2$	$+3x$	-1
B	$3x$	$6x^4$	$-3x^3$	$9x^2$	$-3x$
C	-2	$-4x^3$	$2x^2$	$-6x$	2

$$6x^4 \quad -7x^3 \quad +11x^2 \quad -9x \quad +2$$

The game shown at right, for example, represents the multiplication of $(3x - 2)(2x^3 - x^2 + 3x - 1) = 6x^4 - 7x^3 + 11x^2 - 9x + 2$.

Most of the squares are blank at the start of the game. While the beginner level provides the factors (in the gray squares), some of the factors are missing in the more advanced levels.

What do you think Andre needs to be able to do to find the other roots?

8-114.   Andre decided to join the craze and try some Polydoku puzzles, but he is not sure how to fill in some of the squares. Help him by answering parts (a) and (b) below about the Polydoku puzzle in the news article he read (found in problem 8-113), then complete part (c).

   a.   Explain how the term $2x^2$ in cell C3 of the news article was generated.

   b.   What values were combined to get $-7x^3$ in the news article answer?

   c.   Copy and complete the Polydoku puzzle at right.

	1	2	3	4	5
A	$\times$	$4x^3$	$+6x^2$	$-2x$	-5
B	$2x$				
C	-3				

8-115.   POLYDOKU TEAM CHALLENGE

Work with your team to complete the puzzle at right. Find the factors and the product for the puzzle. If you get stuck, you can consult parts (a) through (c) below for ideas.

	1	2	3	4	5
A	$\times$			$-2x$	
B	x	$2x^4$			
C	-4		$12x^2$		

$12x$

   a.   How is cell B2 related to the answer?

   b.   How did you find the third term in the answer?

   c.   What cells did you use to get the value in cell B5?

8-116.   Jessica is about to start the intermediate-level Polydoku puzzle shown at right. Show Jessica how to complete the puzzle. Make sure you can justify your solution.

Use your results to complete the statements below.

	1	2	3	4
A	$\times$			
B	$2x$			
C	$+5$			

$6x^3$ $+7x^2$ $-16x$ $+10$

$$\frac{6x^3 + 7x^2 - 16x + 10}{2x + 5} = \underline{\hspace{2cm}} \quad \text{and} \quad (2x + 5) \cdot \underline{\hspace{2cm}} = \underline{\hspace{2cm}}$$

8-117.   Unfortunately, Jessica made a mistake when she copied the problem. The constant term of the original polynomial was supposed to have the value + 18 (not + 10). She does not want to start all over again to solve the puzzle.

    a.   Jessica realizes that she would now have 8 remaining from the original expression. What is the significance of this 8?

    b.   Jessica writes her work as shown below:

$$\frac{6x^3 + 7x^2 - 16x + 18}{2x + 5} = \frac{(6x^3 + 7x^2 - 16x + 10) + 8}{2x + 5} = 3x^2 - 4x + 2 \text{, remainder 8.}$$

Gina thinks that there is a way to write the answer without using the word "remainder." Discuss this with your team and find another way to write the result. Be prepared to share your results and your reasoning with the class.

    c.   Use Jessica and Gina's method to divide $(6x^3 + 11x^2 - 12x - 1) \div (3x + 1)$.

8-118.   Create your own Polydoku puzzles that can be used to solve each of the polynomial-division problems below. Express any remainders as fractions and use your results to write a multiplication and a division statement like those in problem 8-117.

    a. $\dfrac{6x^4 - 5x^3 + 10x^2 - 18x + 5}{3x - 1}$ b. $(x^4 - 6x^3 + 18x - 4) \div (x - 2)$

    c. $x - 3 \overline{\smash{)}x^3 + x^2 - 14x + 3}$ d. $\dfrac{x^5 - 1}{x - 1}$

8-119.   Now work with your team to help Andre solve his original problem (problem 8-113). Find all of the roots (exact zeros) of the polynomial.

ETHODS AND MEANINGS

Polynomial Division

The examples below show two methods for dividing $x^4 - 6x^3 + 18x - 1$ by $x - 2$. In both cases, the remainder is written as a fraction.

Using long division:

$$
\begin{array}{r}
x^3 - 4x^2 - 8x + 2 \\
x-2\overline{)x^4 - 6x^3 + 0x^2 + 18x - 1} \\
\underline{x^4 - 2x^3} \\
-4x^3 + 0x^2 \\
\underline{-4x^3 + 8x^2} \\
-8x^2 + 18x \\
\underline{-8x^2 + 16x} \\
2x - 1 \\
\underline{2x - 4} \\
3
\end{array}
$$

Answer: $x^3 - 4x^2 - 8x + 2 + \frac{3}{x-2}$

Using area models:

	x^3	$-4x^2$	$-8x$	$+2$	Remainder
x	x^4	$-4x^3$	$-8x^2$	$+2x$	3
-2	$-2x^3$	$+8x^2$	$+16x$	-4	

$$x^4 - 6x^3 \quad +0x^2 \quad +18x \quad -1$$

Answer: $x^3 - 4x^2 - 8x + 2 + \frac{3}{x-2}$

Therefore, $(x^4 - 6x^3 + 18x - 1) \div (x - 2) = x^3 - 4x^2 - 8x + 2 + \frac{3}{x-2}$ and
$(x-2)(x^3 - 4x^2 - 8x + 2 + \frac{3}{x-2}) = x^4 - 6x^3 + 18x - 1$.

8-120.   Carlos is always playing games with his graphing
          calculator, but now his calculator has contracted a
          virus. The [TRACE], [ZOOM], and [WINDOW] functions
          on his calculator are not working. He needs to
          solve $x^3 + 5x^2 - 16x - 14 = 0$, so he graphs
          $y = x^3 + 5x^2 - 16x - 14$ and sees the graph at right
          in the standard window.

          a.   From the graph, what appears to be an integer
                solution to the equation?

          b.   Check your answer from part (a) in the equation.

          c.   Since $x = -7$ is a solution to the equation, what is the factor associated
                with this solution?

          d.   Use polynomial division to find the other factor.

          e.   Use your new factor to complete this equation:

                $$x^3 + 5x^2 - 16x - 14 = (x + 7)(\textit{other factor}) = 0$$

          f.   The "other factor" leads to two other solutions to the equation. Find these
                two new solutions and give all three solutions to the original equation.

8-121.   Now Carlos needs to solve $2x^3 + 3x^2 - 8x + 3 = 0$, but his calculator will still
          only create a standard graph. He sees that the graph of $y = 2x^3 + 3x^2 - 8x + 3$
          crosses the x-axis at $x = 1$. Find all three solutions to the equation.

8-122.   Without actually multiplying, decide which of the following polynomials could
          be the product of $(x - 2)(x + 3)(x - 5)$. Justify your choice.

          a. $x^3 - 4x^2 - 11x - 5$ b. $2x^3 - 4x^2 - 11x + 30$

          c. $x^3 - 4x^2 - 11x + 30$ d. $2x^3 - 4x^2 - 11x - 5$

8-123. Which of the following binomials could be a factor of $x^3 - 9x^2 + 19x + 5$? Explain your reasoning.

  a. $x - 2$ b. $x - 5$ c. $x + 3$ d. $x + 2$

8-124. Now divide $x^3 - 9x^2 + 19x + 5$ by the factor that you chose in the preceding problem. If it is a factor, use it and the resulting factor to find all the zeros of the polynomial. If it is not a factor, reconsider your answer to the preceding problem and try a different factor.

8-125. Consider the equation $5x^2 - 7x - 6 = 0$ as you answer the questions in parts (a) through (d) below.

  a. What are the factors of $5x^2 - 7x - 6$?

  b. What are the solutions to the equation?

  c. Explain the relationship between the factors of the polynomial expression and the solutions to the equation.

  d. How are the solutions to the equation related to the lead coefficient and constant term in the original polynomial?

8-126. The city of Waynesboro is trying to decide whether to initiate a composting project where each residence would be provided with a dumpster for garden and yard waste. The city manager needs some measure of assurance that the citizens will participate before launching the project, so he chooses a random sample of 25 homes and provides them with the new dumpster for yard and garden waste. After one week the contents of each dumpster is weighed (in pounds) before processing. The sorted data is shown below:

0	0	0	0	1.7	2.6	2.9	4.2	4.4
5.1	5.6	6.4	8.0	8.9	9.7	10.1	11.2	13.5
15.1	16.3	17.7	21.4	22.0	22.2	36.5		

Checksum 245.5

Problem continues on next page →

8-126.   *Problem continued from previous page.*

    a.   Create a combination boxplot and histogram. Use an interval of 0 to 42 pounds on the *x*-axis and a bin width of 6 pounds.

    b.   Describe the center, shape, spread and outliers.

    c.   What is a better measure of center for this distribution the mean or median and why?

    d.   What is a better measure of spread the standard deviation or IQR and why?

    e.   The city can sell the compost, and engineers estimate the program will be profitable if each home averages at least 9 pounds of material. The city manager sees the mean is nearly 10 pounds and is ready to order dumpsters for every residence. What advice would you give him?

8-127.   This problem is a checkpoint for solving and graphing inequalities. It will be referred to as Checkpoint 8A.

Graph the inequality in part (a) and the system of inequalities in part (b).

    a. $|x+1| \geq 3$ b. $y \leq -2x+3$

                                                   $y \geq x$

                                                     $x \geq -1$

Check your answers by referring to the Checkpoint 8A materials located at the back of your book.

Ideally, at this point you are comfortable working with these types of problems and can solve them correctly. If you feel that you need more confidence when solving these types of problems, then review the Checkpoint 8A materials and try the practice problems provided. From this point on, you will be expected to do problems like these correctly and with confidence.

8-128.   Given the equation: $3x+y-z=6$.

    a.   Draw a graph.

    b.   Is (1, 2, –1) on the graph? Justify your answer.

8.3.2 How can I solve it?

Factors and Integral Roots

You already know several methods for solving quadratic equations, such as factoring, completing the square, and using the Quadratic Formula. Mathematicians have developed formulas for solving third- and fourth-degree polynomial equations, but these formulas are far more complicated and messy than the Quadratic Formula is, and they are rarely used. Furthermore, for polynomials of degree greater than four, there is no single formula to use. For many polynomials, you can develop more useful methods than a formula based on what you already know.

8-129.   SEARCHING FOR ROOTS OF POLYNOMIALS

By combining what you know about graphing, factoring, polynomial division, and solving quadratic equations, you will be able to find the roots of the higher-degree polynomial functions in this lesson.

Your Task: Find all of the zeros of the polynomial below and then write the polynomial in factored form with factors of degree 2 or 1.

$$P(x) = x^4 - x^3 - 5x^2 + 3x + 6$$

Discussion Points

What are some possible linear factors?

How can the graph help us decide which factors to try?

How can we use the known factors to figure out other factors?

What do we need to do to write the polynomial in factored form and find the zeros?

Further Guidance

8-130.   Given the polynomial $P(x) = x^4 - x^3 - 5x^2 + 3x + 6$, list all of the possible linear factors $(x \pm a)$ of the polynomial. Use only integer values for a.

   a.   Could $x - 5$ be included on your list of possible linear factors? Explain.

   b.   Not all of the *possibilities* will actually be factors. Use your graphing calculator to decide which of the factors you listed are the best possibilities.

   c.   Now that you have shortened the list of possibilities, which factors on the shortened list really are factors of $P(x)$? Justify your answer.

   d.   If you have not already, divide the polynomial by one of the factors from part (c) and write the polynomial as a product of a linear and a cubic factor.

   e.   Now divide the cubic factor from part (d) by the other linear factor that worked, and write the original polynomial as a product of two linear factors and one quadratic factor.

   f.   From the factored form, you can find all of the solutions to $x^4 - x^3 - 5x^2 + 3x + 6 = 0$ and the exact x-intercepts for the graph of $P(x)$. What are they?

===   *Further Guidance*   ===
       section ends here.

8-131.   LEARNING LOG

As a team, look back over the work you did to find the linear factors of $P(x)$ and make a list of steps you can use to find all of the zeros of a given polynomial. Then record your ideas in your Learning Log. Use diagrams, arrows, and other math tools to help demonstrate your ideas. Title this entry "Factors and Roots of Polynomial Functions" and label it with today's date.

8-132.   Your teacher will assign your team one of the following polynomial functions. Use the list of steps your team developed to factor the polynomial and find all of its roots. Then prepare a poster in which you illustrate and justify each of your steps. Be sure to include the graph on your poster and clearly explain the relationship between the solutions of the equation and the x-intercepts.

a. $Q_1(x) = x^3 + 3x^2 + 1x - 5$

b. $Q_2(x) = 6x^4 + 7x^3 - 36x^2 - 7x + 6$

c. $Q_3(x) = x^4 + 2x^3 + 10x^2 + 18x + 9$

d. $Q_4(x) = x^4 - 8x^3 + 18x^2 - 16x + 5$

e. $Q_5(x) = x^5 - 4x^3 - x^2 + 4$

f. $Q_6(x) = x^3 + x^2 - 7x - 7$

8-133.   **LEARNING LOG**

Make additions and/or adjustments to your Learning Log entry from problem 8-131 to reflect what you leaned from the posters that you and your classmates presented for problem 8-132.

8-134.   Use the procedures you developed to factor each of the following polynomial expressions. Each final answer should be a linear factor times a quadratic factor. Look for patterns in the factors.

a. $x^3 - 1$ b. $x^3 + 8$

c. $x^3 - 27$ d. $x^3 + 125$

8-135.   If you generalize the patterns for the factors in problem 8-134, you will discover a shortcut for factoring cubic polynomials that are described as the sum or difference of two cubes. Write the factors for each polynomial expression below.

a. $x^3 + a^3$ b. $x^3 - b^3$

8-136.   Are there similar patterns for $x^4 + a^4$ and $x^4 - b^4$? Explain.

8-137.   BUILDING POLYNOMIALS

For each of the following descriptions of polynomial functions with integral coefficients, answer each question below.

     i.   What are the possible numbers of real zeros?

     ii.   How many complex zeros are possible?

     iii. For each number of possible real zeros, give an example of a polynomial in factored form.

  a.   A third-degree polynomial function.

  b.   A fourth-degree polynomial function.

  c.   A fifth-degree polynomial function.

METHODS AND MEANINGS

Polynomial Theorems

Factor Theorem: If $x = a$ is a zero of the polynomial $p(x)$, then $(x - a)$ is a factor of the polynomial, and if $(x - a)$ is a factor of the polynomial, then $x = a$ is a zero of the polynomial.

Example: $x = -3$, $x = 2$, and $x = 1 \pm i\sqrt{7}$ are zeros of the polynomial $p(x) = x^4 - x^3 + 20x - 48$. According to the Factor Theorem, $(x + 3)$, $(x - 2)$, $(x - (1 + i\sqrt{7}))$, and $(x - (1 - i\sqrt{7}))$ are factors of the polynomial.

Fundamental Theorem of Algebra: The Fundamental Theorem of Algebra states that every one-variable polynomial has at least one complex root (remember that every real number is also a complex number). This theorem can be used to show that every polynomial of degree n has n complex roots. This also means that the polynomial has n linear factors, since for every root a, $(x - a)$ is a linear factor.

Note that the total of n roots might include roots that occur multiple times. For example, the third degree polynomial $p(x) = x^3 - 3x^2 + 4$ has three roots—a root at $x = -1$ and a double root at $x = 2$. The three linear factors are $(x + 1)$, $(x - 2)$, and $(x - 2)$.

Integral Zero Theorem: For any polynomial with integral coefficients, if an integer is a zero of the polynomial, it must be a factor of the constant term.

Example: Suppose the integers a, b, c, and d are zeros of a polynomial. Then, according to the Factor Theorem, $(x - a)(x - b)(x - c)(x - d)$ are factors of the polynomial. When you multiply these factors together, the constant term will be $abcd$, so a, b, c, and d are factors of the constant term.

Remainder Theorem: For any number c, when a polynomial $p(x)$ is divided by $(x - c)$, the remainder is $p(c)$. For example, if the polynomial $p(x) = x^4 - x^3 + 20x - 48$ is divided by $(x - 5)$, the remainder is $p(5) = 552$.

Note that it follows from the Remainder Theorem that if $p(c) = 0$, then $(x - c)$ is a factor. For example, if $p(x) = x^3 - 3x^2 + 4$, one solution to $x^3 - 3x^2 + 4 = 0$ is $x = -1$. Since $p(-1) = 0$, then $(x + 1)$ is a factor.

8-138.   Carlo was trying to factor the polynomial
$p(x) = x^4 - 4x^3 - 4x^2 + 24x - 9$ to find all of its
roots. He had already found one factor by making
a guess and dividing the polynomial, so he had
$p(x) = (x - 3)(x^3 - x^2 - 7x + 3)$. He was trying to
factor $x^3 - x^2 - 7x + 3$, so he had tried dividing it
by $(x + 3)$, $(x + 1)$, and $(x - 1)$, but none worked
without a remainder. Then Teo came by and said,
"You should look at the graph."

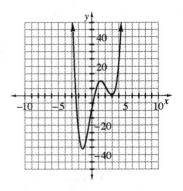

a.   How does the graph help?

b.   Complete the problem.

8-139.   Spud has a problem. He knows that the solutions for a quadratic equation are
$x = 3 + 4i$ and $x = 3 - 4i$, but in order to get credit for the problem he was
supposed to have written down the original equation. Unfortunately, he lost the
paper with the original equation on it. Luckily, his friends are full of advice.

a.   Alexia says, *"Just remember when we made polynomials. If you wanted 7
and 4 to be the answers, you used $(x - 7)(x - 4)$. So you just do x minus the
first one times x minus the other."* Use $(x - (3 + 4i))(x - (3 - 4i))$ to find the
quadratic equation.

b.   Hugo says, *"No, no, no. You can do it that way, but that's too
complicated. I think you just start with $x = 3 + 4i$ and work backward. So
$x - 3 = 4i$, then, hmmm... Yeah, that'll work."* Try Hugo's method.

c.   Whose method do you think Spud should use? Explain your choice.

8-140.   So far you have been able to extend the rules for real numbers to add, subtract, and multiply complex numbers, but what about dividing? Can you use what you know about real numbers to divide one complex number by another? In other words, if a problem looks like this:

$$\frac{3+2i}{-4+7i}$$

What needs to be done to get an answer in the form of a single complex number, $a + bi$?

Natalio had an idea. He said, *"I'll bet we can use the conjugate!"*

"How?" asked Ricki.

"Well, it's a fraction. Can't we multiply the numerator and denominator by the same number?" Natalio replied.

a.   Natalio was not very clear in his explanation. Show Ricki what he meant they should do.

b.   Using Natalio's ideas you probably still came up with a fraction in part (a), but the denominator should be a whole number. To write a complex number such as $\frac{c+di}{m}$ in the form $a + bi$, just use the distributive property to rewrite the result as $\frac{c}{m} + \frac{d}{m}i$. Rewrite your result for part (a) in this form.

8-141.   Use the method developed in problem 8-140 to do the following division problems.

a. $\frac{2-5i}{1-2i}$ b. $(-3+i) \div (2 + 3i)$

8-142.   Find the inverse of $g(x) = (x + 1)^2 - 3$ with the domain $x \geq -1$. Sketch both graphs and state the domain and range of the inverse function.

8-143.   Sketch the graph of each polynomial function below and find all of the zeros.

a. $y = x^3 + 1$ b. $y = x^3 - 8$

8-144. Solve the system of equations at right for (x, y, z).

$$x = y + z$$
$$2x + 3y + z = 17$$
$$z + 2y = 7$$

8-145. Solve $\sqrt{x^2 + 6} = x + 2$.

8-146. Sketch the graph of each equation below.

　a.　$y = 3 \sin (x + \frac{\pi}{2})$ 　　　　　　b.　$y = -2 \sin (4x)$

8-147. Spud has done it again. He's lost another polynomial function. This one was a cubic, written in standard form. He knows that there were two complex zeros, $-2 \pm 5i$ and one real zero, -1. What could his original function have been?

8-148. Given the polynomial $p(x) = x^3 - 6x^2 + 7x + 2$.

　a.　What is $p(2)$?

　b.　Use the Remainder Theorem to find one factor of $x^3 - 6x^2 + 7x + 2$. (See the Math Notes box in Lesson 8.3.2 above.)

　c.　Use (b) to find another factor.

　d.　What are all the solutions of $x^3 - 6x^2 + 7x + 2 = 0$?

8-149. Rewrite each of the following division problems as a single complex number.

　a.　$\frac{5+3i}{5-3i}$ 　　　　　　b.　$\frac{7+3i}{1-i}$

8-150.   Megan is an industrial engineer for Bowler Cola Company. She takes a random
         sample of cola cans from the production line each day to determine if the
         product meets various specifications. One of the measurements she records is
         the mass (in grams) of the filled cans. The following sorted data are from of a
         sample of 30 regular and diet cola cans.

         Note: The data is sorted so it is easy to work with without a statistical
         calculator.

         Regular

361	362	363	365	366	366	367	367	367	368
368	368	369	369	369	369	370	370	370	371
370	371	371	371	373	375	375	376	376	380

Checksum 11088

         Diet

349	349	350	351	353	353	353	354	354	354
354	355	355	355	356	357	358	361	361	361
361	361	361	362	362	363	364	365	366	366

Checksum 10724

   a.   Find the five number summary (minimum, third quartile, median, first
        quartile, maximum) for each soda.

   b.   Make a combination histogram and boxplot for each type of soda. Include
        the five number summary. Use an interval of 348 to 384 grams on the
        x-axis and a bin width of 4 grams.

   c.   Describe the center, shape, spread, and any outliers, of each histogram.

   d.   Compare the two samples.

   e.   Each can is marked as containing 12 fluid ounces. Twelve ounces is about
        341 grams. Why is there so much variation from 341 grams in the
        samples?

8-151.   Sketch both the circle $x^2 + y^2 = 25$ and the parabola $y = x^2 - 13$.

   a.   How many points of intersection are there?

   b.   Find the coordinates of these points algebraically.

8-152.   Solve each equation. Be sure to check your answers.

   a. $\sqrt{x} + 2 = x$ b. $\sqrt{x} + 2 = \sqrt{x+6}$

8-153.   Sketch a graph of each of the following trigonometric functions.

   a. $y = \sin(0.5(x - \pi))$

   b. $y = 10\sin(3x) - 2$

   c. $y = 5\cos(x + \frac{\pi}{4})$

   d. $y = \cos(2(x - \frac{\pi}{4}))$

8-154.   The graph of $p(x) = x^3 + 4x^2 + x - 26$ is shown at right.

   a.   Use the graph to find one solution to $p(x) = 0$, then use the Factor Theorem to find a factor of $p(x)$. Read about the Factor Theorem in the Math Notes box in this lesson.

   b.   Determine all the real and complex zeros of $p(x)$. Then write $p(x)$ in factored form.

8-155.   For each equation, find two solutions $0 \le x < 2\pi$, which make the equation true. No calculator should be necessary.

   a. $\cos x = -\frac{1}{2}$

   b. $\tan x = \frac{\sqrt{3}}{3}$

   c. $\sin x = 0$

   d. $\cos x = \frac{\sqrt{2}}{2}$

8-156.   Rewrite each of the following division problems as a single complex number in simplest form.

   a. $\frac{2-6i}{4+2i}$

   b. $\frac{5}{1+2i}$

8-157.   A long lost relative died and left you $15,000! Your parents say that you need to save the money for college, so you put it an account that pays 8% interest compounded annually. How many years will it take until your account is worth $25,000?

8-158.   Solve each equation.

   a. $\log_3(2x - 1) = -2$

   b. $5^{\log_5(x)} = 3$

   c. $\log_2(x) - \log_2(3) = 4$

   d. $\log_3(5) = x$

8-159.   Verify that the graphs of the equations $x^2 + y^3 = 17$ and $x^4 - 4y^2 - 8xy = 17$ intersect at $(3, 2)$.

8-160.   The graphs of $y = \log_2(x-1)$ and $y = x^3 - 4x$ intersect at two points: $(2, 0)$ and approximately $(1.1187, -3.075)$. Use that information to solve $\log_2(x-1) = x^3 - 4x$.

8-161.   Solve each equation below for x.

a. $1234x + 23456 = 987654$

b. $\frac{10}{x} + \frac{20}{x} = 5$

c. $5x^2 - 6x + 1 = 0$

d. $x^3 - 3x^2 + 2x = 0$

8-162.   Use your knowledge of the unit circle to explain why the graphs of $y = \sin\theta$ and $y = \cos(\theta - \frac{\pi}{2})$ are the same.

8-163.   For homework, Londa was asked to simplify the expression $\sqrt{-7} \cdot \sqrt{-7}$. She got the answer 7, but when she checked, she learned that the correct answer was -7.

a.   Show Londa the steps she could take to get -7.

b.   What steps do you think Londa took to get 7 as a result?

c.   What does she need to consider to avoid making this mistake in the future?

d.   Londa's example means that it is not always true that $\sqrt{a} \cdot \sqrt{b} = \sqrt{ab}$ for real numbers a and b. What restriction needs to be placed on the numbers a and b?

8-164.   Change each angle from degrees to radians.

a. $60°$ b. $75°$ c. $210°$ d. $225°$

8.3.3 How can I use it?

An Application of Polynomials

In this lesson, you will have the opportunity to use the equation and graph of a polynomial function to solve a problem involving a game at the County Fair.

8-165.   COUNTY FAIR GAME TANK

The Mathamericaland Carnival Company wants to create a new game. It will consist of a tank filled with Ping-Pong balls of different colors. People will pay for the opportunity to crawl around in the tank blindfolded for 60 seconds, while they collect Ping-Pong balls. Most of the Ping-Pong balls will be white, but there will be a few of different colors. The players will win $100 for each red, $200 for each blue, and $500 for each green Ping-Pong ball they carry out of the tank.

The tank will be rectangular, open at the top, and will be made by cutting squares out of each corner of an 8.5-meter by 11-meter sheet of translucent miracle material that can be bent into shape. The owner of the company thinks that she will make the greatest profit if the tank has maximum volume. She has hired your team to figure out the exact dimensions of the tank that creates the maximum value.

Your Task: Your team will write a report of your findings to the Carnival Company that includes each of the following elements.

- Any data or conjectures your team made based on experimental paper tanks.

- A diagram of the tank with the dimensions clearly labeled with appropriate variables.

- A graph of the volume function that you found with notes on a reasonable domain and range.

- An equation that matches your graph.

- Your conclusions and observations.

8-166. Use a full sheet of 8.5" x 11" paper, which is the same shape as the material for the tank. Each member of your team should choose a different sized square to cut out of the corners. Measure the side of the square you cut out and write along the edge of the large piece of paper. Use either inches or centimeters. Your paper should look like the figure at right.

Fold the paper up into an open box (fold on the dotted lines). Then tape the cut parts together so that the box holds its shape. Measure the dimensions of the tank. Record the dimensions directly on the model tank.

8-167. Make a table like the one below for your team's results. Consider "extreme" tanks, the ones with the largest possible cutout and the smallest possible cutout. For example, imagine cutting a square out of each corner zero inches on a side.

Height of Tank	Width of Tank	Length of Tank	Volume of Tank

a. Examine the data in the table with your team and make some conjectures about how to find the maximum volume.

b. Label the height as x. Using x for the height, find expressions for the length and width.

c. Write an equation to represent the volume of the tank.

d. Sketch the graph of your function by using the roots and determining the orientation.

e. What domain and range make sense for your function?

f. Approximate the maximum volume of the tank and the dimensions of the tank that will generate this volume.

8-168.   Use your graph and your tank model to write your report. Include your answers
          to the following questions.

          a.   Which points on the graph represent tanks that can actually be made?
                Explain.

          b.   How are the dimensions of the tank related? In other words, what happens
                to the length and width as the height increases?

          c.   Make a drawing of your tank. (You may want to use isometric dot paper.)
                Label your drawing with its dimensions and its volume.

                                        Further Guidance
                                        section ends here.

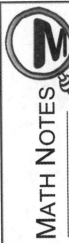

METHODS AND MEANINGS

Factoring Sums and Differences

MATH NOTES

The difference of two squares is factored as: $a^2 - b^2 = (a+b)(a-b)$

The sum of two cubes is factored as: $a^3 + b^3 = (a+b)(a^2 - ab + b^2)$

The difference of two cubes is factored as: $a^3 - b^3 = (a-b)(a^2 + ab + b^2)$

Review & Preview

8-169.   A polynomial function has the equation $P(x) = x(x-3)^2(2x+1)$. What are the
          x-intercepts?

8-170.   Sketch a graph of a fourth-degree polynomial that has no real roots.

8-171.   By setting the polynomial equal to zero and solving the quadratic equation, you can work backwards to "force factor" any quadratic. Use the solutions of the corresponding quadratic equation to write each of the following expressions as a product of two linear factors.

   a. $x^2 - 10$

   b. $x^2 - 3x - 7$

   c. $x^2 + 4$

   d. $x^2 - 2x + 2$

8-172.   Decide which of the following equations have real roots, and which have complex roots without completely solving them.

   a. $y = x^2 - 6$

   b. $y = x^2 + 6$

   c. $y = x^2 - 2x + 10$

   d. $y = x^2 - 2x - 10$

   e. $y = (x - 3)^2 - 4$

   f. $y = (x - 3)^2 + 4$

8-173.   Determine whether $x = -2$ is a solution to the equation $x^4 - 4x = 8x^2 - 40$. Show why or why not.

8-174.   This problem is a checkpoint for solving complicated equations. It will be referred to as Checkpoint 8B.

   Solve each equation. Check your solutions.

   a. $2|x - 3| + 7 = 11$

   b. $4(x - 2)^2 = 16$

   c. $\sqrt{x + 18} = x - 2$

   d. $|2x + 5| = 3x + 4$

   Check your answers by referring to the Checkpoint 8B materials located at the back of your book.

   Ideally, at this point you are comfortable working with these types of problems and can solve them correctly. If you feel that you need more confidence when solving these types of problems, then review the Checkpoint 8B materials and try the practice problems provided. From this point on, you will be expected to do problems like these correctly and with confidence.

8-175.   Let $p(x) = x^3 - 3x^2 - 7x + 9$.

      a.   Find $p(5)$.

      b.   Verify the Remainder Theorem. Read about the Remainder Theorem in the Math Notes box in Lesson 8.3.2.

8-176.   The roots of two quadratic polynomials are given below. Write possible quadratic functions in standard form.

      a. $x = -i, x = i$ b. $x = 1 + \sqrt{2}, x = 1 - \sqrt{2}$

8-177.   Graph two cycles of each function.

      a. $y = -2\cos(x + \frac{\pi}{2})$ b. $y = \sin(x - \frac{\pi}{2})$

Chapter 8 Closure What have I learned?

Reflection and Synthesis

The activities below offer you a chance to reflect about what you have learned during this chapter. As you work, look for concepts that you feel very comfortable with, ideas that you would like to learn more about, and topics you need more help with. Look for connections between ideas as well as connections with material you learned previously.

① **TEAM BRAINSTORM**

What have you studied in this chapter? What ideas were important in what you learned? With your team, brainstorm a list. Be as detailed as you can. To help get you started, a list of Learning Log entries and Math Notes boxes are below.

What topics, ideas, and words that you learned *before* this chapter are connected to the new ideas in this chapter? Again, be as detailed as you can.

How long can you make your list? Challenge yourselves. Be prepared to share your team's ideas with the class.

Learning Log Entries

- Lesson 8.1.1 – Graphing Polynomials
- Lesson 8.3.2 – Factors and Roots of Polynomial Functions

Math Notes

- Lesson 8.1.1 – Polynomials, Degree, Coefficients
- Lesson 8.1.2 – Roots and Zeros
- Lesson 8.1.3 – Notation for Polynomials
- Lesson 8.2.1 – Imaginary and Complex Numbers
- Lesson 8.2.2 – The Discriminant and Complex Conjugates
- Lesson 8.2.3 – Graphing Complex Numbers
- Lesson 8.3.1 – Polynomial Division
- Lesson 8.3.2 – Polynomial Theorems
- Lesson 8.3.3 – Factoring Sums and Differences

②   MAKING CONNECTIONS

Below is a list of the vocabulary used in this chapter. Make sure that you are familiar with all of these words and know what they mean. Refer to the glossary or index for any words that you do not yet understand.

coefficient	complex number	conjugate
degree	discriminant	factor
imaginary number	integral roots	polynomial
quotient	real number	remainder
root	solution	*x*-intercept
zero		

Make a concept map showing all of the connections you can find among the key words and ideas listed above. To show a connection between two words, draw a line between them and explain the connection. A word can be connected to any other word as long as you can justify the connection. For each key word or idea, provide an example or sketch that shows the idea.

While you are making your map, your team may think of related words or ideas that are not listed here. Be sure to include these ideas on your concept map.

PORTFOLIO: EVIDENCE OF MATHEMATICAL PROFICIENCY

This section gives you an opportunity to show growth in your understanding of key mathematical ideas over time as you complete this course.

Part 1: You may have done this in a previous chapter. You have grown mathematically since then. Be sure to include everything you have learned since the last time you did this problem.

How many different kinds of graphs can you create that have:

i. No *x*-intercepts?   *ii.* One *x*-intercept?

iii. Two *x*-intercepts?   *iv.* Three or more *x*-intercepts?

For each type of graph, show a sketch, label the key points, and give its equation. Make sure that each graph you give as an example represents a different family and describe the family in words or with a general equation. Show how to calculate the *x*-intercepts of each of your sample graphs.

Part 2: Compare your responses to this "Growth Over Time" problem. Write an evaluation of your growth based on your responses. Consider each of the following questions as you write your answer.

• What new concepts did you include the second time you did the problem? In what ways was your response better than your first attempt?

• If you did the problem three times, how was your final version different from the first two? What new ideas did you include?

• Did you omit anything in your later versions that you used in one of the earlier versions? Why did you omit it?

• Rate your attempts by making three bars like the ones below and shading each bar to represent how much you knew on each attempt.

First Attempt:	
Second Attempt:	
Final Attempt:	

• Is there anything you want to add to your current version? If so, add it and keep this version for future reference.

Core Connections Algebra 2

④ WHAT HAVE I LEARNED?

Most of the problems in this section represent typical problems found in this chapter. They serve as a gauge for you. You can use them to determine which types of problems you can do well and which types of problems require further study and practice. Even if your teacher does not assign this section, it is a good idea to try these problems and find out for yourself what you know and what you still need to work on.

Solve each problem as completely as you can. The table at the end of the closure section has answers to these problems. It also tells you where you can find additional help and practice with problems like these.

CL 8-178. Decide if each of the following equations is a polynomial. If it is, state the degree. If it is not, explain how you know.

a. $f(x) = 3x^3 - 2x + 5$

b. $y = 0.25x^7 - 5x$

c. $y = 3^x - x^2$

d. $f(x) = x^2 - \sqrt{x} + 2$

e. $Q(x) = 3(x-4)^2(x+2)$

f. $y = x^2 - 3x + 5 - \frac{2}{x-2}$

CL 8-179. Where do the graphs of each of the following functions cross the x-axis?

a. $f(x) = (x-2)^2 - 3$

b. $f(x) = (x-19)^2(x+14)$

CL 8-180. Write a polynomial equation for a graph that passes through the point $(1, 56)$ and has three x-intercept: $(-3, 0)$, $(2, 0)$, and $(5, 0)$.

CL 8-181. Decide if each of the following functions has real or complex roots.

a. $y = 3x^2 + 5x + 4$

b. $y = 3x^2 + 5x - 4$

CL 8-182.   Make a sketch of a graph $q(x)$ such that $q(x) = 0$ would have the number and type of solutions indicated below.

   a.   7 real solutions

   b.   5 real and 2 complex solutions

   c.   4 complex solutions

   d.   2 complex and 4 real solutions

CL 8-183.   Sketch graphs of each of the following polynomial functions. Be sure to label the x- and the y-intercepts of each graph.

   a. $y = x(2x + 3)(2x - 5)$

   b. $y = (11 - 2x)^2(x - 2)$

CL 8-184.   Simplify each expression.

   a. $(3 + 4i) + (7 - 2i)$

   b. $(3 + 5i)^2$

   c. $(7 + i)(7 - i)$

   d. $(3i)(2i)^2$

   e. i^3

   f. i^{32}

CL 8-185.   Divide: $(2x^3 + x^2 - 19x + 36) \div (x + 4)$

CL 8-186.   The graph of $f(x) = x^3 + 3x^2 + x - 5$ is shown at right. Use it to determine all real and complex roots.

CL 8-187.   The roots of a quadratic polynomial are given below. Find a possible quadratic equation in standard form.

   a. $x = 2i, x = -2i$

   b. $x = 2 + \sqrt{3}, x = 2 - \sqrt{3}$

CL 8-188.   For each equation determine the amplitude, period, locator point, and sketch part of the graph.

   a. $y = 3\cos(2x)$

   b. $y = \tan(x - \frac{\pi}{2})$

CL 8-189.   Write an equation for each of the following graphs. If you have a graphing calculator, use it to check your equation (be sure to set your window to match the picture).

a.

b.

c.

d.
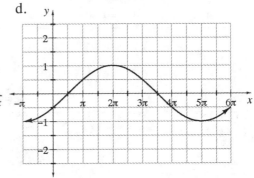

CL 8-190.   Use the system below to answer each question.

$$y = 2x$$
$$y = x^2 + 5$$

a.   Without graphing, what is the solution to the system?

b.   What does the solution to the system tell you about the graphs?

CL 8-191.   Check your answers using the table at the end of this section. Which problems do you feel confident about? Which problems were hard? Have you worked on problems like these in math classes you have taken before? Use the table to make a list of topics you need help on and a list of topics you need to practice more.

Answers and Support for Closure Activity #4
What Have I Learned?

Note: MN = Math Note, LL = Learning Log

Problem	Solutions	Need Help?	More Practice
CL 8-178.	a. Yes; degree 3 b. Yes; degree 7 c. No; it contains an exponent of x d. No; it contains a non-integer exponent $\left(\frac{1}{2}\right)$ e. Yes; degree 3 f. No; it contains a term that is a fraction with x in the denominator	MN: 8.1.1 and 8.1.3	Problems 8-9, 8-17, 8-28, 8-39, and 8-55
CL 8-179.	a. $x = \pm\sqrt{3} + 2$ b. $x = 19$ and $x = -14$	Lesson 8.1.1 and 8.1.2 MN: 8.1.2	Problems 8-19, 8-20, 8-21, 8-36, 8-37, 8-106, 8-125, 8-132, and 8-169
CL 8-180.	$y = 3.5(x+3)(x-2)(x-5)$	Section 8.1	Problems 8-38, 8-50, 8-56, and 8-57
CL 8-181.	a. complex roots b. real roots	Lessons 8.2.1 and 8.2.2 MN: 8.2.2 and 8.3.2	Problems 8-88, 8-110, and 8-172
CL 8-182.	a. b. c. d.	Sections 8.1 and 8.2 LL: 8.1.1	Problems 8-104, 8-105, and 8-170

Problem	Solutions		Need Help?	More Practice
CL 8-183.	a	b.	Lessons 8.1.1 and 8.1.2 LL: 8.1.1	Problems 8-8, 8-35, and 8-107
CL 8-184.	a. $10 + 2i$ c. 50 e. $-i$	b. $-16 + 30i$ d. $-12i$ f. 1	Lesson 8.2.1 MN: 8.2.1	Problems 8-76, 8-111, 8-141, 8-149, and 8-156
CL 8-185.	$2x^2 - 7x + 9$		Lesson 8.3.1 MN: 8.3.1	Problem 8-124
CL 8-186.	$x = 1, -2 \pm i$		Lesson 8.3.2 LL: 8.3.2	Problems 8-120, 8-121, 8-124, 8-138, 8-148, and 8-154
CL 8-187.	a. $y = x^2 + 4$ b. $y = x^2 - 4x + 1$		Sections 8.1 and 8.2 MN: 8.1.2 and 8.3.2 LL: 8.3.2	Problems, 8-87, 8-139, 8-147, and 8-176
CL 8-188.	a. Locator: $(0, 3)$ Amplitude: 3 Period: π b. Locator: $(\frac{\pi}{2}, 0)$ Period: π There is no amplitude.		Chapter 7 MN: 7.2.4 LL: 7.2.4	Problems 7-141, 7-144, 7-159, 8-14, 8-94, 8-146, 8-153, and 8-177

Problem	Solutions	Need Help?	More Practice
CL 8-189.	a. $y = \cos x$, $y = \sin(x + \frac{\pi}{2})$ or $y = -\sin(x - \frac{\pi}{2})$ b. $y = -3 - \sin x$ c. $y = 5 \sin 4x$ d. $y = \sin \frac{1}{3}(x - \frac{\pi}{2})$	Chapter 7 MN: 7.2.4 LL: 7.2.4	Problems 7-129, 8-62, and 8-94
CL 8-190.	a. $(1 \pm 2i, 2 \pm 4i)$ b. The graphs do not intersect.	Lesson 8.2.1	Problems 8-11, 8-68, 8-69, and 8-161

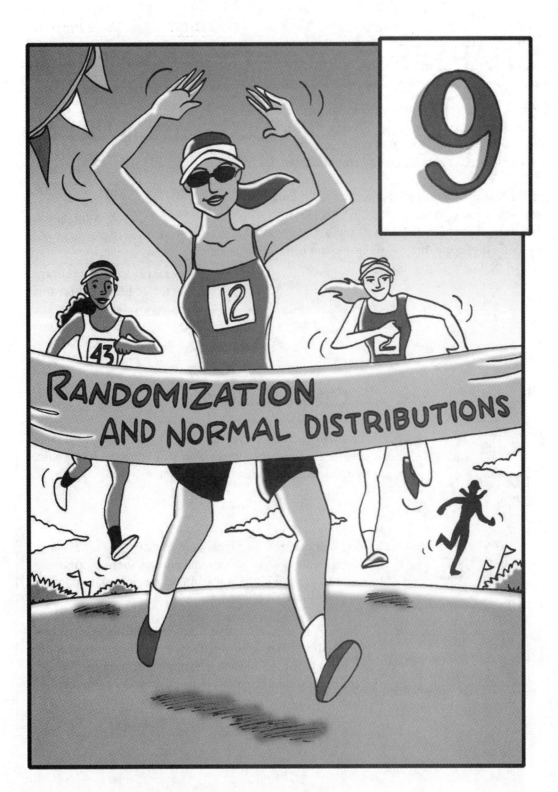

9

RANDOMIZATION
AND NORMAL DISTRIBUTIONS

CHAPTER 9 Randomization and Normal Distributions

In this chapter you will learn some basic techniques of performing opinion surveys along with their limitations and pitfalls. You will learn why randomness is a cornerstone of statistical studies.

In the last section of the chapter, you will create a histogram with percentages called a relative frequency histogram. You will learn a new way to describe the shape of a distribution, and use it to model certain distributions.

Guiding Question

Mathematically proficient students attend to precision.

As you work through this chapter, ask yourself:

How can I use the appropriate degree of precision for this problem—in my mathematics, in my vocabulary, and in how I ask survey questions?

Chapter Outline

Section 9.1 You will create a survey and learn how to avoid bias in creating survey questions. You will learn the importance of randomness in observational studies.

Section 9.2 You will perform an experiment and contrast other experiments with observational studies such as opinion surveys. You will learn the importance of randomness for experiments.

Section 9.3 You will construct relative frequency histograms. When the conditions are appropriate, you will model the relative frequency histogram with a normal distribution. With the help of a calculator, you will use the model to find the proportion of the sample (or population) with certain characteristics.

9.1.1 What questions will I ask?

Survey Design

Have you heard statements like the ones below?

- "81% of public school students are not satisfied with the food provided by their schools."

- "The President has an approval rating of 72%."

How do news sources get this information? Do they ask every public school student? Do they ask every citizen? What questions do they ask? How reliable are their results? Do you believe them?

In this chapter, you will learn some of the methods used by statisticians to justify claims such as these. You will also apply these methods to investigate your own questions.

9-1. **WHAT DO WE WANT TO KNOW?**

Before you can figure out a way to find information, you need to know what information you are looking for! Work with your team to brainstorm research questions that you find interesting. Be clear about the **population** (the entire group) in which you are interested. Here are some examples to get your thinking started:

- What do voters in this town think about raising taxes?

- What percentage of students at your school are vegetarians?

- How many children in this area consider themselves to be multiracial?

a. Work with your team to brainstorm research questions that might be investigated with a short survey.

b. Next, as a team, discuss your ideas and decide on one research question that you will investigate together. When you have made a decision, call your teacher over to confirm that your question will work.

c. Talk with your team about how you might go about gathering information about your question. Write down your ideas and be prepared to share them with the class.

9-2.   BIAS IN SURVEY QUESTIONS

Shortly, you will write survey questions for your own investigation. However, before you do that, it is important to understand how the questions that you ask can influence your results. Influence on a study that favors a certain outcome is called **bias**.

Discuss each of the following survey questions with your team. For each one,

- Look for ways in which the question may contain bias.

- Rewrite the question to reduce the bias you found.

- Be prepared to share your ideas with the class.

a.   Do teenagers worry about getting poor grades?

b.   Do you support the Governor's education plan that ensures that students will be more successful in school?

c.   Does the frequent occurrence of brutal violence in movies and video games have a negative affect on the young people exposed to them?

d.   Do you believe the current movie ratings system is effective?

e.   Should your teachers be paid more?

f.   Moderate exercise is necessary to stay healthy. Do you exercise regularly?

9-3. Consider the following descriptions of common sources of bias in survey questions. Look back at the survey questions in problem 9-2 to see if you can find any of these types of bias in those questions. Note that some of these questions may refer to bias that you already identified, while some may help you see new sources of bias.

   a. **Question Order:** Sometimes two questions are asked in an order such that the first question suggests an answer to the second. Which of the poll questions uses the biased question order technique? Why would you expect it to influence responses?

   b. **Preface:** Some questions start with statements that can bias the result of the question that follows. Which of the survey questions presented to your class uses this technique? Why would you expect such statements to influence responses?

   c. **Two Questions in One:** This technique involves asking two questions at once. Survey respondents may agree with one part and disagree with another part, but they are only allowed to give one answer. Which of the survey questions presented to your class uses this technique?

   d. **Biased Wording:** By using pleasing or unpleasant words, the surveyor can influence results. Which of the survey questions presented to your class uses this technique?

   e. **Desire To Please:** Research shows that many survey takers will answer in the ways that they perceive will please the surveyor. Which of the survey questions presented to your class are likely to be biased in this way? Are some more severely biased than others?

9-4. CREATING BIAS

You and your team members have been asked by the U.S. Department of Education to survey people about the President's new proposal to extend the school year from the current length of 180 days to 200 days. A survey question might be, *"Do you think students should attend school for 180 days as they do now, or for 200 days?"*

Work with your team to rewrite this question in as many ways as you can to *introduce* bias. For each new question you write, note in which direction the bias is likely to influence responses.

9-5.   Now you and your team will write your own
         survey.

a.   Work with your team to write a short survey
     that you could use to investigate the research
     question that you selected in problem 9-1.
     Do your best to minimize bias in your
     questions.

b.   Trade survey questions with another team. Read their questions and
     decide whether you see bias in any of them. If so, write a brief
     explanation of what type of bias you see and offer suggestions for
     rewording the questions to reduce bias.

c.   Get your survey questions back from the team that offered you feedback.
     Consider their feedback and make any revisions that you decide will help
     improve your survey.

9-6.   There are many considerations involved when writing a survey. For example
         consider the following two survey questions:

         Question 1: What is your favorite way to exercise?

         Question 2: Which of the following ways to exercise do you prefer?

               Running   Swimming   Team Sports   Dancing   Skiing

a.   Discuss these two ways of asking people about their exercise preferences.
     What are the possibilities and limitations of each question?

b.   Question 1 is an example of an **open question**,
     while Question 2 is a **closed question**. Open
     questions allow respondents to offer any
     response they like, while closed questions limit
     them to some set number of responses from
     which to choose. Discuss these question types
     with your team. Is one type likely to give
     more accurate information? Why? Is one type
     likely to be more convenient? Why? When
     might you want to choose to ask an open or a closed question?

c.   Make changes to your survey questions so that you have *at least one* open
     question and *at least one* closed question. Be careful! Changing the
     format of a question can introduce new kinds of bias.

d.   Store your survey questions in a safe place. They will be needed later in
     this chapter.

Core Connections Algebra 2

METHODS AND **M**EANINGS

MATH NOTES

Population Parameters and Sample Statistics

The entire group that you are interested in studying and making conclusions about is called the **population**. Some questions can be investigated by studying every member of the population. For example, you can figure out how many students in your class have siblings by asking every student. This process of measuring every member of a population is called taking a **census**. Numerical summaries, such as mean and standard deviation, computed from a population census are called **parameters** of that population.

The United States government performs a census every ten years. The government uses this data to learn such things as how the population is changing, where people live, what types of families exist, and what languages are spoken. For example, the 2010 U.S Census counted 308,745,538 people and 4,239,587 of them were over the age of 85.

To answer some questions, a census is not possible. It might be too expensive or impractical. For example surveying every math student in your state may be too time consuming. It might be that the object being measured is destroyed during the experiment, as when determining how strong bicycle tires are by filling every single bicycle tire with air until it explodes. When it is not possible or practical to take a census, a portion of the population, called a **sample**, is measured or surveyed. Numerical summaries of a sample are called **statistics**.

For example, if all of the people in this class make up our population, then every fifth member of our class is a possible sample. The whole-class (population) average on the final exam is a parameter. The average test score of the students in the sample is a statistic.

9-7.   Read the Math Notes box in this lesson. For each question, describe the population of interest. Then state whether a census is practical or whether it makes more sense to take a sample. Justify your response.

a.   What is the average time it takes U.S. employees to commute to work?

b.   What is the average bedtime for students in your math class?

c.   How much Vitamin A is in an average carrot?

d.   What is the public approval rating of the Governor?

e.   How much weight can an elevator cable support?

f.   What are your friends' favorite movies?

9-8.   Katelyn owns a 24-hour coffee shop in front of a downtown office building. She recorded the number of cups of coffee sold each hour during a 48-hour time period.

Katelyn sorted the data and made the following histogram:

Cups of Coffee Sold		
1	22	37
5	22	38
7	23	38
12	24	40
12	25	41
12	26	41
12	26	42
12	29	47
14	29	47
16	30	49
17	30	51
19	31	52
20	32	55
21	33	55
21	35	59
22	36	76
checksum 1444		

a.   Using the sorted data from the table and the histogram, find the five number summary (minimum, first quartile, median, third quartile, maximum) without using your calculator.

b.   Describe the distribution of coffee sales per hour.

9-9.   Consider the polynomial $x^4 - 6x^3 - 6x^2 + 6x - 7$.

   a.   Using only integers, list all the possible linear factors.

   b.   Is $(x+1)$ a factor of the polynomial? Is $(x-1)$ a factor? Show how you know without graphing.

9-10.   Find all values of a for which the equation $ax^2 + 5x + 6 = 0$ has solutions that are real numbers. Express a in terms of one or more inequalities.

9-11.   Solve each equation for $0 \le \theta \le 360$. You may need your calculator, but remember that your calculator only gives *one* answer. Most of these problems have more than one answer. Think about all four quadrants.

   a. $\sin \theta = 0.5$ b. $\cos \theta = -0.5$

   c. $4 \tan \theta - 4 = 0$ d. $3 \sin^2 \theta = 1$

9-12.   Verify algebraically that $g(x) = \frac{5x-2}{3}$ is the inverse function of $f(x) = \frac{3x+2}{5}$.

9-13.   The **Richter scale** assigns a magnitude number to quantify the energy released by an earthquake. The magnitude of an earthquake was defined by Charles Richter to be $M = \log \frac{I}{S}$ where I is the intensity of the earthquake (measured by the amplitude of a seismograph reading taken 100 km from the epicenter of the earthquake) and S is the intensity of a "standard earthquake" (whose amplitude is 1 micron $= 10^{-4}$ cm). For example, an earthquake measuring 3.6 on the Richter scale is $10^{0.2}$ or approximately 1.6 times as intense as an earthquake measuring 3.4 on the Richter scale.

   a.   How many times stronger is an earthquake that measures 6.5 on the Richter scale than an earthquake that measures 5.5?

   b.   How many times stronger is an earthquake that measures 5.1 than an earthquake that measures 4.3? Give your answer both as a power of 10 and as a decimal. Make sure your answer has the same level of precision as the Richter measurements.

   c.   What is the magnitude of an earthquake that is half as strong as an earthquake measuring 6.2 on the Richter scale?

9-14.   The roots of a polynomial are given below. Find two linear factors and the corresponding quadratic factor.

   a. $x = -2 + \sqrt{3}, x = -2 - \sqrt{3}$ b. $x = -2 + i, x = -2 - i$

9-15.   Joanne was making repairs to her deck and needed to buy some supplies. She purchased two posts, three boards, and four piers for $52. When she needed more materials, she went back to the lumberyard and bought one post and five boards for $13. Realizing she did not need the piers, she made a third trip in which she bought three more boards, returned the four piers, and ended up with a refund of $34. What was the cost of each item?

9.1.2 Whom should I survey?

Samples and the Role of Randomness

In order to decide whether you like a particular soup, do you need to eat the whole pot? Usually, you can get a good sense of the flavor of the soup by taking a small taste, or a sample.

When conducting a study, it is usually not possible to survey every person or object in the population in which you are interested (for example, all the residents of the United States, all the students at your school, or all teenage shoppers). However, just as you can learn about the flavor of a soup with a small taste instead of eating the whole pot, you can learn about a population by **sampling** instead of taking a census. Unfortunately, large groups of people are much harder to stir than pots of soup to get a representative mix of their populations.

In this lesson, you will consider ways that statisticians do the equivalent of "stirring" populations in order to take samples that represent the whole population well.

As you work with your team today, consider the following questions.

> How should we decide what is "typical" of a group?

> How do random selection and intentional selection compare?

9-16.   How should you choose people for your survey to make up a sample that you think represents the population for your research question?

   a.   Discuss this question with your team and write down your ideas. Be sure to justify why your ideas will help you choose a representative sample.

   b.   Do you think your sampling method is better than randomly selecting members of the population? Why or why not?

9-17.   Some astronomers believe that a number of small objects, called Vulcanoid
          asteroids, exist between Mercury and the Sun. Other scientists, however, do not
          believe that these asteroids exist. The brightness of the sun has prevented direct
          observations, so the controversy remains unresolved.

Imagine the following scenario.
Scientists invent a special camera that can
photograph these asteroids, even though
they are so close to the sun. They put the
camera on a satellite and send it off. To
their joy and amazement, the satellite
begins to transmit images back to the
earth and the asteroids are visible!
Vulcanoids are real!

Unfortunately, in just five seconds, the heat of the sun destroys the camera and
the transmission stops. Due to a technical malfunction, the five seconds of
video images were not recorded. The scientists who were watching have to rely
on their memories of the images.

a.   Help the scientists determine the size
      of a "typical" Vulcanoid asteroid by
      modeling this scenario. First, look
      at your "video" picture (Lesson
      9.1.2A Resource Page) for exactly
      five seconds. Then, *without talking
      to anyone*, write down your estimate
      of a typical asteroid diameter in
      millimeters.

b.   Follow your teacher's instructions to contribute your estimate to the
      class's histogram. Sketch the histogram on your paper and describe its
      attributes, including the center, shape, spread, and the presence of any
      outliers.

9-18.   Now suppose that the camera on the satellite and the recording equipment were repairable and the scientists were able to record a good still photograph of the Vulcanoid asteroids. Now you have much more reliable information with which to determine the size of a typical asteroid.

   a.   Look at your photograph on the Lesson 9.1.2A Resource Page. Again, *without talking to anyone*, pick ten "typical" asteroids and measure the diameter of each in millimeters. Write down each of your measurements and then calculate the mean diameter. Do you think this result is a better estimate of the size of a typical asteroid than the one you estimated in problem 9-17? Why or why not?

   b.   Again, follow your teacher's instructions to contribute your calculated mean to the class's new histogram. Sketch the histogram on your own paper and describe how this histogram compares to the histogram of the class's estimates from problem 9-17.

   c.   In general, which set of estimates is more accurate? How can you tell? Be sure to use your comparison of the histograms to help justify your answer.

9-19.   You will use your calculator's ability to generate random numbers to help you to randomly select 10 asteroid images.

   a.   First, your teacher will give you instructions to make sure that your calculator does not generate the same random numbers as someone else's calculator.

   b.   Your teacher will now give you instructions to use your calculator to randomly select ten asteroids. It is possible that some will be repeated. Each member of your team should generate his or her own set of random numbers.

        Measure the ten asteroids that were randomly chosen by your calculator. If you have repeated numbers, measure those asteroids twice. Calculate the mean diameter of your ten asteroids.

   c.   Again, follow your teacher's instructions to contribute your calculated mean to the class's new histogram of randomly selected asteroids. Sketch the histogram on your own paper and describe how this histogram compares to the histograms of the class's estimates from problems 9-17 and 9-18.

9-20.   HOW SHOULD SAMPLES BE CHOSEN?

Based on the data collected by your class, discuss the following questions with your team. Be prepared to contribute your ideas and questions to a class discussion.

a.   Which selection method produced the most consistent (least variable) results? Why does this result make sense?

b.   Look in particular at the differences in data produced by intentionally-chosen samples and randomly-chosen samples. Why do the differences make sense? Be sure to consider differences in center, shape, spread, and outliers.

c.   Which sampling method seems to produce the best estimate of the size of a "typical" asteroid? How can you tell?

d.   Your teacher will provide you with the actual measures of central tendency of the sizes of the asteroid images. Does your idea about which sampling method is best change?

9-21.   CHOOSING YOUR SAMPLE

Talk with your team about what it would mean to randomly choose a sample from the population in your survey (problems 9-1 and 9-6). How might you do that? Could your calculator help you? Will it be possible to survey a randomly-selected sample? Why or why not?

Store your survey questions in a safe place. They will be needed later in this chapter.

9-22. Consider each of the following survey questions. For each one, explain any bias you find. If you think the question is unbiased (or fair), explain why.

a. Do you agree that it is important to make ending homelessness a high priority?

b. Which of the following factors is most important to address in order to slow global climate change?

A. Car emissions B. Airplane emissions

C. Pollutants from private industry D. Dependence on oil

c. How important is it to raise teacher salaries?

9-23. Consider each of the following research conditions. For each one, write a research question that would be subject to such conditions.

a. Sampling must be used because the population is too large to measure.

b. Sampling must be used because measuring the population would destroy it.

c. A census can be used because the population is measurable.

d. A census can be used, even though the population is very large.

9-24.   When vapor under high pressure is released into the air, the resulting noise can severely damage people's hearing. This is a concern for large industrial facilities like power plants and factories. To help control this noise pollution companies install silencers, which work on the same principles as car mufflers. Hector is an engineer for Vapor Kinetics. He is testing two different models of silencers, the Hush Puppy and the Quiet Down, by measuring the sound energy in decibels (dB) each silencer is producing at various temperatures and pressures. The data has been sorted and is shown below:

Hush Puppy

19.7	22.8	26.3	27.4	29.5	38.8	39.3	44.5	46.7	50.0
51.2	52.4	53.4	56.6	58.0	58.6	60.7	62.3	66.4	67.0
68.6	69.6	70.1	70.9	71.3	72.9	76.4	76.5	76.7	79.5

Checksum 1664.1

Quiet Down

14.2	16.3	19.3	24.6	26.0	30.5	35.8	37.4	39.9	40.0
40.1	47.3	52.9	53.5	53.7	56.0	56.6	56.7	59.1	59.8
61.3	62.6	63.3	64.3	66.5	67.1	71.8	95.7	101.2	102.1

Checksum 1575.6

a.   Create a combination boxplot and histogram for each silencer. For the histograms, scale the x-axis from 12 to 108 and use a bin width of 12 dB.

b.   Describe the center, shape, spread and outliers for each silencer. Make sure your results have the same level of precision as the measurements.

c.   Hector needs to recommend one design for production. Which one do you suggest and why?

d.   The decibel scale is logarithmic, not linear. For example, a 105 dB sound is 8 times louder than a 75 dB sound. This is roughly the difference in noise between running a kitchen blender and running a chain saw. Does this information change your answer to part (c)? Why or why not?

9-25.   Rearrange the equation $y = 2x^2 + 8x + 5$ into a more useful form for graphing. State the locator point and draw the graph.

9-26.   Solve this system for y and z: $\frac{z+y}{2} + \frac{z-y}{4} = 3$

$$\frac{4z-y}{2} + \frac{5z+2y}{11} = 3$$

9-27. Solve each equation.

  a. $\log_2(x) + \log_2(x-2) = 3$ b. $\log(2x) - \log(x^2) = -2$

9-28. Convert the following angle measurements from degrees to radians.

  a. $30°$ b. $15°$ c. $-75°$ d. $630°$

9-29. Find the exact equation of the graph at right.

9-30. A conveyor belt carries grain to the top of a barn, where it drops the grain so that it forms a pile on the ground. The pile is in the shape of a cone. Recall that the volume of a cone is one-third the area of the base times the vertical height.

  a. Find the volume of the grain when the height of the pile is ten feet and the radius of the base is 4 feet. Use appropriate precision on your results.

  b. As the pile grows, the cones formed remain similar. If the radius of the base is four feet when the height is ten feet, what is the radius of the base when the height is 15 feet?

  c. Consider the angle the side of the cone-shaped pile makes with the ground. Is this angle changing? Justify your answer. If not, what is the measure of the angle?

9.1.3 What if random is not possible?

....

Bias in Convenience Samples

In Lesson 9.1.2, you learned that random samples generally represent populations from which they are selected more closely than intentionally-selected samples. Partly for this reason, randomization is an important part of statistics.

However, it is often the case that it is neither possible nor practical to sample a population randomly. For example, if you wanted to survey voters in the United States about their choice for a presidential candidate, random sampling might not be practical. Even if you designed a method to select 1000 names randomly from the population of American voters, how would you find those 1000 people to survey in a timely and cost effective manner?

Sometimes statisticians are restricted to sampling strategies based on who is available to them, a practice known as **convenience sampling**. When this sampling technique is used, it is often impossible to make responsible claims about the original population. Consider these ideas as you work on the following problems with your team.

9-31. Delilah is a pollster and she wants to know what American voters think about a possible federal income tax increase to fund education. She stands outside of a grocery store one evening and surveys every adult who is registered to vote. 62% of the voters Delilah surveyed support the tax increase.

a. Can Delilah claim that this result is representative of American voters in general? Be sure to justify your thinking.

b. With your team, think about the population that Delilah is actually finding information about. Whom can she responsibly claim her 62%-in-favor result represents?

c. How might Delilah improve her sampling technique to better represent the population of American voters? Discuss this with your team and be prepared to share your ideas with the class.

9-32.   Sometimes pollsters try to predict the sorts of bias that they are likely to introduce with their sampling methods so that they can report their results appropriately. For example, Delilah might notice that many of the voters she surveyed had school-age children with them, and she might reason that they are more likely than average to support policies that fund public education.

For each of the following sampling methods, consider the actual population it could represent. What sorts of biases might you expect from these groups about Delilah's question from problem 9-31? What biases might you expect them to have about your own team's research question? Be prepared to share your ideas with the class.

a.   A call-in survey on a morning television talk show.

b.   Questionnaires mailed to addresses found in an online phone list.

c.   A survey of every student on the bus to school.

9-33.   Often when it is not possible to use a truly random sample, statisticians try to incorporate as much randomness as they can into their samples. For example, statisticians might divide the population into smaller clusters that each represent the population and randomly choose clusters to sample. They might divide the populations into groups that are each alike (stratified) for a particular characteristic, then randomly sample from each group. Or they might systematically choose every fifth person or every tenth person, which is just as good as random if there is no order to the subjects.

Consider this idea as you talk with your own team about the survey you have been designing. Make a plan for sampling that considers the following questions. Be prepared to share your plan with your teacher.

- What is the population you are interested in?

- How will you select a sample of your population? How can you incorporate some degree of randomness into your selection process?

- How can you justify claims you will make about how representative this sample is of your population?

Store your survey questions in a safe place. They will be needed later in Chapter 11.

9-34.   In 1988, a committee of the Physicians Health Study Research Group released
         the results of a five-year experiment conducted on over 22,000 male physicians
         aged 40 to 84. The research on this sample suggested that the participants who
         took an aspirin every other day had a lower rate of heart attacks.

   a.   Can you conclude from this experiment that aspirin reduces the risk of
        heart attacks for all people? Why or why not?

   b.   Can you conclude from this experiment that aspirin reduces heart attacks
        for all men? Why or why not?

   c.   Can you conclude from this experiment that aspirin is linked to reduced
        heart attacks for all men aged 40 to 84? Why or why not?

   d.   Can you conclude from this experiment that aspirin reduces heart attacks
        for male physicians aged 40 to 84? Why or why not?

   e.   Can you conclude from this experiment that male physicians aged 40 to 84
        should take aspirin? Why or why not?

9-35.   LEARNING LOG

         With your team, discuss what you have learned in
         Section 9.1 about survey design, sampling strategies and
         avoiding bias. What are the types of bias that can be
         present in a survey? How can you avoid them in the questions that you ask?
         How can you sample the population in which you are interested to best be able
         to confidently answer your question? Summarize your ideas and include
         examples in your Learning Log. Title this entry "Survey Design and Bias" and
         label it with today's date.

9-36.   For each question below, describe a realistic method to collect information to
         answer the question. Be sure to indicate whether you would use a sample or
         census and whether your results would be parameters or statistics.

   a.   What percentage of American League baseball players had a batting
        average above .300 this season?

   b.   How much pressure can be exerted on a chicken egg before it breaks?

   c.   How many hours of television does a high school student watch per day?

9-37.   Label each of the following questions as either "open" or "closed."

   a.   How often do you exercise?

      A.   Every day

      B.   Once a week or more

      C.   Less than once a week

   b.   What is your favorite way to exercise?

   c.   What is your favorite time of year?

   d.   In which country were you born?

9-38.   For each question in problem 9-37 that you decided is open, give examples of answers that might be difficult to compare and quantify. For each question that you decided is closed, explain how the information you get from an answer may not be as accurate as it could be.

9-39.   What is the probability that $x^2 + 7x + k$ is factorable if $0 \le k \le 20$ and k is an integer?

9-40.   Victoria is playing with her balance scale and balances 3 blue blocks and 2 red blocks on one side with 5 blue blocks and a red block on the other. Later, her brother balances 2 red blocks and a blue block with a 40-gram weight. How much does each block weigh?

9-41.   This problem is a checkpoint for writing and solving exponential equations. It will be referred to as Checkpoint 9A.

When rabbits were first brought to Australia, they had no natural enemies. There were about 80,000 rabbits in 1866. Two years later, in 1868, the population had grown to over 2,400,000!

   a.   Why would an exponential equation be a better model for this situation than a linear one? Would a sine function be better or worse? Why?

   b.   Write an exponential equation for the number of rabbits t years after 1866.

   c.   How many rabbits do you predict were present in 1871?

   d.   According to your model, in what year was the first pair of rabbits introduced into Australia? Is this reasonable?

   e.   Actually, 24 rabbits were introduced in 1859, so the model is not perfect, but is close. Is your exponential model useful for predicting how many rabbits there are now? Explain.

Check your answers by referring to the Checkpoint 9A materials located at the back of your book.

Ideally, at this point you are comfortable working with these types of problems and can solve them correctly. If you feel that you need more confidence when solving these types of problems, then review the Checkpoint 9A materials and try the practice problems provided. From this point on, you will be expected to do problems like these correctly and with confidence.

9-42.   Factor and reduce to simplify $\frac{3x+6}{x^2+7x+10}$. Justify each step.

9-43.   Simplify and add $\frac{x-4}{x+2} + \frac{4x+12}{x^2+5x+6}$. Justify each step.

9-44.   Change the angle measurements below from radians to degrees or from degrees to radians.

   a.   144°   b.   300°   c. $\frac{5\pi}{9}$

   d. $\frac{17\pi}{12}$ e. $\frac{19\pi}{2}$ f.   220°

9.2.1 How can an experiment show cause and effect?

Testing Cause and Effect with Experiments

METHODS AND MEANINGS

MATH NOTES

Observational Studies and Experiments

In an **observational study**, data is collected by observing but without imposing any kind of change. A survey is one type of observational study. Observational studies are often plagued by **lurking variables**, that is, hidden variables that are not part of the study, but that are the true cause of an association. For example, the number of firefighters at a fire is associated with the amount of damage at the scene of the fire. But of course firefighters are not the cause of the damage! The lurking variable, "size of the fire," causes both the number of firefighters and the amount of damage to increase.

To determine cause and effect, often a randomized, controlled **experiment** is conducted. In an experiment, subjects are randomly divided between two or more groups, and a **treatment** (a change) is imposed on at least one of the groups. Randomized experiments can be used to determine cause and effect because the influence of lurking variables, even though they are unknown, has mostly been equalized among all the groups. If there is a difference among groups, it is most likely due to the treatment since everything else is mostly the same.

Chapter 9: Randomization and Normal Distributions

461

9-45. Consider this question: *"Does a new type of motor oil improve gas mileage?"* Assuming this new motor oil was already available to the public, you could survey some car owners who use the oil and some who do not and compare their mean gas mileages.

a. What problems might arise from using this method? What are some possible lurking variables that could affect the outcome of the study?

b. After reading the Math Notes box in this lesson, design an experiment to help decide whether the new motor oil improves gas mileage.

c. Sometimes a group gets no treatment. If people are involved, they may get a **placebo** (a treatment with no effect) so the psychological effects of participating in an experiment are the same among the groups. If you have not already done so, include a no-treatment or placebo group in your experiment.

9-46. Testing to see how many drops of water fit on a penny would be an observational study. You would simply look to see how much water ordinary pennies can hold.

Today, a treatment has been added to a random sample of pennies to make it an experiment. Your teacher has cleaned a sample of pennies using a mild acid. The research question is, *"Does cleaning pennies cause them to hold a different amount of water than ordinary uncleaned pennies?"*

You will be assigned a sample of pennies and a workstation to test your pennies. Use the test procedures outlined by your teacher. Make class histograms and boxplots for the clean pennies and the regular pennies.

9-47. As a class, compare the histograms and boxplots, discuss your results, and write a brief conclusion.

9-48. Suppose your results from problems 9-46 and 9-47 were seriously biased by a lurking variable. The effects of this lurking variable can be defeated by using proper experimental procedures. As a class, discuss improvements that could be made in the testing procedures.

9-49.　Repeat the experiment using the revised testing procedures. Create the new histograms and box plots. Write a conclusion to the question: *"Do clean pennies hold a different amount of water than regular pennies?"*

9-50.　Statistical results can be affected by psychological issues. Researchers who conduct experiments need to eliminate sources of bias for their statistical analysis to be meaningful. What are some potential causes of bias in the following samples?

　　a.　Super Cola paid for a taste test study comparing it to Amazing Cola. Participants were asked to taste both drinks and pick their favorite. Super Cola was labeled "m" and the Amazing Cola was "q." The majority of participants picked the drink labeled "m," which was Super Cola.

　　b.　A survey was conducted in the following manner: "The Bill of Rights guarantees the right to bear arms so that we can protect our families and our country. Recently, attempts have been made to enact stricter gun controls. Do you want these restrictions?"

　　c.　Another survey was conducted in the following manner: "Last year over 15,000 people were murdered by handguns, which accounted for 68% of all murders. Recently, attempts have been made to enact stricter gun controls. Do you want these restrictions?"

9-51.　As you discovered in the asteroid activity in Lesson 9.1.2, people are not very good at picking representative samples. Similarly, it is actually quite difficult to "fake" randomness.

In this problem, you will perform a brief survey to get an idea of people's "random" behavior. For this particular survey, you are not concerned with any particular population, so you can choose any sample that is convenient. You should talk with at least 10 people among your friends and family, but try for more to make your results more interesting.

Use the same survey method for everybody: text messaging, phone call, or personal interview. Carefully record the responses you get.

Problem continues on next page →

9-51.   *Problem continued from previous page.*

    a.   Why would using a mass email or a social networking site not be a good plan?

    b.   Ask each of your respondents to make each of the following choices randomly. Make sure you read the choices exactly the same way to each respondent.

       1. Pick a number between 1 and 4.

       2. Pick a vowel (a, e, i, o, or u).

       3. Choose a color.

    c.   Make a bar graph for the responses to each of the three questions in your survey. Write the precise wording of the question with each bar graph.

    d.   Do your results show that people's choices were truly random? Why or why not?

    e.   Try to explain any trends or interesting patterns that you observe. Were the results similar to what you expected? Why or why not?

9-52.   Because gathering data for entire populations is often impractical, most of the data we analyze are samples. In order to make the sample standard deviation more closely estimate the population standard deviation, statisticians modify the way they calculate the standard deviation for a sample.

Refer to the Math Notes box in Lesson C.1.3 in Appendix C to remind you of how to calculate standard deviation (for a population). The calculation of standard deviation of a *sample* is slightly different. When computing the mean of the distances squared, instead of dividing by the number of values in the data set, divide by *one less* than the number of values in the set.

A non-profit consumer health organization measured the fat content of five low fat raspberry muffins purchased at random Sunbucks coffee shops. Find the mean and standard deviation of the fat content in this sample. Do the computations step by step, without using the "standard deviation" function on your calculator. The fat content follows: 6, 8, 8, 9, 7 grams of fat. (Hint: After showing all of your computations, the correct sample standard deviation is 1.14g.)

9-53.   Solve the system of equations at right.

$$8x - 3y - 2z = -8$$
$$-2x + 8y + 7z = 26$$
$$4x + y - 5z = 23$$

9-54.   Divide $(x^3 - 2x^2 + 25x - 50) \div (x - 2)$.

9-55.   Use your answer from the previous problem to solve $x^3 - 2x^2 + 25x - 50 = 0$.

9-56.   If $\cos\theta = \frac{8}{17}$, find $\sin\theta$.

9-57.   If $a = 2 + 3i$ and $b = 1 - i$, compute each of the following operations:

a. $a + b$ b. $a - b$ c. ab d. $\frac{a}{b}$

9-58.   Solve each equation.

a. $\frac{15}{x-2} = \frac{16}{x}$ b. $\frac{1}{x} + \frac{1}{2x} = 9$

9.2.2 How can I answer the question?

Conclusions From Studies

You will often see headlines in everyday life announcing the results of some statistical study. Today you will critically analyze the possible meanings of such headlines.

9-59.   For each question:

- Does a census or sample make more sense in this situation?

- Should an observational study or an experiment be carried out to answer the question?

- If an observational study is possible, explain how you would carry out the study. How would you get a representative sample from the population?

- If surveys are necessary, list a potential source of bias in the question(s).

- If the study asks for an association between variables, discuss the effects of at least two possible lurking variables.

- If an experiment would be suitable, outline an experimental design.

a.   Is there a relationship between the amount of physical activity a person gets and his or her perceived level of stress?

b.   What is the mean of the 2009 SAT math scores for the state of Arizona? Is it higher than the corresponding mean score for West Virginia?

c.   What percentage of high school students would be willing to donate $10 or an hour of time to help a local food bank?

d.   What is the mean weight of backpacks carried on college campuses? Is it different than the mean weight of backpacks carried on high school campuses?

e.   Would wearing neckties increase standardized test scores for boys in middle school?

f.   What is the average number of absences for the freshman class at your school?

g.   What proportion of refurbished cell phones are defective?

h.   How much cholesterol is in a chicken egg?

i.   Do the seniors at your school do less homework than the sophomores?

9-60. Answer some of the same questions posed in problem 9-59 for these actual newspaper headlines. If an observational study was done, explain how. Explain why an experiment was not possible. If the study shows an association between variables, discuss the effects of at least two possible lurking variables. If you believe an experiment was done, state so, and outline a possible experimental design. If surveys were necessary, list a potential source of bias in the question(s), and a potential difficulty in getting a representative sample from the population.

a. "STUDY STICKS IT TO TRADITIONAL BACK CARE. Acupuncture – real and fake – gets better results for pain than the usual treatments."

b. "MARITAL STRIFE A HEART WRECKER? Bad marriage can increase risk of coronary disease, researchers say."

c. "BREASTFEEDING MAY CUT BREAST CANCER RISK. Women with a family history of breast cancer who have ever breastfed reduce their risk of getting premenopausal breast cancer by nearly 60%, according to a new study."

d. "STUDY: ORAL DRUG BETTER THAN LOTION TO KILL LICE… A new study has found that in tough cases, a (new) oral medication kills the parasites more effectively than a prescription lotion applied to the scalp."

9-61. LEARNING LOG

With your team, discuss the similarities and differences between observational studies, surveys, and experiments. What are the advantages and disadvantages of each? What are some of the important things to consider when conducting an observational study versus a survey or designing an experiment? How confident can you be about your conclusions? Summarize your thoughts in your Learning Log. Title this entry "Surveys Versus Experiments" and label it with today's date.

9-62.   Suppose you were conducting a survey to determine what portion of voters in your town supports a particular candidate for mayor. Consider each of the following methods for sampling the voting population of your town. State whether each is likely to produce a representative sample and explain your reasoning.

a.   Call one number from each page of an online phone listing for your town between noon and 2 p.m.

b.   Survey each person leaving a local grocery store.

c.   Survey each person leaving a local movie theater.

d.   Walk around downtown and survey every fourth person you see.

e.   Could you make a representative sample by surveying a few people from each of the situations described in parts (a) through (d) above? Explain, and consider what problems might still remain.

9-63.   Consider the question: "Does a traditional classroom SAT preparation course improve scores more than an online study course?"

Design an experiment that could help to answer this question. Refer to problem 9-45 for ideas.

9-64.   Suppose you were asked to find lurking variables that would be associated with the news headline: "Study: Kids who were spanked have lower IQs." Certainly, there are plenty of lurking variables to cast doubt on cause and effect. Think about what it would take to do an experiment to determine if spanking causes lower IQs. Design an experiment and point out why it is not ethical.

9-65.   In an effort to determine the amount of food a male yellow-billed magpie eats in a day, a sample of 5 birds from pet stores was observed. The birds ate the following amount of food: 60, 60, 50, 40, and 50 grams. Find the mean and standard deviation weight of food in this sample. Do the computations step by step, without using the "standard deviation" function on your calculator, as in problem 9-52.

Core Connections Algebra 2

9-66.　How many solutions are there to the system of equations at right? Justify your response.

$$y = x^2 - 2x + 2$$
$$y = 2x - 2$$

9-67.　Graph $y = \sqrt{(4 - x^2)}$. Imagine revolving this graph around the x-axis, faster and faster, so that it appears to form a sphere. Sketch the sphere and then find its volume. Note: The volume of a sphere is given by $V = \frac{4}{3}\pi r^3$.

9-68.　What is the probability that $x^2 + kx + 12$ will factor if $0 \le k \le 8$ and k is an integer? Make an organized list (sample space) to help you determine the probability.

9-69.　Graph at least two cycles of the following functions.

a.　$f(x) = 3\sin 2(x - \frac{\pi}{4}) + 1$　　　　b.　$g(x) = \frac{1}{2}\cos\frac{1}{4}(x + \pi)$

9.3.1 What percent is it?

Relative Frequency Histograms

In this lesson you will learn how to make a new kind of histogram, called a relative frequency histogram. A relative frequency histogram helps you find the proportion of the population with a certain characteristic.

9-70.   In order to make the standard deviation of a sample more closely estimate the population standard deviation, statisticians modify the way they calculate the standard deviation for a sample.

   a.   If the data set contains the entire population, you divide by n, the number of values in the data set, when finding the population standard deviation. If the data set is a sample from the population, you divide by $n-1$ to find the sample standard deviation. Which standard deviation has a larger value?

   b.   One of the reasons the sample standard deviation needs to be increased has to do with outliers. Why might the presence of outliers in the population make the standard deviation of a sample too small compared to the standard deviation of the population?

   c.   Refer to problem 9-65. The amounts the five birds ate were: 60, 60, 50, 40, and 50 grams. Explore the functions on your calculator to find the mean and the sample standard deviation for the five birds.

   d.   What if the five birds were the entire population of birds? What would the mean and population standard deviation be? Use the correct symbols, referring as needed to the Math Notes box at the end of this lesson.

9-71.   VISORS FOR RUNNERS, Part 1

The Style & Comfort Headgear Company makes
printed visors as gifts for women running in
charity marathons. Marathons in different cities
have different numbers of participants. S & C
Headgear needs a method for deciding how many
visors of each size to print for each event. The
company collected the data below for women's
head circumference by measuring 40 randomly
selected runners at charity events.

Head circumference (cm)							
55.5	53.7	53.7	53.4	53.1	55.2	53.9	53.8
53.1	52.2	54.8	54.5	53.2	52.3	55.3	53.2
51.9	53.1	53.1	52.2	51.2	55.4	53.3	51.4
52.6	53.7	52.7	52.8	51.9	54.3	55.4	53.7
53.0	52.7	53.0	54.6	52.5	52.9	53.1	51.9

checksum 2133.3

a.   What are the mean head circumference and standard deviation for these
      women?

b.   On your calculator, make a histogram of the distribution of women's head
      circumferences and sketch it. Use an interval from 50 cm to 57 cm with a
      bin width of 1.

c.   Hat size is determined by the whole-number portion of a woman's head
      circumference. For example, a woman with a head measuring 55.8 cm
      would need a size 55 hat. According to your histogram, how many
      women in this sample need a size 52 hat?

d.   What percent of the women in this sample have a hat size less than 54?

9-72. Questions about percentages, like those in part (d) of problem 9-71 above, are easier to answer if you make a table of **relative frequencies**. Relative frequency is the **proportion** of hats: the percent of hats in that size out of the total 40 hats, written as a decimal.

a. Copy and complete the following table.

Women's hat sizes		
size interval	frequency (# of hats)	relative frequency (proportion of hats)
50–51	0	0
51–52	5	0.125
52–53	9	0.225
53–54	17	
54–55		
55–56		
56–57		

b. Your teacher will show you how to make a **relative frequency histogram** from the table above. Sketch the relative frequency histogram. Label the top of each bar with its relative frequency. What do you notice about the shape of the relative frequency histogram?

c. Relative frequency histograms make percentages easier to visualize. Use the histogram to compute the percent of hats in this sample between size 52 and 55.

d. What percent of hats in this sample are below size 56? Show a computation.

9-73.   CHARITY RACE TIMES, Part 1

The 40 women in the sample recorded their race times in various charity 5K
races in the table below.

Race time (min)							
22.2	22.6	24.9	23.5	22.8	23.3	23.1	21.6
21.3	22.9	25.7	23.3	23.3	22.5	24.4	22.7
24.1	23	22.5	23.2	24.7	24.4	23.3	23.5
23.1	22.5	22.3	22.6	23.6	23.3	23.3	23.4
23.0	23.1	24.5	23.9	20.6	23.5	22.8	24.4

checksum 928.7

a.   Find the mean and standard deviation
of the race times to four decimal
places. Justify your choice of standard
deviation.

b.   Create a relative frequency histogram with your calculator, and sketch it.
Use an interval from 19 to 27 with a bin width of 1. Label the top of each
bar with its relative frequency.

c.   Use the relative frequencies on your histogram to calculate the percentage
of racers in this sample that had a time faster than 22 minutes. Remember,
smaller times are faster.

d.   What percentage of racers in this sample completed a race between 22 and
25 minutes? What is the relationship between the area of the bars and the
percentage of the population?

9-74.   LEARNING LOG

With your team, discuss the similarities and differences
between a histogram and a relative frequency histogram as
a way to represent a distribution of single-variable data.
What is the meaning of the *area* of the bars on a relative
frequency histogram? Summarize the directions for creating a relative
frequency histogram, including examples. Title this entry "Relative Frequency
Histograms" and label it with today's date.

METHODS AND **M**EANINGS

MATH NOTES

Symbols for Standard Deviation

In statistics, standard variables are used to represent the mean and standard deviation.

The number of values in a data set is often represented with n.

The population parameters are written using lower-case Greek letters such as μ (pronounced "myoo") for the mean, and σ (pronounced "sigma") for the population standard deviation.

When the data are a sample, $\bar{x}$ (pronounced "x-bar") represents the sample mean, and s is used to represent the sample standard deviation.

Review & Preview

9-75.   Bias can take many forms. Sometimes it is created unintentionally by conditions in an experiment. Other times it is more intentional. For each example below, comment on possible bias.

a.   In a TV commercial an interviewer asks people on the street to name their favorite radio station. All five that he asked claimed the same station as their favorite.

b.   A university campus wants to increase fees in order to build a new recreation hall. It surveys students to determine support. Survey booths are placed outside the university gym. The resulting survey showed overwhelming support.

c.   A study shows that many more accidents occur on I-95 during the day than at night. Is it therefore safer to drive at night?

d.   An active citizens' group claimed that a nuclear facility was operating at below average safety levels and therefore should be shut down.

9-76.   Design experiments for the following statistical
         questions. If it would be unethical to conduct
         such an experiment, state why.

         a.   "Does listening to classical music during a
               math test improve scores?"

         b.   "Do seat belts save lives in car crashes?"

         c.   "Does vitamin C help prevent colds?"

9-77.   Simplify each expression below.

         a. $3^{-2} \cdot 3^4$ b. $3^{-4} \cdot 3^4$

         c. $(3^{-1} + 3^{-3}) \cdot 3^4$ d. $\frac{3^{-2} - 3^{-1}}{3^{-3} + 3^{-4}}$

9-78.   John has to graph a set of parabolas of the form $y = x^2 - 4x + 2^n$ where n is an
         integer and $0 \le n \le 6$. What is the probability that one of these parabolas,
         chosen at random, will have:

         a.   One x-intercept?

         b.   Two x-intercepts?

         c.   No x-intercepts?

9-79.   If $\tan\theta = \frac{1}{2}$ and $\pi \le \theta \le \frac{3\pi}{2}$, what is the value of $\sin\theta$?

9-80.   Denae and Gina were trying to solve $\sqrt{x+5} + \sqrt{x} = 5$. They knew they would have to square the equation to get rid of the radicals, but when they tried it, they got $x + 5 + 2\sqrt{x(x+5)} + x = 25$, which did not look much easier to deal with. Gina had an idea.

"Let's start by putting the radicals on opposite sides of the equation and then squaring." she said. Her work is shown at right.

$$\sqrt{x+5} + \sqrt{x} = 5$$
$$\sqrt{x+5} = 5 - \sqrt{x}$$
$$x + 5 = 25 - 10\sqrt{x} + x$$

"But there's still a radical!" she exclaimed, disappointed.

"That's okay," said Denae, *"there's only one now, so we can get the term with the radical by itself and then square everything again."*

a.   Follow Denae's advice and solve this equation.

b.   Use Denae and Gina's method to solve $\sqrt{2x-2} - \sqrt{x} = 1$.

9-81.   If you deposit $1000 into an account that pays 6% interest compounded monthly, how long do you have to wait until the account is worth $4000?

9-82.   Graph each of the following trig functions.

a. $y = 2\sin(x)$ and $y = \cos(x)$ on the same set of axes.

b.   Use your answer to part (a) to graph $y = 2\sin(x) + \cos(x)$.

9-83.   You are given a bag that you are told contains eight marbles. You draw out a marble, record its color, and put it back.

a.   If you repeat this eight times and you do not record any red marbles, can you conclude that there are not any red marbles in the bag? Explain.

b.   If you repeat this 100 times and you do not record any red marbles, can you conclude that there are not any red marbles in the bag? Explain.

c.   How many times do you have to draw marbles (putting them back each time) to be absolutely certain that there are no red marbles in the bag?

9.3.2 How can I make predictions?

The Normal Probability Density Function

By creating a mathematical model of data, you can describe the data to others without giving them a list of all the data, and you can make predictions based on the data. In previous courses you created a model when you drew a line of best fit as a model for data in a scatterplot. Using the line of best fit, you were able to describe the association in the data, and you were able to make predictions from the model.

Much of the real data that is encountered in science, business, and industry can be modeled with a bell-shaped curve, called a **normal probability density function**. This function is given by the following mathematical formula:

$$f(x) = \frac{1}{\sqrt{2\pi\sigma^2}} e^{-\frac{(x-\mu)^2}{2\sigma^2}}$$

Although this looks intimidating, your calculator can draw the graph very easily based on the mean and standard deviation of the data.

9-84.   CHARITY RACE TIMES, Part 2

Reread problem 9-73 "Charity Race Times" from Lesson 9.3.1. Recreate the relative frequency histogram on your calculator, and record the mean and standard deviation. Use an interval from 19 to 27 with a bin width of 1.

Your teacher will demonstrate how to model the women's 5K times with a normal probability density function ("**normal distribution**"). Sketch the histogram with your model on top of it.

How well does your model represent the data? What are the strengths and weaknesses of your model?

9-85.   If you wanted to use the relative frequency histogram to find the percent of
women in this sample that have run times between 22.5 and 24.5 minutes, you
would add up the bars between 22.5 and 24.5. But since your histogram is not
drawn conveniently with those bins, you would have to redraw the histogram.
However, your model of the data comes to the rescue!

a.   The height of the bars between 22.5 and
24.5 can be modeled with the area under the
normal distribution between 22.5 and 24.5,
as shaded black in the diagram at right.

Your teacher will show you how to use the
normalcdf function on your calculator to find
the area under the curve between 22.5 and
24.5. In general, on a TI83/84+ calculator,
you enter [2nd] [DISTR] normalcdf(*lower limit,
upper limit, mean, standard deviation*) to
have your calculator find the proportion for
the interval.

What percent of women in this sample have running times between 22.5
and 24.5 minutes?

b.   Your model represents the percentages of women in the sample that have
various run times. But it does much more than that – since the sample of
40 randomly selected women represents the whole population of women
that run in 5K races, your model can tell you about percentages in the
whole population. (You will refine these techniques in more advanced
statistics classes.) If your model represented the whole population, what
percentage of all women that run 5K races have race times between 20 and
25 minutes?

c.   Even though the fastest (smallest) time in the sample of 40 women was
20.6 minutes, the model that you chose – the normal probability density
function – starts at negative infinity and goes all the way to positive
infinity. What percentage of all women in the population run faster than
26 minutes according to your model? Since your calculator may not have
an infinity key, instead enter -10^{99} for the lower limit.

d.   Using your model, make a prediction for the percentage of women that fall
below the mean running time. Does your answer make sense?

Core Connections Algebra 2

9-86.   VISORS FOR RUNNERS, Part 2

The Style and Comfort 5K Race for Charity is coming
up. The Style and Comfort Headwear Company
expects 775 racers. Based on a model for hat size
distributions for all women, they will need to order
hats for the event.

a.   On your calculator, recreate the relative frequency histogram for the 40
      women's hat sizes in problem 9-71. Use an interval from 50 cm to 57 cm
      with a bin width of 1.

b.   Use the mean and standard deviation of hat sizes that you calculated in
      problem 9-71 to make a model of the data using a normal distribution.
      You will need your calculator. Sketch the histogram and the model.

c.   Using your model to represent all women running 5K races, determine
      what percentage of women racers wear a size 51 hat. Shade this
      proportion on a new sketch of the model, and calculate the proportion
      using normalcdf on your calculator. How does the percentage predicted
      by the model compare to the percentage observed in your sample?

d.   How many size 51 hats should Style and Comfort order for the anticipated
      775 racers at the Style and Comfort 5K Race for Charity?

e.   Use the model to predict how many of the racers at the Style and Comfort
      5K Race for Charity are expected to have a hat size below 51. Sketch
      these proportions on a new sketch of the model.

f.   How many racers would you expect to have a hat size over size 56?
      Between 51 and 56?

g.   Does your answer to part (f) make sense
      when compared to the answers from part (e)?

h.   What percentage of racers does your normal
      distribution model predict have hat sizes
      between negative infinity and infinity? Does
      your model make a sensible prediction?

9-87.   LEARNING LOG

With your team, discuss the similarities and differences
between a relative frequency histogram as a way to
represent a sample, and the normal distribution as a model
for the population represented in the random sample. Review the directions and
include some examples for drawing a normal distribution and for finding
percents represented by areas under the normal distribution. Title this entry
"Relative Frequency Histograms and Normal Distributions," and include
today's date.

9-88.   Some students at North City High are abusing the
privilege of being allowed to leave campus for
lunch. The number of students tardy to Mrs.
Greene's period after lunch is too high. In the
last 30 school days, she recorded the number of
tardy students shown in the relative frequency
histogram at right.

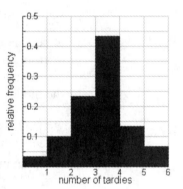

   a.   Describe the distribution of tardy students by
         estimating the height of each bin.

   b.   How many days were 3 or more students tardy?

   c.   What percent of the days were no students tardy?

9-89.   Coach Pham claims that his new 6-week agility program will increase an
         athlete's vertical leap by 10 centimeters more than traditional workouts.

   a.   Design an experiment to test the coach's claim.

   b.   If the group using Coach Pham's techniques improved their leaping
         significantly more than the group using traditional methods, would this
         provide evidence that the new agility program is the cause?

9-90.   A properly randomized and controlled experiment can determine cause and
         effect, unlike an observational study, which can be plagued by lurking variables.
         Why do we not conduct an experiment for every study? Why do observational
         studies at all?

Core Connections Algebra 2

9-91. Graph the inequalities $y \geq |x-2|$ and $y \leq 4-|x|$, then find the area of the enclosed region.

9-92. Use the equation $f(x) = (x+3)^3 - 1$ to complete each of the following tasks.

    a. Find the inverse equation.

    b. Graph the inverse equation.

    c. Is the inverse a function? Explain.

9-93. Make a sketch of the graph of each of the following functions. Describe the graphs.

    a. $y = (x+1)^2 (x-2)^2 (x-5)^2$
    b. $y = -(x+1)^2 (x-2)^2 (x-5)^2$

9-94. Given the function $h(x) = -2(x+3)^2 + 2$:

    a. What are the intercepts?
    b. What are the domain and range?

9-95. Rewrite each equation in graphing form and identify the key points.

    a. $y = \frac{1}{4}x^2 + \frac{1}{2}x + \frac{5}{8}$
    b. $y = \frac{1}{4}x^2 + 5x + 41$

9-96. Find the distance between the two points.

    a. (x, y) and $(-3, y)$
    b. (x, y) and $(-3, 2)$

9.3.3 How well did I do?

Percentiles

9-97.   The ACT is a test that colleges use to help make admissions decisions for potential students. Nationwide, the scores are normally distributed, with a mean score of 21 (out of a possible 36) and a standard deviation of 4.7.

   a.   Model the scores of all test takers on your calculator using a normal distribution. An appropriate value for the maximum of the relative frequency axis is 0.1.

   b.   Adèle scored 25 on the ACT. With your team, explore how well she did. Remember your normal distribution is a model for the bars of a histogram. Shade the "bars" (the area under the normal distribution) for all the scores below Adèle's score. What percent of scores are below Adèle's score? Round to the nearest whole number.

   c.   Since 80% of test-takers scored below Adèle, you can say that Adèle scored in the 80th **percentile**. Rémy scored a 16 on the ACT. What was Rémy's percentile?

   d.   Antoinette scored 21 on the ACT. *Without a calculator*, make a sketch of the scores below Antoinette on a normal distribution and indicate what percentile Antoinette fell in.

9-98.   Percentiles are not just for normal distributions. They can be used for any set of data to report the percent of scores that fell below a given score. The following data are the test scores on Mrs. Abraha's Chapter 3 test in Geometry.

Chapter 3 Geometry Test Scores						
75	72	91	90	83	60	89
86	17	71	58	86	81	86
94	94	79	60	53	89	42
89	56	57	93	93	94	76
80	80	94	75	92	69	75

checksum 2679

a.   Make a histogram of the data on your calculator and sketch it. Use a bin width of 5.

b.   Lateefa is modeling the data using a normal distribution, but her partner Farid thinks that it is not a good idea. What advice would you give them about using a normal distribution?

c.   Lateefa scored 86 on the test, and Farid scored 92. What percentile did each score in?

d.   What score is at the 25th percentile? 75th percentile?

e.   Find the five number summary (minimum, first quartile, median, third quartile, maximum) for this data. How does your answer compare to part (d) above?

9-99.   The March 2004 issue of *Ichthyological Research* reported the relative frequencies for the length of 98 larvae of the ayu sweetfish is shown at right.

a.   Estimate the 90th percentile for the length of ayu larvae.

b.   Would you recommend making a model using a normal distribution for the data to answer part (a)? Why or why not?

c.   Estimate the 50th percentile. What is another name for the 50th percentile?

9-100.   Rachna's physics class is going out to the football
field to launch rockets today. The rocket that Rachna
is launching has historically had a mean flight
distance of 74 m with a standard deviation of 26 m.
A rocket's flight distance is modeled with a normal
distribution.

a.   Make a graph of the distribution of Rachna's
rocket flight distances on your calculator, and
sketch it. An appropriate value for the maximum
of the relative frequency axis is 0.02.

b.   From your graph, visually estimate the two flight distances between which
the rocket will land 90% of the time. Shade this portion of your sketch.

c.   Use your calculator to check your estimate. How close to 90% did you
come?

d.   The middle 90% (or 95% or 99%) of the data is an important computation
in statistics. It tells you what "typical" data might look like without
considering the small or large extremes at either end. Statistical
computations will reveal that the lower bound of the middle 90% of
normally distributed data is at -1.6449 times the standard deviation, and
the upper bound is at 1.6449 times the standard deviation. Use this new
information to make a new, more accurate, determination of the two
distances between which the rocket will land 90% of the time.

9-101.   Rachna and her sister, Rakhi, were both in the same physics class. They made a
bet with each other on whose rocket would go farther. The loser would have to
wash the family dishes for a month! Unfortunately, Rakhi was assigned a very
different style rocket from the one Rachna got, so it was difficult to make a fair
comparison. They decided to compare the percentiles. Rakhi's style of rocket
had a mean flight distance of 30 m with a standard deviation of 6 m.

Rachna's rocket went 66.74 m, while Rakhi's went 28.17 m. Use percentiles to
determine who had to wash the dishes for a month.

9-102.   In response to a judging controversy during the 2002 Winter Olympics, a new
scoring system for ice dancing was implemented in 2006. The new system uses
a "grade of execution" (GOE) as part of the overall score. The GOE goes from
-3 to 3, and can be modeled with a normal distribution with mean of 0 and
standard deviation of 1. Isabella and Tony scored a 2 on the GOE. What
percentile are they in? What percentage of ice dancers had higher scores?

Core Connections Algebra 2

METHODS AND MEANINGS

MATH NOTES

Normal Probability Density Function

For many situations in science, business, and industry, data may be represented by a bell-shaped curve. In order to be able to work mathematically with that data – describing it to others, making predictions – an equation called a **normal probability density function** is fitted to the data. This is very similar to how a line of best fit is used to describe and make predictions of data on a scatterplot.

The normal probability density function ("normal distribution") stretches to infinity in both directions. The area under the normal distribution can be thought of as modeling the bars on a relative frequency histogram. However, instead of drawing all the bars, a curve is drawn that represents the tops of all the bars. Like bars on a relative frequency histogram, the area under the normal distribution (shaded in the diagram below) represents the portion of the population within that interval.

The total area under the curve is 1, representing 100% of the population. The mean of the population is at the peak of the normal distribution, resulting in 50% of the population below the mean and 50% above the mean.

The width of the normal distribution is determined by the standard deviation (the variability) of the population under study. The more variability in the data, the wider (and flatter) the normal distribution is.

9-103. North City High School has served the following number of lunches since the beginning of the school year. The data has been sorted.

Number of lunches sold per day							
576	605	632	660	671	689	723	774
584	606	636	661	671	695	738	785
594	613	640	663	675	698	745	
595	618	640	665	677	703	755	
603	630	652	666	678	721	774	

checksum 24711

a. What are the mean and standard deviation number of lunches in the sample?

b. What is the five number summary of the distribution?

c. Make a relative frequency histogram of the number of lunches served. Use a scale from 560 to 800 lunches, with a bin width of 40 lunches. Sketch the histogram and label the height of each of the bins.

d. Describe the distribution. Make sure you consider the center, shape, spread, and outliers.

e. Using your histogram, determine the percent of days on which fewer than 600 lunches were sold.

f. Using the histogram, estimate the percent of days on which between 600 and 700 lunches were sold.

9-104.   Do you remember the students tardy to Ms. Greene's class? Now that you have
           investigated how to create and use a normal distribution, model the number of
           tardy students Ms. Greene actually recorded using a normal distribution. The
           data Mrs. Greene gathered for 30 days is shown in the table below.

Number of tardy students per day					
2	4	3	3	4	2
1	3	3	4	3	2
2	3	1	2	3	3
3	0	2	3	2	5
5	3	3	3	4	1
					checksum 82

   a.   On your calculator, recreate the relative frequency histogram for the
        number of tardy students that is shown in problem 9-88.

   b.   Find the mean and standard deviation of the number of tardy students.

   c.   On your calculator, model the data with a normal distribution by pressing
        [Y=] and entering [2nd] [DISTR] normalpdf(X, *mean, standard deviation*).
        Sketch the model with the histogram.

   d.   According to your model, on what percentage of days were 4 people
        tardy? Shade this proportion on a new sketch of the model, and calculate
        the proportion using normalcdf(*lower, upper, mean, standard deviation*)
        on your calculator.

   e.   Assume that the last 30 days in Mrs. Greene's class were representative of
        the 180 days in the whole school year. According to your model, how
        many days this year can Mrs. Greene expect 4 or more tardy students?
        Sketch the area representing these days on a new graph of the model.

9-105.   Due to natural variability in manufacturing, a 12-ounce can of soda does not
           usually hold exactly 12 ounces of soda. The quality control department at a
           soda factory allows cans to hold a little more or a little less. According to
           specifications, a soda-can filling machine must fill each can with a mean of
           12 ounces of soda and a standard deviation of 0.33 ounces. The amount of soda
           in a can filled by filling machines can often be modeled with a normal
           distribution.

   a.   Use your calculator to create a graph of a normal distribution using
        normalpdf. Sketch the graph. An appropriate value for the maximum of
        the relative frequency axis is Ymax = 1.5.

   b.   How often do you actually get a 12 oz can of soda containing more than
        12 oz?

   c.   What percent of cans contain between 11.5 and 12.5 ounces of soda?
        Shade your diagram from part (a) to represent these cans.

9-106. Use the properties of logarithms to rewrite each expression as an equivalent one using only one logarithm.

a. $\log_3(5) + \log_3(m)$

b. $\log_6(p) - \log_6(m)$

c. $\log_2(r) + 3\log_6(z)$

d. $\log(90) + \log(4) - \log(36)$

9-107. Simplify each expression.

a. $\dfrac{x+2}{x^2-2x-3} + \dfrac{x}{x^2-2x}$

b. $\dfrac{2}{x} - \dfrac{x}{x-2}$

c. $\dfrac{x^2-x-6}{x^2-x-20} \cdot \dfrac{x^2+6x+8}{x^2-x-6}$

d. $\dfrac{x^3+8}{x} \div \dfrac{x+2}{x^2}$

9-108. Solve each equation.

a. $\dfrac{x+1}{5} = \dfrac{5}{x-1}$

b. $\dfrac{1}{x} + \dfrac{1}{x+2} = 3$

9-109. Graph in three dimensions.

a. $(2, -1, -3)$

b. $6x - 3y + 9z = 18$

9-110. Find the distance between each pair of points.

a. $(17, 29)$ and $(-1, -1)$

b. (x, y) and $(-1, -1)$

9-111. This problem is a checkpoint for finding the equation for the inverse of a function. It will be referred to as Checkpoint 9B.

Consider the function $f(x) = 2\sqrt{3(x-1)} + 5$.

a. Find the equation for the inverse of $f(x)$.

b. Sketch the graph of both the original and the inverse.

Check your answers by referring to the Checkpoint 9B materials located at the back of your book.

Ideally, at this point you are comfortable working with these types of problems and can solve them correctly. If you feel that you need more confidence when solving these types of problems, then review the Checkpoint 9B materials and try the practice problems provided. From this point on, you will be expected to do problems like these correctly and with confidence.

Chapter 9 Closure What have I learned?

Reflection and Synthesis

The activities below offer you a chance to reflect
about what you have learned during this chapter.
As you work, look for concepts that you feel very
comfortable with, ideas that you would like to learn
more about, and topics you need more help with.
Look for connections between ideas as well as
connections with material you learned previously.

①   TEAM BRAINSTORM

What have you studied in this chapter? What ideas were important in what you
learned? With your team, brainstorm a list. Be as detailed as you can. To help
get you started, a list of Learning Log entries and Math Notes boxes are below.

What topics, ideas, and words that you learned *before* this chapter are connected
to the new ideas in this chapter? Again, be as detailed as you can.

Learning Log Entries
- Lesson 9.1.3 – Survey Design and Bias
- Lesson 9.2.2 – Surveys Versus Experiments
- Lesson 9.3.1 – Relative Frequency Histograms
- Lesson 9.3.2 – Normal Probability Density Function

Math Notes
- Lesson 9.1.1 – Population Parameters and Sample Statistics
- Lesson 9.2.1 – Observational Studies and Experiments
- Lesson 9.3.1 – Symbols for Standard Deviation
- Lesson 9.3.3 – Normal Probability Density Function

②   MAKING CONNECTIONS

Below is a list of the vocabulary used in this chapter. Make sure that you are familiar with all of these words and know what they mean. Refer to the glossary or index for any words that you do not yet understand.

bias	census	convenience sample
experiment	five number summary	lurking variable
mean	median	normal distribution
observational study	parameter	population
random sample	sample	standard deviation
statistic	treatment	variable

Make a concept map showing all of the connections you can find among the key words and ideas listed above. To show a connection between two words, draw a line between them and explain the connection. A word can be connected to any other word as long as you can justify the connection.

While you are making your map, your team may think of related words or ideas that are not listed here. Be sure to include these ideas on your concept map.

③   PORTFOLIO: EVIDENCE OF MATHEMATICAL PROFICIENCY

This section gives you an opportunity to show growth in your understanding of key mathematical ideas over time as you complete this course. Several options are presented below. Follow your teacher's directions for which options you should complete.

Part 1: You may have done this problem before in a previous chapter. You have grown mathematically since then. Be sure to include everything you have learned since the last time you did this problem.

Explain everything that you know about $f(x) = 2^x - 3$.

Activity continues on next page. →

     Core Connections Algebra 2

③ *Activity continued from previous page.*

Part 2: Compare your responses to this "Growth Over Time" problem. Write an evaluation of your growth based on your responses. Consider each of the following questions as you write your answer. If you only did the problem twice, then answer accordingly.

- What new concepts did you include the second time you did the problem? In what ways was your response better than your first attempt?

- How was your final version different from the first two? What new ideas did you include?

- Did you omit anything in your later versions that you used in one of the earlier versions? Why did you omit it?

- Rate your three attempts by making three bars like the ones below and shading each bar (left to right) to represent how much you knew on each attempt.

First Attempt:
Second Attempt:
Final Attempt:

- Is there anything you want to add to your current version? If so, add it and keep this version for future reference.

Alternatively, your teacher may have you complete the following problem and add it to your portfolio:

Corbin is concerned about the amount of sodium in breakfast cereal. After examining labels from a random sample of cereal brands, he discovers that the amount of sodium in breakfast cereal is approximately normally distributed with a mean of 6.5 milligrams sodium per gram of cereal and a standard deviation of 1.6 mg/g. Corbin has listed his three favorite cereals and their sodium content below and wants to know how they compare to the population of breakfast cereals as a whole. For each cereal listed below, find its sodium content percentile and provide Corbin an explanation of what each percentile means.

a. Tweeties cereal has 7.3 milligrams sodium per gram of cereal.

b. Apple Flakes cereal has 4.5 mg/g.

c. Korn Crispies cereal has 3.9 mg/g.

WHAT HAVE I LEARNED?

Most of the problems in this section represent typical problems found in this chapter. They serve as a gauge for you. You can use them to determine which types of problems you can do well and which types of problems require further study and practice. Even if your teacher does not assign this section, it is a good idea to try these problems and find out for yourself what you know and what you still need to work on.

Solve each problem as completely as you can. The table at the end of the closure section has answers to these problems. It also tells you where you can find additional help and practice with problems like these.

CL 9-112.   Stephanie is interested in laws concerning the death penalty. She gives the following survey question to her government class.

"The constitution allows individual states the freedom to enact laws which are not contradictory to federal laws. For example, capital punishment is permissible in some states but not in others. Are you in favor of the U.S. Congress passing legislation to override every individual state law and ban the practice of capital punishment?"

Thirty-eight percent of the students respond in favor of a federal law governing the use of capital punishment. Stephanie concludes that there is insufficient popular support to pass a federal law banning capital punishment.

a.   Is 38% a parameter or statistic? How do you know? What population is Stephanie making her conclusion about?

b.   What sources of bias are present in the wording of her question?

c.   What sampling technique did Stephanie use and how might it introduce bias into her conclusion?

CL 9-113.   Suppose Stephanie wanted to determine whether students in her ceramics class have a significantly different opinion towards capital punishment legislation than those in her government class. She finds 55% of the ceramics students in favor of federal oversight of capital punishment and concludes that taking ceramics causes opposition to the death penalty. Why is her conclusion unreasonable? Design an experiment that would test her conclusion.

CL 9-114.   It is inventory time at the Mathletes Shoe Super Store. To speed up the process, Iris, the storeowner, decided to find the value of the inventory by counting the number of pairs of shoes that belong in $30 intervals. She made the following table:

Value ($)	# of pairs
0 up to 30	47
30 up to 60	67
60 up to 90	60
90 up to 120	46
120 up to 150	18
150 up to 180	6
180 up to 210	4
210 up to 240	2

a.   Make a relative frequency histogram of the distribution of shoes in the store.

b.   Which intervals contain the median, the first quartile and third quartile?

c.   Describe the distribution of shoe values in terms of center, shape, spread and outliers.

d.   What proportion of shoes are valued at least $150?

e.   Calculate an estimated proportion of shoes that cost between $50 and $100.

f.   Calculate an estimated mean price for a pair of shoes. Assume every pair of shoes in each dollar interval is valued at the middle price for that interval.

CL 9-115.   Park rangers study the pellets of hawks to determine their eating habits. Hawks regurgitate the indigestible portion of their diet in a pellet. Pellets are about one or two inches long, and can contain the bones, fur, feathers, and claws of their prey.

In order to determine if hawks were changing their diet to cope with a particularly harsh winter, rangers collected a random sample of ten pellets. The rodent bones in the pellets had mass: 7.3, 12.1, 4.1, 11.9, 6.3, 4.9, 10.7, 6.3, 0.0, 7.0 grams.

From the sample park rangers will make predictions for the population using a normal model. What is the mean and standard deviation they will use in their model? Use an appropriate precision in your response based on the precision of the data.

CL 9-116.   Consider the Integral Zero Theorem.

a.   Using only integers, list all the possible linear factors of $(x^3 + 8)$.

b.   Is $(x+8)$ a factor of $(x^3 + 8)$? Is $(x+2)$ a factor of $(x^3 + 8)$? Show how you know without graphing.

CL 9-117. Solve the system of equations at right.
$$\tfrac{x}{4} + \tfrac{y}{3} = 1$$
$$2x - \tfrac{y}{3} = 17$$

CL 9-118. Use the graph at right to solve $2^x + 1 < 3^x$.

CL 9-119. Check your answers using the table at the end of this section. Which problems do you feel confident about? Which problems were hard? Have you worked on problems like these in math classes you have taken before? Use the table to make a list of topics you need help on and a list of topics you need to practice more.

Answers and Support for Closure Activity #4
What Have I Learned?

Note: MN = Math Note, LL = Learning Log

Problem	Solution	Need Help?	More Practice
CL 9-112.	a. 38% is a statistic because it represents the opinions of the sample, her government class. Her conclusion is making a statement about the voting U.S. population.	Lessons 9.1.1, 9.1.2, and 9.1.3 MN: 9.1.1	Problems 9-22, 9-23, 9-36, 9-37, 9-38, 9-50, 9-51, 9-62, and 9-75
	b. Stephanie's question has a lead-in statement about the constitution, which may persuade survey-takers that states should be allowed to determine whether or not to use capital punishment.		
	c. Stephanie probably used a convenience sample because it was easy to survey those in her government class. Those students have many things in common like age, location, and level of education, and so do not represent the U.S. population as a whole. Because they are in a government class, they may be more aware of state rights versus federal authority.		

Problem	Solution	Need Help?	More Practice
CL 9-113.	Stephanie is using samples from her high school that are not representative of a larger population. Also, it is likely that students choose for themselves whether or not to take ceramics so it is plausible that the kind of student who likes ceramics is already opposed to the death penalty rather than ceramics changing the political opinions of students. To demonstrate cause and effect, Stephanie would need to take a group of student volunteers and randomly assign them to government or ceramics courses. After the course is completed, she could poll them about capital punishment and compare the results.	Lessons 9.2.1 and 9.2.2 MN: 9.2.1	Problems 9-63, 9-76, and 9-89

CL 9-114. a.

Shoe Value ($)

b. Q1 $30–60, Med $60–90, Q3 $90–120

c. The distribution is positive or right skewed so the median and IQR would describe the center and spread. You would need the actual data points to find these values precisely but the center is approximately $65 and the IQR is about $60. There are no gaps or outliers.

d. $(6 + 4 + 2) / 250 = 0.048$ or 4.8%

e. Using one third of the $30-60 interval and one third of the $90-120 interval $((1/3)67 + 60 + (1/3)46) / 250 = 0.391$ or 39.1%

f. $15(47) + $45(67)+ $75(60) + $105(46) + $135(18) + $165(6) + $195(4) + $225(2) / 250 = $70.8

(Need Help?) Lesson 9.3.1

(More Practice) Problems 9-72, 9-73, 9-88, 9-103, and 9-104

Problem	Solution	Need Help?	More Practice
CL 9-115.	Mean 7.1 g, sample standard deviation 3.8 g (not population standard deviation 3.6 g).	Problems 9-52 and 9-70	Problems 9-65, 9-73, and 9-103
CL 9-116.	a. $(x \pm 1), (x \pm 2), (x \pm 4), (x \pm 8)$ b. $(x+8)$ is not a factor, $(x+2)$ is a factor. Use the Remainder Theorem and determine whether -8 and -2 are zeros. Or, divide and see that $(x+8)$ is not a factor because there is a remainder. $(x+2)$ is a factor because there is no remainder.	Lesson 8.3.2 MN: 8.3.2	Problems 8-125, 8-138, 9-9, 9-39, and 9-68
CL 9-117.	$(8, -3)$	Lesson 4.1.1 LL: 4.1.1	Problems 8-11 and 9-26
CL 9-118.	$x > 1$	Lesson 4.2.3 MN: 4.2.3 and 4.2.4	Problems 7-28, 8-41, 8-89, and 9-91

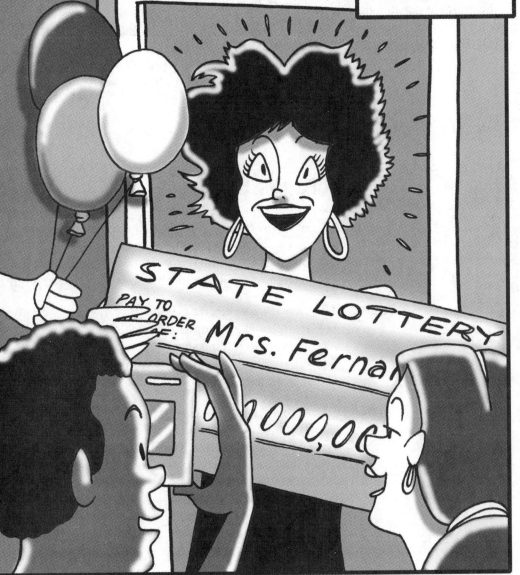

Chapter 10

In this chapter you will revisit and add to what you already know about arithmetic and geometric sequences. In Sections 10.1 and 10.2 you will use what you know about sequences and multiple representations to write series and find their sums.

In Section 10.3 you will use what you learned about combinations to develop the Binomial Theorem, which is useful for simplifying some algebraic manipulations, as well as solving some probability problems.

Guiding Question

Mathematically proficient students look for and express regularity in repeated reasoning.

As you work through this chapter, ask yourself:

How can I extend the pattern from smaller sums to larger sums?

Chapter Outline

Section 10.1 In this section, you will revisit arithmetic sequences as you learn about arithmetic series and devise methods for finding their sums. You will learn to recognize the difference between a series and a sum.

Section 10.2 Here, you will revisit geometric sequences as you learn about geometric series and their sums. In addition to finding sums of geometric series where the last term is determined, you will learn how to represent and calculate sums of some infinite series.

Section 10.3 In this section, you will learn about Pascal's Triangle, and you will connect it to your knowledge of combinations to develop the Binomial Theorem, which can be used to solve some algebraic problems as well as probability problems.

10.1.1 Can I find a sum without adding?

Introduction to Arithmetic Series

Have you ever had to carefully add a long list of numbers? When the numbers are unrelated to each other, there may be no alternative, but if there is a pattern or relationship between the terms in your list, it is often possible to develop strategies to make your calculation much easier.

For example, if ticket sales double each day in the month before a concert, is there a faster method for calculating the total number of tickets sold than by adding the sales for each day one at a time? Similarly, if a mine produces 150 tons more iron each year than in the previous year, how can the amount of iron produced during an entire century can be quickly calculated?

In this section you will explore problems like these and develop new strategies for making these calculations.

Today your team will consider different ways to find the sum of a sequence of terms. As you work, use the following questions to focus and advance your mathematical discussions.

> What do the terms (of the sequence) represent? What does the sum represent?
>
> Is there another way to find the sum?
>
> How can we verify our result?

10-1. COUNTING ON COLLEGE!

When Angela turned eighteen, her Uncle Zachary explained to her that he had been saving money for her college education since she was born. He told her that when she was one month old, he put $50 into a safe deposit box, and the month following he added $53. He continued adding money like this for the last 18 years, each month putting in $3 more than he had the previous month. The money that had been saved would now pay for Angela to attend any college of her choosing.

a. Write out the sizes of the deposits for the first few months as an arithmetic sequence. How much was added to Angela's college fund on the 12th month?

b. Work with your group to find a formula for the arithmetic sequence that determines the amount deposited on the nth month. Check that when n is 1 (representing the first month) your formula gives $50. Using your formula, determine how much was in the final deposit on the last month of the 18th year.

10-2.   Angela continued to think about Uncle Zachary's savings.

   a.   Angela wrote the equation for the sequence as $t(n) = 47 + 3n$. But Uncle
        Zachary wrote $t(n) = 50 + 3(n-1)$. Which equation gives the correct
        sequence? What is the advantage of writing the equation like Angela did?
        What is the advantage of writing it like Uncle Zachary did?

   b.   Determine the amount of money in Angela's college fund at the time of
        her first birthday, after her Uncle had made exactly 12 deposits.

   c.   How much was saved by Angela's 5th birthday? Can you think of ways
        you might be able to figure this out without having to add the money for
        every month? Be ready to share your ideas with the class.

10-3.   SERIES

In problem 10-1, the total amount of money deposited before
Angela's eighteenth birthday is the sum of an arithmetic
sequence, where each term in the sequence represents the
amount of money added by her uncle in one month. When the terms of a
sequence are added instead of listed, the result is called a **series**. When a
sequence is arithmetic, meaning each term differs from the previous one by
some constant amount, then its corresponding *series* is called an **arithmetic
series**. The series representing the first year in problem 10-1 could be written:

$$50 + 53 + 56 + \ldots + 80 + 83$$

A matryoshka, a set of Russian nested dolls, can help illustrate the difference
between a sequence and its corresponding series. These dolls are special
because each doll fills the space inside the doll of the next larger size. When
the dolls are placed one inside the other, as in the picture, they are "nested."

   a.   When the dolls are nested, their diameters steadily increase. (Note: The
        top half of only the innermost doll is shown in the picture.) If the smallest
        doll in the diagram has a diameter of 5 cm, and each doll has a diameter
        that is 1 cm longer than the next-smallest doll, write a sequence that
        represents the diameters from shortest to longest.

   b.   In what situation might you want to find the sum of all of the diameters of
        these dolls? Discuss this with your team, then write the series and
        calculate its sum.

   c.   Some matryoshka have as many as 20 dolls! For one such matryoshka, the
        diameter (in millimeters) of each doll from smallest to largest can be
        represented with the sequence $t(n) = 8 + 3(n-1)$, where the domain of n is
        the integers from 1 to 20.

        If all 20 dolls were arranged in a line with each doll touching the one next
        to it, how long would the line of dolls be? Write a series to represent this
        problem and calculate its sum.

10-4.   FINDING THE SUM

When an arithmetic series has many terms, adding them all one at a time can be tedious. It is useful to have other strategies to calculate the sum. To look for a strategy, consider a new situation:

Flo is preparing to run the 100-meter race at her next track meet. Her coach decides to collect data to learn how well Flo is accelerating (speeding up) at the beginning of the race. The sequence below represents approximately how far Flo travels during each second of the first six seconds of a practice race, in meters.

$$1, 3, 5, 7, 9, 11$$

a.   Find the equation, $t(n)$, in first term form, for this sequence. In the context of Flo's race, explain the meaning of the first term and the common difference. Be sure you include units.

b.   What does the *series* in this situation represent?

c.   Flo decided to use square tiles as shown in the diagram below to represent her distance from the starting line as time passed.

| 1ˢᵗ sec | 2ⁿᵈ sec | 3ʳᵈ sec | 4ᵗʰ sec | 5ᵗʰ sec | 6ᵗʰ sec |

She rearranged her tiles on a graph like the one at right. How are the terms of the sequence (the distance covered in each second) shown in this graph? How is the series (the total distance run) represented?

d.   Finding the area of the long rectangle Flo made in part (c) requires adding all the terms. However, if the columns in Flo's graph can be rearranged to form a single rectangle, its area can be found more easily. How might this work? Discuss this with your team and be prepared to share your ideas with the class.

10-5.   Calculate the sum of the arithmetic series represented by the graphs below. Try to do this without adding all of the individual terms of the sequence.

a.

b.

c.

d.

10-6.   TEAM CHALLENGE

How much information do you need to be able to write an arithmetic series and find its sum? For each arithmetic series described below, work with your team to write the series, find its sum, or both. If it is not possible, explain why not.

a. What if you know that the first term is 18, the last term is 72, and the common difference is 4.5? What is the series? What is the sum?

b. What if you know that there are 6 terms, the last and smallest term is 21, and the sum is 336? What is the series?

c. What if you know that the series has 9 terms and the last term is 18? What is the series? What is the sum?

d. What if the third term of an 18-term series is 29 and the terms are increasing by 10? What is the series? What is the sum?

Core Connections Algebra 2

METHODS AND MEANINGS

Permutations and Combinations

MATH NOTES

Eight people are running a race. In how many different ways can they come in first, second, and third?

This is a problem of counting **permutations**, or arrangements, and the result can be represented $_8P_3$, which means the number of ways to choose and arrange three different (not repeated) things from a set of eight, in which *order matters*. There are several ways to write and compute $_8P_3$:

$$_8P_3 = \frac{8!}{(8-3)!} = \frac{8!}{5!} = \frac{8\cdot7\cdot6\cdot5\cdot4\cdot3\cdot2\cdot1}{5\cdot4\cdot3\cdot2\cdot1} = 8 \text{ choices} \cdot 7 \text{ choices} \cdot 6 \text{ choices} = 336$$

In general, $_nP_r = \frac{n!}{(n-r)!} = n(n-1)(n-2)...(n-r+1)$ for n items chosen r at a time.

Lists of groups, *without regard to the order* within the group, are called **combinations**. In selecting committees, it matters who is selected but not the order of selection or any arrangement of the groups. Selections such as those with committees are called combinations. Note that combinations do not include repeated elements.

For example: Eight people are eligible to receive $500 scholarships, but only three will be selected. How many different ways are there to select a group of three?

This is a problem of counting combinations. $_8C_3$ represents the number of ways to choose three from a set of eight. This is sometimes read as "eight choose three."

To compute the number of combinations, first calculate the number of permutations and then divide by the number of ways to arrange each permutation.

$$_8C_3 = \frac{_8P_3}{3!} = \frac{8!}{5!3!} = 56$$

In general:

Number of ways to choose $= \dfrac{\text{\# of ways to choose and arrange}}{\text{\# of ways to arrange}} = {_nC_r} = \frac{_nP_r}{r!} = \frac{n!}{(n-r)!r!}$.

10-7.   Uncle Zachary decided to increase the amount he was saving for Angela by $5 each month instead of three.

    a.   How much would he deposit on the month of her second birthday?

    b.   Write a formula for the nth term of this sequence.

    c.   How much money is in the account the month of her first birthday, just after he made his 12th deposit?

10-8.   The 300 people who were lined up outside the amusement park had all entered by 8:15 a.m. By 8:30, 550 more had entered. The number who entered each 15 minutes increased steadily by 250 after that. All of the people were planning to stay for the parade at noon.

    a.   How many people entered between 11:45 and noon, just in time for the parade?

    b.   Represent the problem as a series and write a formula for the nth term.

10-9.   Write a formula for the nth term of each of the following series.

    a. $3 + 10 + 17 + \ldots$ b. $20 + 11 + 2 + \ldots$

10-10.   If the third term of an arithmetic sequence is 13 and the seventeenth term is –29, what is the eighth term?

10-11.   Graph each of the following functions and label the x- and y-intercepts.

    a. $f(x) = 3(x - 4)^2 - 5$ b. $g(x) = 2x^2 - 3x - 5$

10-12.   Aurora is starting a fitness program at her school and needs to find an easy measure of fitness to assign workouts and gauge improvement. She decides that using resting heart rate would be helpful. Assume that the resting heart rate of young women is approximately normally distributed with a mean of 74 beats per minute (bpm) with a standard deviation of 5 bpm.

   a.   Aurora found a chart that said resting heart rates between 70 and 79 (inclusive) are considered average for women her age. What proportion of her classmates would she expect to find in the average range?

   b.   The chart also claims that resting heart rate of 66 or less indicates excellent fitness in otherwise healthy young women. What portion of her classmates would she expect to find in excellent shape?

   c.   If Aurora's fitness program lowers the mean heart rate of her female classmates by 4 bpm, what will be the *increase* in the proportion of women now classified as being in excellent shape?

10-13.   Find the distance between each of the following pairs of points.

   a. $(-6, 9)$ and $(2, -4)$ b. (x, y) and $(5, 2)$

10-14.   If Emily bought three pounds of oranges and four pounds of bananas for $8.53 and Beth bought four pounds of oranges and two pounds of bananas for $7.74, how much should Jenel expect to pay for nine pounds of oranges and seven pounds of bananas?

10-15.   How many people were in the amusement park in problem 10-8 to watch the noontime parade?

10-16.   Chloe wants to place her matryoshka dolls in a row on a windowsill that is 92 cm long. Will her entire set of 20 dolls fit if their diameters in *millimeters* are given by the formula $t(n) = 13 + 3(n - 1)$?

10-17.   Find the sum of $1 + 6 + 11 + 16 + 21 + ...$ if the series has 10 terms.

10-18.   A series has 9 terms. The last term is 18 and the fifth term is 6. What is the series?

10-19. Is 435 a term in the sequence 3, 11, 19, …? If so, which term is it? If not, justify why not.

10-20. Twelve people signed up to play darts during lunch. How many ways can a three-person dart team be chosen? For help, refer to the Math Notes box in this lesson.

10-21. Andrea has just purchased a five-digit combination lock. It allows her to set up her own combination. She can use the numbers 0 through 9 for her combination, and she must use five digits. For help with this problem, refer to the Math Notes box in this lesson.

    a.   How many five-digit combinations can she make so that no digit is repeated?

    b.   How many five-digit combinations are possible if she *can* repeat the digits?

10-22. For what values of n does the equation $2x^2 + nx + 9 = 0$ have exactly one root?

10-23. Without using a calculator, simplify and evaluate each of the following log expressions. Your result should be an expression without logarithms.

    a. $\log(4) + \log(25)$ b. $\dfrac{7^{\log_7(3)}}{\log_5 5^4}$

10-24. Consider the graph of $f(x) = \sin(x)$.

    a.   Describe the graph.

    b.   Could this graph be an example of any other function? Explain why $f(x) = \sin(x)$ cannot be a polynomial function.

10.1.2 How can I find a sum without a graph?

More Arithmetic Series

In Lesson 10.1.1, you explored ways to use a graph of a series to find its sum without adding every term. Can the strategies that you developed help you find the series when you do not have a graph? As you work with your team to answer this question, remember to talk together about how to describe a term or series generally and to ask each other if the answers you find make sense.

10-25. While trying to find the sum of an arithmetic series, Antonio rearranged the terms so that the last term is combined with the first term, the second-to-last term is combined with the second term, etc. (as shown at right). Use his graph to answer the questions below.

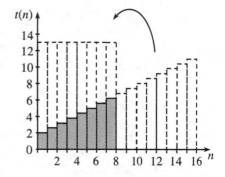

a. How can Antonio be sure that the result of stacking the terms this way will be a rectangle?

b. What is the sum of Antonio's series? How do you know?

c. Which terms of the series form the first column? What is the height of this column?

d. Write out Antonio's series and find the sum.

10-26. With your team, create a series that has an odd number of terms. How could you apply Antonio's method to this series? Be prepared to share your ideas with the class.

10-27. Will Antonio's method work for all arithmetic series? Why or why not? Use an example to explain your conclusion.

10-28.   Do you think that Antonio's method can be altered to find the sum of an arithmetic series without a graph? Work with your team to find the dimensions of the transformed rectangle for each arithmetic series below without graphing the series. Then find the sum.

a. $11 + 18 + 25 + \ldots + 74$

b.   14 terms with $t(1) = 8$ and $t(14) = 151$

c. $t(n) = 4 + 6(n-1)$, for integer values of n starting at 1 and ending at 25

10-29.   Remember Angela from problem 10-1? Her Uncle Zachary has been depositing an increasing amount of money each month to be given to her for college on her 18th birthday. In her first month of life, he started by depositing \$50 and then each month deposited an amount that was \$3 more than the previous month. Use Antonio's strategies and those that you used in problem 10-28 to determine how much money Uncle Zachary will have for Angela on her 18th birthday.

10-30.   Decide whether each situation below involves a series or a sequence and give a reason for your choice. Then answer the question.

a.   Hornets build nests by constructing hexagonal cells around a center, as shown at right. As this hexagonal pattern forms, the first ring of cells has 6 cells, the next has 12, and the next has 18. If a colony of hornets builds 10 rings, how many cells will they have?

b.   Thanks to fundraising, the balance of the math club's savings account grows by \$55 each month. The balance during the first month of the school year was \$190. At the end of the year, the club's treasurer produced a report showing the balance for each month of the school year. What was the balance after the 8th month?

c.   Starting after his birthday, Evan's allowance increases \$0.25 each week. He decides to save his money in order to buy a new πPod, which costs \$180. If his allowance on his birthday is \$1.50, will he have enough savings on his next birthday to buy the πPod?

10-31.   JACKPOT FEVER!

While Ms. Fernandez is standing in line to
buy her lottery ticket, she noticed that a
different state has a jackpot that may go even
higher. Then she realizes that because of a
time difference, it has more hours to grow!
She has already predicted that the jackpot in her state will be $50,900,000 when
tickets are drawn, and she has to decide quickly if she should buy tickets in the
other state.

On a nearby television screen, she sees a news report explaining that the other
state started the day with a jackpot of $29,000,000 and that each additional
ticket sold will increase the jackpot by $1.00. The news also mentioned that
1,800,000 tickets were sold in the first hour and hourly ticket sales have steadily
increased by 20,000 tickets per hour throughout the day. If the drawing in that
state occurs 14 hours after stores have opened, which state will have the larger
jackpot? Show how you found your answer.

10-32.   With your team, find the sum of the arithmetic series $t(1) + t(2) + t(3) + \ldots + t(n)$.

10-33.   LEARNING LOG

Describe how to find the sum of an arithmetic series in your
Learning Log. Be sure to include examples in your
description. Title this entry "Arithmetic Series" and label it
with today's date.

METHODS AND MEANINGS

Series

The sum of the terms of a sequence is called a **series**. If the terms have a constant difference (meaning that they increase or decrease linearly), they form an **arithmetic series**. If the terms instead have a constant ratio or multiplier (meaning that they change exponentially), they form a **geometric series**.

Examples of arithmetic and geometric series are shown below.

arithmetic series: $2 + 6 + 10 + 14 + \ldots + (4n - 2)$

geometric series: $1 + \frac{1}{2} + \frac{1}{4} + \frac{1}{8} + \ldots + \frac{1}{2^n}$

Review & Preview

10-34. Examine each of the series below.

Odd numbers: $1 + 3 + 5 + \ldots + 149$

Even numbers: $2 + 4 + 6 + \ldots + 150$

a. Write an expression for the nth term of each series.

b. What is the sum of each series?

10-35. Consider the series $21 + 17 + 13 + \ldots + -99$ as you answer the questions in parts (a) through (c) below.

a. Write an expression for the nth term.

b. How many terms are in the series? How can you tell?

c. What is the sum of this series?

10-36. On a six-person bowling team, only four players bowl in any game. How many different four-person teams can be made if the order in which they bowl does not matter?

10-37.   How many different bowling lineups of four
          players can be made in the previous problem
          if order does matter?

10-38.   State the degree of $f(x) = (x+4)(x+1)^2(x-2)$
          and sketch its graph.

10-39.   Find the equation of a third degree polynomial that has the roots 3, 2, and –1
          and passes through the point (1, 1).

10-40.   Complete the square to convert each of the following quadratic functions to
          graphing form. State the vertex and sketch the graph.

          a. $f(x) = x^2 + 6x + 7$ b. $f(x) = x^2 - 10x$

10-41.   David and Regina are competitive racers, and they both aim to break 2 minutes
          in their races. They are trying to figure out which who has the more difficult
          challenge, since they compete in different sports. David runs the 800-meter
          race and Regina swims the 200-meter freestyle. They agree to accept the
          following standards for high school boys and girls: boys' 800-meter mean time
          is 149 seconds with a standard deviation of 13.6 seconds, girls' 200-meter
          freestyle mean time is 145 seconds with a standard deviation of 8.2 seconds.

          Currently, David's best time is 2:02 minutes and Regina's best time is 2:10
          minutes. Assuming times in their respective events are normally distributed,
          find the percentile in which each David and Regina fall. Which athlete is
          relatively faster for their sport?

10-42.   Convert the following degree measures to radians.

          a.   45°   b.   75°   c.   –15°   d.   450°

10.1.3 How else can I see it?

General Arithmetic Series

So far, you have developed strategies that help find the sum of a given series for a given number of terms. However, what if the number of terms is unknown? For example, in the lottery example from Lessons 10.1.1 and 10.1.2, what if the time of the drawing has not yet been set? How can you find a general expression that would represent the total number of tickets sold after any number of hours?

As you work with your team today, pay attention to the different ways to study a series. Many of the strategies introduced today may be helpful in the future when thinking about the sum of other types of series. When your team finds a new way to "see" the sum of a series, be sure to share the idea with your classmates.

10-43.   Consider the series $1 + 2 + 3 + 4 + ... + n$.

a.   What is the sum of the first 3 terms? The first 10 terms?

b.   What is the sum of the first n terms? That is, find $1 + 2 + 3 + 4 + ... + n$. Justify your answer.

c.   Legend has it that long ago, when famous mathematician Carl Gauss was a young student, his teacher tried to keep his class busy by giving them the task of finding the sum $1 + 2 + 3 + 4 + ... + 99 + 100$. He stunned his teacher and his classmates by finding the sum quickly without assistance. What is the sum?

10-44.   In problem 10-43, you found a general expression that gives the sum of the first n counting numbers, but what about other types of numbers? For example, what is the sum of the first n odd numbers? Or the first n even numbers? Find expressions for both of these cases below. Look for new strategies and justify your answer.

a.   Sum of the first n even numbers: $2 + 4 + 6 + 8 + ... + 2n$

b.   Sum of the first n odd numbers: $1 + 3 + 5 + 7 + ... + (2n - 1)$

c.   Use your expressions from parts (a) and (b) to find the sum of the first 100 even numbers and then the sum of the first 100 odd numbers.

Core Connections Algebra 2

10-45. Terrell noticed that if he adds the first terms, second terms, third terms, etc. of the two arithmetic series at right, he gets a brand new series!

original series $\longrightarrow$ $\begin{cases} 1+2+3+4+\ldots+n \\ 2+4+6+8+\ldots+2n \end{cases}$

new series $\longrightarrow$ $\quad 3+6+9+12+\ldots+3n$

a. Describe his new series. Is it arithmetic? How many terms does it have?

b. Use the expressions for the sums of the original series to find an expression for the sum of the new series.

c. Is there another way you could have found the expression for the sum of the series $3+6+9+\ldots+3n$? Be prepared to explain your strategy to the class.

d. If you have not done so already, verify that your strategy in part (c) resulted in an expression equivalent to your expression from part (b).

10-46. In problem 10-45, you used the sums of two different series to find the sum of a new series. How else can the sum of one series be used to find the sum of another series? Consider this as you work on the problems below.

a. How can the sum of $1+2+3+4+\ldots+n$ be used to find the sum of $2+4+6+8+\ldots+2n$? Test your idea algebraically using the expressions for the sums of these series.

b. How can the sum of $2+4+6+8+\ldots+2n$ be used to find the sum of $1+3+5+7+\ldots+(2n-1)$? Test your idea algebraically using the expressions for the sums of these series.

10-47. Flo saw the sum of odd numbers from part (b) of problem 10-44 differently. She decided to represent the arithmetic series with the tile pattern below, where the area of each figure is equal to the term of the series.

Fig. 1   Fig. 2   Fig. 3   Fig. 4   Fig. *n*

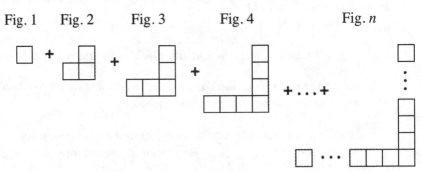

a. How many tiles are in the nth term? Justify your conclusion.

b. What is the sum of the first 3 terms? The sum of the first 5 terms? How can you represent this sum with the tiles?

c. What is the sum of the first *n* terms? Represent the sum algebraically in terms of *n* and with a diagram with tiles.

d. Based on Flo's representation, what is the sum of the first $(n+1)$ odd numbers? Justify your answer.

10-48. Use one or more of the series below to create a new series you have not summed before. Then use the algebraic expressions for the sums to generate an expression for the sum of your new series. Be ready to share your new series and explain its sum to the class.

$$1+2+3+4+\ldots+n$$

$$2+4+6+8+\ldots+2n$$

$$1+3+5+7+\ldots+(2n-1)$$

METHODS AND MEANINGS

Arithmetic Series

An arithmetic sequence can be represented in general by a formula for its nth term:

$$t(n) = a + (n-1)d$$

The first term (when $n = 1$) is a, and the common difference is d.

An arithmetic series is the sum of the terms of an arithmetic sequence.

$$t(1) + t(2) + t(3) + \ldots + t(k)$$

The total sum of this series can be found by adding the first and last terms, multiplying by the number of terms k and dividing by 2:

$$S(k) = \frac{k(t(1) + t(k))}{2}$$

The sum of a series can be represented with the area in the diagram at right, where each column represents a term of the series.

Note that when the diagram is rearranged as shown, the region becomes a rectangle with a height of $t(1) + t(k)$ and a width of $\frac{k}{2}$.

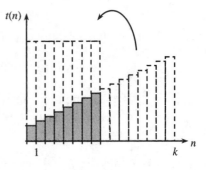

Review & Preview

10-49. Find the sum of the arithmetic series below.

a. $5 + 10 + 15 + 20 + \ldots + 400$

b. $3 + 8 + 13 + 18 + \ldots + 398$

c. $80 + 74 + 68 + 62 + \ldots + 14$

10-50. Consider the sequence of multiples of 11 that are less than 100. Write them as a series and find the sum.

10-51.   Lorna is looking at the series $5+3+10+8+15+\ldots+400+398$.

"The sequence definitely isn't arithmetic, but it does have a pattern," Lorna told her team, *"I wonder if we can still find the sum of the series?"*

a.   What patterns do you see in Lorna's series? Describe them as completely as you can.

b.   Do you agree with Lorna's statement that this sequence is not arithmetic? Justify your conclusion. Do you think it is still possible to find a sum for the series?

c.   *"I think I see it!"* Lorna exclaimed. *"I think we can separate the terms into the two different arithmetic series shown below, kind of like unzipping a zipper."* Her work is shown below.

$$5 + 10 + 15 +\ldots+ 395 + 400$$
$$3 + 8 + 13 +\ldots+ 393 + 398$$

How can you use Lorna's two series to find the sum of the original series? State the sum and describe your process.

10-52.   Your midterm exam contains 12 questions and you must answer any 10.

a.   How many different combinations of questions are possible?

b.   If everyone must answer questions one, two, and three, how many different combinations are possible?

10-53.   Verify that $3+i\sqrt{2}$ is a solution of $x^2-6x+11=0$.

10-54.   Show and explain why the equation $2^x = 5-x$ has only one real solution.

10-55.   At McDugal's Golden Parabola, Ramona bought four hamburgers and two milkshakes for $13.50. Inez bought three hamburgers and one milkshake and spent $9.25. What is the cost of a hamburger? A milkshake?

10-56.   Solve:

a. $\log_7(3x-2)=2$

b. $2^x \cdot 2^{x-2} - 16^2 = 0$

10-57.   Sketch a graph of $y=-x^2(x-2)^2(x+2)^2$.

10.1.4 How else can I express it?

Summation Notation and Combinations of Series

So far in this chapter you have focused your work on arithmetic series represented algebraically, geometrically, and graphically. Today you will be introduced to a new notation for arithmetic series and you will look at methods for writing equations to find sums.

As you work today, keep the following questions in mind to focus your team discussions:

How does this connect to what we have done before?

How can we simplify it?

How can we describe it?

10-58. Remember Gauss, the mathematician from Lesson 10.1.3, whose teacher tried to keep him busy by asking him to add up the numbers from 1 to 100? Legend has it that Gauss did not show any of his work (shocking!), but he is commonly said to have used a method that starts with the steps below:

$$\begin{array}{r} S = 1 + 2 + 3 + \ldots + 98 + 99 + 100 \\ S = 100 + 99 + 98 + \ldots + 3 + 2 + 1 \\ \hline 2S = 101 + 101 + 101 + \ldots + 101 + 101 + 101 \end{array}$$

a. Examine his work. What is he doing? Discuss this with your team, and then summarize each step on your paper.

b. How can you simplify his resulting equation to find the sum of the series $1 + 2 + 3 + \ldots + 100$? Show and explain on your paper.

c. How is the process from parts (a) and (b) related to how you have used a graph to find the sum of a series? Discuss with your team and write your conclusions.

d. Show how to use this strategy to find the sum of the series below. Show all of your work.

$$S = 2 + 5 + 8 + 11 + \ldots + 59$$

10-59. The series in part (d) of problem 10-58 can also be represented using **summation notation**, as shown below:

$$\sum_{c=1}^{20}[2+3(c-1)]$$

The symbol "Σ" is the Greek letter "sigma," and indicates that the terms generated as c changes from 1 to 20 are summed. The expression $2+3(c-1)$ is the rule for the terms of the series. As you can see in the table at right, when $c=1$, $t(1)=2+3(1-0)=2$, and so on. So, as c changes from 1 to 20, the series below is generated:

c	$t(c)$
1	2
2	5
3	8
$\vdots$	$\vdots$
20	59

$$2+5+8+\ldots+59$$

The letter c is used here as an **index**, which temporarily represents the term number as the series terms are determined. The same series could be written:

$$\sum_{p=1}^{20}[2+3(p-1)] \text{ or as } \sum_{p=1}^{20}(-1+3p)$$

It is also possible for the series to be written with a different starting value, such as:

$$\sum_{p=0}^{19}(2+3p)$$

a. Use summation notation to represent the series $15+19+23+27+31$.

b. Expand the series $\sum_{t=1}^{6} t^2$ and find its sum.

10-60. In problem 10-51 you separated Lorna's complicated series into two different arithmetic series, as shown below.

$$5+3+10+8+15+\ldots+400+398 = 5+10+15+\ldots+400$$
$$+3+8+13+\ldots+398$$

a. Write each of the two arithmetic series using summation notation.

b. How could you use your expressions from part (a) to write an expression for Lorna's complicated series using summation notation?

10-61.　Find the sum of each arithmetic series described below.

a.　$\displaystyle\sum_{t=1}^{10}(-5+13t)$

b.　

c.　$4+10+16+22+\ldots+(4+6(n-1))$

d.　$\displaystyle\sum_{t=1}^{30}(10-5t)$

METHODS AND MEANINGS

MATH NOTES

Summation Notation

The capital Greek letter **sigma**, **Σ**, (equivalent to "S" in English) is used in mathematics as a shorter way to indicate the sum of a series. For example:

$$\sum_{k=1}^{5}(2k-3)=-1+1+3+5+7=15$$

Translated, this expression means the sum from $k=1$ to $k=5$ of the terms $2k-3$ equals 15.

Also, the sum of the series $1^2+2^2+3^2$ can be written $\displaystyle\sum_{k=1}^{3}k^2$.

Note: We call k the **index** and k^2 the **argument** of this summation. The values of the index are consecutive integers only, so the values of k in this example are $1, 2,$ and 3.

Review & Preview

10-62.　Write each series in sigma notation and find the sum or an expression for the sum.

a.　$47+34+21+\ldots+(-83)$

b.　$3+10+17+\ldots+(3+7(n-1))$

10-63. Use any method to find the sum of the integers from 100 through 1000. Describe your strategy.

10-64. For many years mathematicians have tried to find a formula to generate prime numbers. One candidate was the expression $n^2 + n + 41$, where n is a positive integer. Try at least 3 or 4 numbers. What do you think of the formula? Does it work? Could you prove it?

10-65. Write each expression in a shorter form.

   a. $3(7 \cdot 3^{n-1})$ b. $0.6(10(0.6)^{n-2})$

10-66. How many different batting orders can be made from the nine starting players on a baseball team? Write the answer using factorials and as a number.

10-67. According to the *National Health Statistics Report*, the average height of adult women in the U.S. is 63.8 inches with a standard deviation of 2.7 inches. Heights can be modeled with a normal probability density function.

   a.   What percent of women are under 4 ft 11 in. tall?

   b.   Most girls reach their adult height by their senior year in high school. In North City High School's class of 324 senior students, how many girls would you expect to be shorter than 4 ft 11 in.? (Note: Assume half of the senior students are girls.)

   c.   How many senior girls do you expect to be taller than 6 ft at North City High?

10-68. Graph each plane in three dimensions.

   a. $2x - 3y + 4z = 12$ b. $2x - 3y = 12$

10-69. Use reference angles, the symmetry of a circle, and the knowledge that $\cos(\frac{\pi}{3}) = \frac{1}{2}$ to write three other true statements using cosine and angles that are multiples of $\frac{\pi}{3}$.

10-70. The Flat Building's roof is 32 feet wide and 60 feet long. An antenna rises 25 feet above the center of the roof, and wires connect the top of the antenna to each corner of the roof and to the midpoint of each edge, as shown in the picture at right.

a. What was the total length of wire used to connect the antenna to the roof (without counting any extra needed for attaching it)?

b. The wires that attach to the corners of the building form an angle with the roof. Find the measure of that angle.

c. Suppose the height of the antenna is x feet (instead of 25 feet). Represent the total length of the wires in terms of x.

10.2.1 What if the series is geometric?

Geometric Series

In this lesson you will work with **geometric series** and develop a method for representing and calculating their sums. Being able to find the sum of a geometric series makes it easy to calculate how much a long-term loan will really cost or how much you will end up paying for something when you buy it on credit. As you work with your team on the problems in this lesson, keep the following discussion questions in mind:

> Can we use any of the strategies we already know?
>
> How can we use what we know about systems of equations?
>
> How can we describe what we have done?
>
> How can we generalize what we have done?

10-71.   Katelyn was helping her younger sister Janelle with her Algebra 1 homework.

a.   Janelle was given the sequence 10, 50, 250, 1250, 6250, … . She wrote the equation $t(n) = 2 \cdot 5^n$ and made the graph at right.

Katelyn cried out, "*No. No. You've written the wrong equation! The correct equation for the sequence is $t(n) = 10 \cdot 5^{n-1}$.*"

Is Katelyn correct? Is Janelle wrong?

b.   What are the advantages of writing the equation like Katelyn did? What are the advantages of writing the equation like Janelle did?

c.   Rewrite the equation $t(n) = 18 \cdot 3^n$ using Katelyn's method.

Core Connections Algebra 2

10-72. PICKING A PAYOUT, Part 1

With a record-setting lottery jackpot
projected for noon tomorrow, Hank stood in
a very long line to buy a ticket. The man
behind him in line tapped him on the
shoulder to ask, *"Hey, have you thought
about how you'd spend the money if you
won?"* Before he could answer, the woman

in front interrupted to say, *"First, you have to decide whether you want to get
your winnings in one lump sum right away, or if you want to receive them
spread out over time. I'm sure one option must be a better deal, but I haven't
figured out which one!"*

When Hank got home he immediately went on the Internet and learned that
lottery winners do have a choice: receive the winnings in a single payment of
51% of the jackpot right away, or spread payments of the jackpot over 20 years.
He also learned that the jackpot is projected to be $50 million! He knew that if
he took the single payment he could invest it right away and earn 4% interest on
that money.

If he chose to receive the payout over 20 years, the Lottery Commission would
invest the money for him. They guarantee to pay $1,500,000 the first year, and
to increase the amount they pay by 5% each year.

At lunchtime, Hank called his brother and told him that if his class could figure
out the difference between the totals for the two payment methods, he would
give that amount to the class if he won the lottery.

a.   If Hank wins the lottery and takes the payments over time, the amounts he
     will receive each year form a geometric sequence. What is the first term?
     What is the growth factor? Write an equation to represent any term in this
     sequence.

b.   If Hank takes the payments over time, how much will he receive in the
     20th year?

c.   When you add up the terms of this sequence to find the total over 20 years,
     you are finding the sum for the geometric series. Show the geometric
     series.

d.   With your team, discuss a *strategy* for calculating the sum without having
     to calculate and add all 20 terms. Consider the graphical method of
     creating rectangles that you used with arithmetic series. Would that work
     for this kind of series? Explain your thinking. You do not need to actually
     sum the series.

10-73.   While working on a strategy to solve the lottery problem, Luann's team decided
          to try to find a strategy by looking at an easier sequence and using fewer terms:

          $$t(n) = 2 \cdot 5^{n-1}$$

          They wrote out the series for the first six terms, represented the sum of the
          series as $S(6)$, and then wrote the series in an equation:

          $$2 + 10 + 50 + 250 + 1250 + 6250 = S(6)$$

          Then Luann remembered the algebraic strategy for finding the sum of an
          arithmetic series where she added the sequence to itself, and then manipulated
          the equations. Is there a similar method you can use for geometric series?
          Work on this as a team. Is there a way to write the equation down twice and
          then rewrite the second equation to eliminate some of the terms when the two
          equations are combined?

10-74.   *"I'm sure that this can be simplified,"* Luann reported to her team. *"But when
          I try to add the series to itself, like we did with the arithmetic series, it just gets
          bigger, and there's no clear pattern. If I subtract it from itself I'm left with
          0 = 0."*

          a.   What are some techniques for rewriting an equation that you use when
                solving systems of equations by elimination? Could these techniques be
                applied in this situation?

          b.   *"A ha!"* Luann almost shouted.

                "Shhh!" her teammate cautioned. *"What have you got?"*

                *"Look! I multiplied both sides of the equation by the sequence
                multiplier."* Luann was really excited about the result. How can you use
                her results and combine the equations to find the sum $S(6)$?

10-75.   Luann wondered if they could use the same method to write an expression for
          the general sum of any number of terms of the series:

          $$2 + 10 + 50 + ... + 2 \cdot 5^{n-1} = S(n)$$

          Show how to use her method to write a general expression for the sum. Make a
          note of what you multiplied by, what was left when you subtracted, and what
          you finally divided by to get the result.

10-76. Antonio is working with a new geometric series generated by the equation $t(n) = 30(1.2)^{n-1}$. His sister has challenged him to find the sum of the first 37 terms. He needs your help.

a. Show Antonio how he can figure out the sum of *any* number of terms without adding them all up.

b. Antonio's sister has challenged him to find the sum of the 38th through the 99th terms of this series. Work with your team to help Antonio meet his sister's challenge.

10-77. PICKING A PAYOUT, Part 2

Look back to your work on problem 10-72. For your convenience, the two payment options are reprinted below. Recall that the jackpot in question is $50,000,000.

Option 1: Receive a single payment of 51% of the jackpot right away. Invest the money and earn 4% interest compounded annually.

Option 2: Receive payments once a year for 20 years. The first payment would be $1,500,000 and the payments would increase by 5% each year.

Your Task: Work with your team to determine which is the best way to collect the money. Should Hank take his winnings immediately and invest the money himself? Or should he choose the guaranteed payout each year for 20 years? With which option would he receive the most money? Be prepared to justify your decision with explanations and calculations.

Discussion Points

How will the amount increase over time if he invests it himself?

How can we represent the amount he would receive each year algebraically if he chooses the annual payout?

How much will there be in total after 20 years in each situation?

10-78.   Imagine taking the single payment of 51% of the jackpot.

   a.   How much will you receive?

   b.   If you invest all of the money at a rate of 4% compounded annually, how much can you expect to have after 20 years?

   c.   Is the answer to part (b) the sum of a series?

10-79.   Imagine instead that you choose to take payments spread over 20 years, starting with $1,500,000 in year 1 and growing by 5 percent each year,

   a.   How much money would you receive in year 2? In year 5?

   b.   Write an equation to show how much money you receive in any given year.

   c.   How much money will you have received after 20 years? Be ready to explain your thinking to the class.

10-80.   With which option would you receive more money? How much more? Which option would you choose? Why?

_____   *Further Guidance*   _____
section ends here.

10-81. Scott and Greg are looking for summer jobs. Their father, who is head of the neighborhood beautification committee, says that if they pick up litter from around the neighborhood for a whole day, he will pay them $0.15 for each piece of trash they collect. Scott realizes that the more litter they pick up, the more difficult it will be to find more pieces, so he proposes a different payment scheme. *"How about you give us $0.10 for the first piece, and increase our pay by 2% for each piece after that? Then we'll get paid more for the pieces we work harder to find."*

a. Write an equation to generate the series Scott is proposing.

b. With Scott's plan, how much will his dad have to pay him for the 100th piece of litter he finds? For the 200th?

c. If Scott collects 150 pieces of litter, how much will he have earned in total? What if he picks up 200 pieces?

d. Greg thinks Scott is crazy to propose an increase of just 2% per piece. After all 2% of 10 cents is just $\frac{2}{10}$ of a cent! Instead, he plans to ask for a one-cent increase for every piece. If their father agrees to this, how much would Greg get paid for the 100th piece he collects? For the 200th piece?

e. If the boys each collect 150 pieces of litter, which payment scheme will earn them the most money?

f. What if they each pick up a total of 200 pieces?

10-82. Drought-conscious Darcy is collecting rainwater in order to water her garden through the hot, dry summer. During the last big rainstorm she filled 12 buckets full to the brim! Each week of the summer, she used the water from one of the 12 buckets to water her plants.

However, Darcy had not counted on evaporation. In the sun, each uncovered bucket loses 0.35 gallons of its water volume each week.

a. If each bucket starts with 15 gallons in it, how many gallons will be in each of the unused buckets after 2 weeks in the sun? After 7 weeks? How much was in the final bucket when Darcy used it on her garden?

b. Is this series arithmetic, geometric, or something else?

c. At the end of the 12th week, how many total gallons of water will Darcy have poured on her plants?

10-83.   Hannah is very interested in genealogy, the study
          of family history. She has traced her family back
          many years and knows the names of her biological
          parents, grandparents, great-grandparents, great-
          great-grandparents, and so on.

    a.   If Hannah counts herself as the first
          generation, how many people are in each of
          the first three generations on her chart?

    b.   What kind of sequence does the number of people in each generation
          form? Is it arithmetic, geometric, or something else? Justify your
          conclusion.

    c.   If Hannah is successful in tracing her true biological ancestors for
          12 generations, how many names will she have?

10-84.   For each of the problems below, decide if the series is arithmetic, geometric, or
          something else. Then, find the sum of the series.

    a. $\displaystyle\sum_{t=0}^{15} 5(2)^t$ b. $\displaystyle\sum_{p=1}^{179}(16-4(p-1))$

    c. $4 + 8 + 12 + \ldots + 392$ d. $\displaystyle\sum_{q=1}^{312} 11q$

    e. $5 + \frac{10}{4} + \frac{10}{8} + \ldots + \frac{10}{4096}$

10-85.   Lucy is working with a series whose first term is 12 and that is generated by the
          expression $t(n) = -9 + 21n$. The sum of her series is 3429. How many terms are
          in her series?

10-86.   Write an entry in your Learning Log that describes what you
          have learned during this lesson. Include information about
          the differences between geometric sequences and geometric
          series, and about how to find the sum of a geometric series.
          What questions do you have about geometric series? Title
          this entry "Geometric Series" and label it with today's date.

10-87. Antonio and Luann were trying to explain their strategy for finding the sum of a geometric series to their homework group. They decided to generate a sequence that would be easy to add up so they could convince the other students that their strategy really worked. They used $t(n) = 3 \cdot 10^{n-1}$.

a. The sum of the first six terms of the series is easy to calculate. You can do it in your head. Write out the first six terms and find the sum.

b. Now explain Luann and Antonio's strategy for finding the sum and use your answer to part (a) to check your result.

c. Represent the first n terms of the series in summation notation and write an expression for the total sum of n terms.

10-88. According to the school secretary, the size of the graduating class of Gauss High has steadily increased since the school has opened. She claims that the number of graduates each year forms the sequence $t(n) = 42 + 12(n-1)$, where n is the number of years the high school has had students graduate. At the end of the year, the administration mails out invitations to all previous graduates to attend the upcoming graduation ceremony.

a. In this situation, what does a sequence represent? What does a series represent?

b. After the 10th graduation ceremony, how many total graduates should there be? Explain how you found your answer.

c. The total number of Gauss High graduates after n years can be represented by the graph at right. If the alumni relations committee wants to invite all graduates to a party to celebrate the nth anniversary of the school, how may invitations will they need to send?

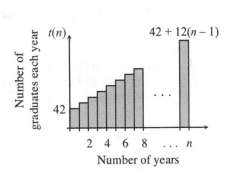

10-89.   Consider the series $8 + 1 + (-6) + (-13) + ... + (-90)$.

     a.   How many terms are there?   b.   What is the sum?

10-90.   Evaluate the sum of the series $\sum_{n=3}^{9} (5n)$. Is the series arithmetic or geometric?

10-91.   Connie and Nora went into Ready Scoop to get ice cream cones, but Nora can't make up her mind. They have 23 flavors and she wants 3 scoops.

     a.   Nora is very particular about the order of the scoops. How many choices does she have if all of the scoops are different?

     b.   Nora changes her mind. She wants a dish (in which the order does not matter), not a cone, but she still wants three different flavors. How many ways can she order?

     c.   Connie says, *"I want a cone with dark chocolate on the bottom and then any other flavors for the two scoops on top."* How many cones are possible with dark chocolate on the bottom?

     d.   Vlad came in as they were leaving and saw Connie's cone. He said, *"Oh, that's what I want, a cone with chocolate on the bottom and then two other flavors."* The clerk, said, *"Okay, but we have four kinds of chocolate."* Vlad replied, *"Any kind of chocolate will do."* How many different cones could fill Vlad's order?

10-92.   Using a graph of $y = \sin x$ as a reference, graph $y = |\sin x|$.

10-93.   Factor and simplify each expression below.

     a. $\dfrac{x^2-4}{x^2+4x+4}$ b. $\dfrac{2x^2-5x-3}{4x^2+4x+1}$

     c.   Justify each step in simplifying the expression in part (a).

10-94.   For each equation below, state the amplitude, period, and locator point, and then sketch two cycles of the graph.

     a. $y = \tan(x)$ b. $y = \tan(x - \pi)$

10-95. Solve each equation.

    a. $\log_5(2x) = 3$ b. $\log_5(x+1) = -1$

    c. $\log(4) - \log(x) = 2$ d. $2\log_3(6) + \log_3(y) = 4$

10-96. Joe's dad is only 40, but he's already thinking about retiring. If he retires early at age 55, he will receive an annual pension starting at $30,000 and increasing at a rate of 3% each year to account for inflation. If he waits until he is 65, his pension will be a larger percentage of his salary at that time. He figures that it will be about $60,000 to start and the same 3% increase after that for inflation. He wants to know which plan will pay out the largest total by age 80. Show him how to find out the answer to his question.

10-97. Ms. Fernandez invested $50,000 of her lottery winnings into two different mutual funds. At the end of one year, both funds together were worth $53,550. One of the funds had produced a return of 8% while the second fund had produced a return of 6.5%. How much money was invested in each fund?

10-98. Eight friends go to the movies. They want to sit together in a row with a student on each aisle. (Assume the row is 8 seats wide including 2 aisle seats.)

    a.   How many ways can they sit in the row?

    b.   If Kristen wants to sit on the far left aisle seat, how many ways can they all sit in the row?

    c.   If Kristen wants either aisle seat, how many ways can the eight students sit?

10-99. Find the distance between each of the following pairs of points.

    a. $(8, 4)$ and $(12, 20)$ b. (x, y) and $(-3, -5)$

10-100. Solve each of the following equations.

    a. $\frac{x}{x+1} = \frac{5}{7}$

    b. $\frac{2}{y} = \frac{3}{y+5}$

    c. $\frac{x}{x+1} + \frac{2}{x-1} = \frac{8}{x^2-1}$

    d. $\frac{2}{y+5} - \frac{3}{y} = \frac{3}{y+5}$

10-101. Solve for x and y in each system below.

    a.
$$2x + y = 12$$
$$xy = 16$$

    b.
$$2x + y = 12$$
$$xy = 20$$

    c. Explain how the graphs of (a) and (b) relate to the solutions to each system of equations.

10-102. Use reference angles, the symmetry of a circle, and the knowledge that $\tan(20°) \approx 0.3640$ to write three other true statements using tangent.

10-103. Use the properties of logarithms to rewrite each equation and then solve. Check for extraneous roots.

    a. $\log(x) + \log(x+21) = 2$

    b. $2\log_4(x) - \log_4(3) = 2$

    c. $\log_2(9x+5) - \log_2(x^2 - 1) = 2$

    d. $\log_7(x+1) + \log_7(x-5) = 1$

10-104. Calculate $(2+i)(3-5i) - (1-4i)^2$.

10.2.2 What if n is very large?

Infinite Series

What is the total distance a ball would travel if you tossed it up and let it bounce? What if a bouncing ball continued to bounce forever? How far would it travel? Today you will discover ways to represent this situation and find the answer to this question.

10-105.   THE BOUNCING BALL

Imagine lying on the ground and tossing a ball straight up 10 meters.

a.   When the ball gets back to you, how far has it travelled?

b.   Instead of catching it, imagine that you let it bounce. The ball has a bounce ratio of 60%, meaning that each time it bounces the ball will bounce to 60% of its previous height. When the ball comes back down to you the second time, how far has it travelled in total?

c.   Imagine that you let the ball bounce until it comes back to you 15 times. Write a geometric series to represent the total distance the ball travels until it comes back to you the 15th time.

d.   What is the total distance the ball will travel up and down?

10-106.   HOW FAR IS IT?

Of course you know that a ball cannot bounce forever, but imagine the ball in the previous problem could. Thinking about this possibility has led to some interesting discoveries. Would the total distance the ball travels up and down continue to grow until it is infinitely large?

Now, imagine starting at 0 on a number line and moving according to the following sequence: move 20 units to the right, and then continue moving right, each time moving 0.6 times the distance you previously moved.

20   12   7.2   • • •

Problem continues on next page →

10-106. *Problem continued from previous page.*

How far along the number line would you travel if you kept going and going and going … forever? That is, what is the total distance the ball would travel if it could bounce forever?

Your Task:

- With your team, investigate the questions above.

- When your team agrees that you have answered the investigation question, create a new infinite geometric series and generalize your results. As you work with your team, keep the following Discussion Points in mind. Then write a strategy for finding the sum of any infinite geometric series.

Discussion Points

What patterns do we see as n increases?

What happens when the multiplier is smaller than one?

How can we represent this?

Is there a simpler equivalent expression?

- Prepare a poster to share your team's findings. Include your examples, generalizations, and justifications.

Further Guidance

10-107. You already calculated the distance for 15 bounces of the ball in problem 10-105. Calculate the distance for 25 moves along the number line, and for several larger values of n.

10-108. Calculate the sums of each of the following geometric series for $n = 10$ and $n = 30$. What do you notice about the results?

a. $200 + 100 + 50 + ... + 200\left(\frac{1}{2}\right)^n$

b. $16 + 24 + 36 + ... + 16\left(\frac{3}{2}\right)^n$

c. What makes the difference in the results for the series in parts (a) and (b)?

10-109.   What do you notice about the results as you use larger values for n? That is, what happens to the total distance the ball travels? Respond to the investigation questions in problem 10-105.

10-110.   Write a strategy for finding the sum of any infinite geometric series. Keep the Discussion Points from problem 10-105 in mind.

═══════════ Further Guidance ═══════════
section ends here.

10-111.   The general formula for the sum of a finite geometric series is

$$S(n) = \frac{r \cdot t(n) - t(1)}{r - 1},$$

where $t(n)$ is the formula for each term. Start with this formula and use it to develop a formula for the sum of an infinite geometric series.

   a.   Since $t(n) = ar^{n-1}$, replace $t(n)$ and $t(1)$ in the formula for $S(n)$ above and simplify.

   b.   It turns out that $S(n) = \frac{a(1-r^n)}{1-r}$ will be the most useful form for the formula for the sum of a geometric series. If you have not done so already, show that your formula in part (a) is equivalent to:

$$S(n) = \frac{a(1-r^n)}{1-r}.$$

   c.   In the bouncing ball problem (problem 10-105), $a = 20$ and $r = 0.6$. What happens to the value of r^n as you use larger and larger values for n? What happens to the value of $1 - r^n$? Discuss these questions with your team.

   d.   For infinite series, the formula can be rewritten as shown below. Explain why this is possible.

$$S = \frac{a}{1-r}$$

   e.   Use this formula for the sum of an infinite series to recalculate the total distance the bouncing ball would travel (in problem 10-105) if it bounced without ending. Compare your results with the results of your investigation in problem 10-106.

10-112.   It is believed that the Greek philosopher Zeno of Alea devised this in about
          450 BCE: The tortoise challenged Achilles to a race. To be fair, Achilles, who
          is known for his tremendous speed, gave the tortoise a head start. Zeno
          proposed that as he ran the race, Achilles would run to the place that the tortoise
          had started. But by that time, the tortoise would have moved forward some
          distance. Then by the time Achilles travels that new distance between him and
          the tortoise, the tortoise will have moved forward again. This would happen
          over and over again. So, even though the tortoise is much slower than Achilles,
          it appears Achilles can never catch up to the tortoise!

          By this same reasoning, you would not ever be able to cross a street. To cross a
          street, you must first cross to the halfway point. After you have gone that far,
          you still have to cross halfway of the remaining distance (which is $\frac{1}{4}$ of the
          whole distance). When you have crossed that, you still have to cross half of the
          remaining distance ($\frac{1}{8}$ of the whole distance). You always have halfway of
          some distance remaining in front of you. It appears you will never be able to
          cross the street!

          Investigate these two paradoxical dilemmas with series.

          a.   Represent the distance you have travelled across the street as an infinite
               geometric series.

          b.   What is the sum of the series?

          c.   Zeno would point out that crossing the street would mean completing an
               infinite number of tasks, which would be impossible. What do you think?

10-113.   Fannie was helping her younger brother Mac with his math homework when
          they came to this problem:

          Change the repeating decimal $0.\overline{63}$ into a fraction.

          Fannie remembered that they could write the problem as an equation and then
          create a second equation by multiplying by a useful power of 10.

          $$N = 0.636363636363....$$
          $$100N = 63.636363636363...$$

          Then they could subtract the first equation from the second and divide to find N
          as follows:

          $$99N = 63$$
          $$N = \tfrac{63}{99} = \tfrac{7}{11}$$

          When she returned to her own homework Fannie thought, "*Whoa! I bet I could
          write $0.\overline{63}$ as an infinite series and use what we just learned about series to get
          the fraction.*"

          a.   Write $0.\overline{63} = 0.636363...$ as an infinite series with a multiplier of 0.01.

          b.   Find the sum of the series and write the answer as a fraction.

Core Connections Algebra 2

10-114.   Use Fannie's method from problem 10-113 to write $0.\overline{143}$ as an infinite series. Then write the decimal as a fraction.

10-115.   What fraction is $0.\overline{9}$ or $0.9999999\ldots$?

10-116.   LEARNING LOG

Write an entry in your Learning Log describing what you learned in this lesson. Include information about infinite geometric series and their sums. What questions do you have about series? Title this entry "Infinite Geometric Series" and label it with today's date.

METHODS AND MEANINGS

MATH NOTES

Geometric Series

A **geometric sequence** can be represented by a formula for its nth term:
$$t(n) = ar^{n-1}$$

The first term is a (for which $n = 1$), and the **common multiplier** (or ratio) is r.

A **geometric series** is the sum of the terms of a geometric sequence:
$$t(1) + t(2) + t(3) + \ldots + t(k)$$

The total sum for a finite series (a series that ends) is:
$$S(k) = \frac{r \cdot t(k) - t(1)}{r-1} = \frac{a(1-r^k)}{1-r}$$

For example, either formula above can be used to find the sum of the series $1000 + 600 + 360 + 216 + 129.6$, which has $a = 1000$ and $r = 0.6$:
$$S(5) = \frac{0.6(129.6) - 1000}{0.6 - 1} = 2305.6 \quad \text{or} \quad S(5) = \frac{1000(1 - 0.6^5)}{1 - 0.6} = 2305.6$$

For an **infinite geometric series** with an initial value of a and a multiplier (or common ratio) r, and $0 < |r| < 1$, the sum of the series can be represented by:
$$S = \sum_{n=1}^{\infty} ar^{n-1} = \frac{a}{1-r}$$

For example: When $a = 100$ and the multiplier is $r = 0.2$, the sum of the infinite series is: $100 + 20 + 4 + 0.8 + \ldots = \frac{100}{1 - 0.2} = 125$

10-117. A hiker decided to spend his days walking around the country. On the first day he walked 25 miles, but on the following days he found he could not keep up that pace. On average he traveled a 5% shorter distance each day. If he could walk forever, how far would he go?

10-118. Given seven points in a plane, no three of which are collinear:

    a.   How many different lines are determined by these points?

    b.   How many distinct triangles can be formed?

    c.   How many distinct quadrilaterals can be formed?

    d.   Explain why the answers to parts (b) and (c) are the same.

10-119. Solve the following equations.

    a. $\frac{3}{x} + \frac{5}{x-7} = -2$ b. $\frac{2x+3}{4} - \frac{x-7}{6} = \frac{2x-3}{12}$

10-120. Betty's Quick Stop makes a 15% profit on its lunches and a 22% profit on its dinners. If Betty took in $2700 on Tuesday and made $513.01 profit, how much did Betty take in on lunch? Write one or two equations, then solve.

10-121. For the polynomial function $f(x) = x^3 - 5x^2 + 11x - 15$, which of the following are possible factors?

    a. $(x+1)$ b. $(x-2)$ c. $(x+4)$ d. $(x-3)$

10-122. Using your answers to the previous problem:

    a.   Factor $f(x) = x^3 - 5x^2 + 11x - 15$.   b.   Solve $f(x) = 0$.

10-123. What fraction is equivalent to the repeating decimal $0.\overline{27}$?

10-124. Find the solutions to the system at right. The solutions may be real or complex.

$$y = x^2 + 2x + 5$$
$$y = 2x^2 + 4x + 7$$

10-125. Why does the formula for the sum of an infinite geometric series contain the condition that $0 < |r| < 1$?

10-126. Find the sum of the first five terms of this series: $3 + 1 + \frac{1}{3} + \ldots$

10-127. Find the value of each of the following combinations.

   a. $_{10}C_8$ b. $_{12}C_7$ c. $_7C_1$

10-128. Without graphing, find where each of the following curves crosses the x-axis. (Find the *exact* points!)

   a. $f(x) = x^2 - x - 12$ b. $f(x) = 2x^2 - 3x - 9$

   c. $f(x) = 2x^2 + x - 7$ d. $f(x) = 3x^2 - 2x + 7$

   e. $f(x) = 3x^3 + 2x^2 - 8x$ f. $f(x) = 2x^3 + 2x^2 + 13x$

10-129. Use properties of exponents to rewrite each expression below so that it involves only multiplication and exponents.

   a. $\dfrac{(-2x)^3 yz^2}{2^{-1}\sqrt{x}y^{-3}}$ b. $\dfrac{3x^2 y^3}{\sqrt{3x}\sqrt[3]{y}}$

10-130. For an object shot into the air, its height h in feet above the ground after t seconds is given by the equation $h = 80t - 16t^2$. Use this equation to answer the following questions.

   a. At what times is the object on the ground?

   b. For what domain is this function reasonable?

   c. How long did it take the object to hit the ground?

   d. For what times is the height greater than 64 feet?

10-131. Dolores says that the solutions for $x^2 - x + 1 = 0$ are $\frac{1}{2} \pm \frac{i\sqrt{3}}{2}$. Is she correct? Explain your answer.

10-132. The graph of $f(x) = x^2 - 3x - 4$ is shown at right. Use the graph to solve:

a. $f(x) = 0$

b. $f(x) \geq 0$

c. $f(x) \leq 0$

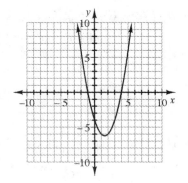

10.3.1 How fast can I rewrite $(x + y)^6$?

Pascal's Triangle and the Binomial Theorem

In this lesson you will use something you learned when studying probability that may seem, at first, to be totally unrelated to the algebra problems you will be rewriting.

When you learned about probability, you explored several kinds of counting problems. You learned to use **combinations**, $_nC_r$, in situations where order does not matter and results are not repeated. For example, when counting the number of ways to choose a 3-member committee out of five volunteers, you calculated $_5C_3 = \frac{5 \cdot 4 \cdot 3}{3!} = 10$. Then you used **permutations**, $_nP_r$, in situations where the order *does* matter, and results are not repeated. For example, when counting how many ways there are to choose the first, second and third place winners from five finalists, you calculated $_nP_r = 5 \cdot 4 \cdot 3 = 60$.

10-133. Work with your team to complete a table for combinations like the one below. Discuss any patterns you notice as you are working.

r, the number of choices

$_nC_r$	0	1	2	3	4	5	6	7	8
0	1								
1	1	1							
2	1	2	1						
3	1	3	3	1					
4			6						
5									
6									
7									
8							28	8	1

n, the total number

10-134. The triangular array at right is another arrangement of the numbers of combinations you entered in the table in problem 10-133. It is known as Pascal's Triangle. Copy the triangle and add several more rows.

n											
0						1					
1					1		1				
2				1		2		1			
3			1		3		3		1		
4		1		4		6		4		1	
5	1		5		10		10		5		1

a. There are many patterns in the triangle, which continues to grow indefinitely. With your team, find and describe as many patterns as you can. You should be able to describe at least three.

b. Discuss with the class the patterns you found. Write down any patterns your classmates found that your team did not find.

c. The single number 1 at the top of the triangle is called Row 0. Label the rows of your triangle to row 10, and describe a rule for writing any new row in the triangle.

10-135. Now consider what may appear to be a completely different problem: the algebraic expansion of the binomial expression $(a+b)^n$. Use what you know about multiplication to complete parts (a) through (d) below.

a. Write $(a+b)^2$ in expanded form. In other words, multiply $(a+b)(a+b)$ and combine like terms. How many terms are there in the resulting polynomial? What are the coefficients of the terms?

b. Multiply and rewrite $(a+b)^3$ in expanded form. How many terms are there, and what are their coefficients? What did you do to expand the polynomial? With your team, discuss possible ways to carry out the polynomial multiplication quickly.

c. How many terms do you think $(a+b)^4$ will have when rewritten in expanded form? Write it in expanded form. What are the coefficients of these terms?

d. How could you use Pascal's Triangle to rewrite the binomial expression $(a+b)^6$ as a sum of monomial terms? Explain your method.

10-136. Explain how you could use Pascal's Triangle to rewrite $(a+b)^n$ in expanded form. What problem would use row 1? Row 0?

10-137. Use Pascal's Triangle to rewrite $(U+V)^3$ in expanded form.

    a.   Pascal's Triangle can be used to expand any binomial raised to a power. Use it to expand the expression $(2x+3)^3$, by substituting $2x$ for U and 3 for V.

    b.   Now use Pascal's Triangle to expand $(x-1)^5$. What will you need to substitute for U and V?

    c.   How many terms are in the answer to part (a)? Part (b)? In general, how many terms would be in the expanded form of the nth power of a binomial?

10-138. To do problems 10-135 through 10-137 you probably noticed that the pattern in Pascal's Triangle appears to be the same pattern in first four powers of $(a+b)^1, (a+b)^2, (a+b)^3, (a+b)^4$. Patterns are powerful and important tools in mathematics. Some have called mathematics "the science of patterns," but to be sure a pattern fits, you need to justify it. Why are the numbers in Pascal's triangle the same as $(a+b)^n$?

Your Task: Discuss this question with your team, write some examples to illustrate your reasoning, and be prepared to explain your reasoning to the class.

Discussion Points

How are the coefficients of the terms in a binomial expansion of
$a + b$ combinations?

How can we use an example?

How are the factors related to the product?

10-139.   Joanna had written $(a+b)^5 = (a+b)(a+b)(a+b)(a+b)(a+b)$ on her paper, when Sareen asked, *"Why did you write that?"*

Joanna replied, *"I thought we could use it as an example. When we did $(a+b)^3$ the variable parts in the expanded form were: a^3, a^2b, ab^2, b^3. What do you think they will be for this one?"*

   a.   For the fifth power make a list of the variable parts of the expressions that will appear in the expanded form.

   b.   Garth jumped in and said, *"I've got an idea, maybe we can look at one of the terms like a^3b^2 and look back at the factors to see where it came from!"*

   "Wait, I think I see it," James chimed in. *"You just use an 'a' from three of the five factors and a 'b' from the other two."*

   What counting formula gives the number of different ways to choose three a's from the five factors? What is the coefficient for a^3b^2 and how could you figure it out without referring to Pascal's Triangle?

―――――   *Further Guidance*   ―――――
section ends here.

10-140.   For his homework assignment, Andrew had to expand $(a+b)^9$. He just realized that he did not have the coefficient for the term a^3b^6. He started writing out the first nine rows of Pascal's Triangle when his friend Robbie said he could find the value using combinations. What combination should Andrew use, and what is the coefficient?

10-141.   Rebecca needs to write the 5th term in the expansion of $(a+b)^{11}$.

   a.   How many terms are in the expansion?

   b.   What is the 5th term of the expansion? (The term is of the form $\_\_ a^7b^4$.)

   c.   Now Rebecca needs to know the 5th term of $(x-2)^{11}$. How can you use your result from part (b)?

10-142.   **Challenge:** Read the Math Notes box about the Binomial Theorem that follows this lesson. Then, use the general form for the Binomial Theorem to show that the sum of the elements of the nth row of Pascal's Triangle is 2^n.

$$_nC_n +_n C_{n-1} +_n C_{n-2} + ... +_n C_2 +_n C_1 +_n C_0 = 2^n$$

10-143. After doing the above challenge problem and noticing that $_2C_0 + _2C_1 + _2C_2 = 2^2$, Duong noticed that $_1C_0 + _1C_1 = 2^1$. He wondered if this worked for 2^3 also.

    a. Does $_3C_0 + _3C_1 + _3C_2 + _3C_3 = 2^3$?

    b. Does $_4C_0 + _4C_1 + _4C_2 + _4C_3 + _4C_4 = 2^4$?

    c. Explain why $_nC_0 + _nC_1 + _nC_2 + \ldots + _nC_n = 2^n$.

10-144. LEARNING LOG

Write an entry in your Learning Log explaining Pascal's Triangle and why it is useful. Include several examples. Title this entry "Pascal's Triangle" and label it with today's date.

METHODS AND MEANINGS

Binomial Theorem

MATH NOTES

The **Binomial Theorem** can be used to write the expansion of binomial expressions of the form $(a+b)^n$. For example:

$$(x+3y)^4$$

$$=_4C_4 x^4(3y)^0 +_4C_3 x^3(3y)^1 +_4C_2 x^2(3y)^2 +_4C_1 x^1(3y)^3 +_4C_0 x^0(3y)^4$$

$$= 1x^4 + 4x^3(3y) + 6x^2(9y^2) + 4x(27y^3) + 81y^4$$

$$= x^4 + 12x^3y + 54x^2y^2 + 108xy^3 + 81y^4$$

In general, $(a+b)^n = {_nC_n}a^n + {_nC_{n-1}}a^{n-1}b + {_nC_{n-2}}a^{n-2}b^2 + \cdots {_nC_1}ab^{n-1} + {_nC_0}b^n$.

Review & Preview

10-145. Use Pascal's Triangle to expand $(x+y)^7$.

10-146. Use the pattern for $(a+b)^5$ to write the fourth term of $(w-4z)^5$.

10-147. George starts a chain letter by sending it to four friends who then send it to four more friends and so on. If George counts as round one and his four friends as round two, how many people will have received the letter after round six?

10-148. Find the sum for each of these infinite geometric series if possible. If it is not possible, explain.

a. $8 + 4 + 2 + \ldots$ b. $3 + 9 + 27 + 81 + \ldots$

10-149. Donna has four bracelets in her jewelry box. They can all be worn together, but each is different from the others. Before she goes to bed at night, she sets out the outfit she will wear the next day, including her accessories. How many different ways can she choose the following: 0 bracelets? 1 bracelet? 2 bracelets? 3 bracelets? 4 bracelets?

a. How do these possible combinations compare to the 4th row ($n = 4$) of Pascal's Triangle?

b. If Donna bought two new bracelets, how many combinations of four bracelets can she choose for her outfit? How can you figure this out without multiplying or using your calculator?

10-150. The Spirit Club recently got a call from the school executive council, asking them to make a committee. They now have 10 volunteers and will need to choose a three-person committee. They need to calculate $_{10}C_3$, the number of possible committees, but they have no calculator with them.

a. Al had a thought: *"I remember that the number of three-person committees you can select from 9 volunteers is 84. This would be the number of committees the tenth volunteer will NOT be on because he or she would be selected from the other nine members."* How would you calculate this number?

b. *"I also know how many committees the new volunteer WILL be on because I can just add his name to each of the two-member committees I had already selected from 9."* How many possible committees would include the tenth volunteer?

c. Without using a calculator (and without multiplying or dividing), explain how Al used parts (a) and (b) to calculate $_{10}C_3$.

d. How is this related to Pascal's Triangle?

10-151.   Sketch a graph of $y = x^3(x-2)(x+2)^2$.

10-152.   Parking meters in a beach resort town cost 25¢ for 15 minutes. A normal distribution with a mean $10 and a standard deviation of $2 can be used to model the amount of money one parking meter makes on a busy summer day.

   a.   Make a graph of the distribution of the money made by one meter on your calculator, and sketch it. An appropriate value for the maximum of the relative frequency axis is Ymax = 0.2.

   b.   From your graph, visually estimate where the middle 90% of meter earnings fall. Shade this portion of your sketch.

   c.   Use your calculator to check your estimate. How close to 90% did you come?

10-153.   Solve the system at right for (x, y, z).

$$2x + y - 2z = 0$$
$$x - y - 4z = -3$$
$$3x + 2y + 2z = -1$$

10-154.   A parabola passes through the points (0, 5), (2, 1), and (6, 17).

   a.   What is its equation?   b.   Where is its vertex?

10-155.   What is the third term of $(2x + \frac{1}{4x})^7$?

10-156.   Find the sum of the first six terms of the series $2 + 6 + 18 + 54 + \dots$.

10-157.   Use the pattern for $(a+b)^4$ to expand $(3x+1)^4$.

10-158.   Complete the square to change the following equations to graphing form. Then sketch the graph of each equation.

   a. $f(x) = x^2 + 4x + 6$ b. $x^2 + 6x + y^2 - 8y = 0$

10-159. Two similar triangles are drawn on a piece of paper. The smaller triangle has an area of 600 square mm and the larger triangle has an area of 960 square mm. If the shortest side of the smaller triangle is 26 mm, how long is the shortest side of the larger triangle?

10-160. Find the equation of the line that is perpendicular to $y = \frac{1}{2}x - 3$ and passes through the point (10, 14).

10-161. For the function $f(x) = \frac{\sqrt{x+4}}{2} - 1$, complete parts (a) through (d) below.

a. Sketch the graph and the inverse.

b. Find the equation of the inverse function.

c. Determine the domain and range of the inverse.

d. Compute $f^{-1}(f(5))$.

10-162. Solve each equation below.

a. $2^{(x-1)} = 64$

b. $9^3 = 27^{(2x-1)}$

c. $x^6 = 29$

d. $6^x = 29$

10-163. A small rocket is launched from five meters below ground level and reaches a height of 3 meters above the ground after 4 seconds. On the way down it is 3 meters above the ground after a total of 8 seconds.

a. What are three data points?

b. Draw a rough sketch of the height of the rocket over time.

c. Find the equation of the parabola based on the data.

d. When will the rocket hit the ground?

e. What is the domain for this function?

f. For what part of the domain is the rocket below ground?

10.3.2 What is *e*?

The Number *e*

So far in this chapter you have learned several things about sums of infinite series and the Binomial Theorem. Now you are going to use this knowledge to look at one particular situation involving an infinite series—compound interest. This work will reveal a new mathematical constant, another **transcendental number** (like π), which has a decimal representation that continues infinitely and does not form a repetitive pattern. This number is called *e*. The number *e* when used as the base of a logarithm is known as a **natural logarithm** and is used widely in the sciences as well as in business and economics.

10-164. Tabitha's uncle gave her $10,000 on her thirteenth birthday. She wants to invest it in a college savings fund. The banker tells her that interest rates have dropped to 3%, but at their bank they will compound the interest at any time interval—daily, even hourly—so their customers can still get a good deal. Tabitha decided to make a table to see how good a deal she could get.

   a. Tabitha knows that a one-year compounding period will result in $10000(1 + .03)^1 = \$10300$. She also knows that she can get the amount for semiannual periods by dividing the rate by 2 and then squaring to compound, or $10000(1 + \frac{0.03}{2})^2 = \$10302.25$. Make a table for shorter compounding periods, including quarterly, monthly, daily, and hourly.

   b. What do you notice about the amounts? Be prepared to share your observations with the class.

10-165. Tabitha was disappointed, but she decided the daily compounding would have to do. Her friend Veronica was more of a dreamer. She asked, *"What if you could earn 100% interest and compound that?"*

   "Wow, that should grow fast!" said Tabitha. *"I've got my calculator. Let's just start with one dollar to make it easy, and we can multiply by any initial amount later."*

   Veronica added, *"Yes, and that makes our formula easier."*

   a. What is the easier version of the formula Veronica is thinking of?

   b. With your team, make a table for at least 12 values of *n*, including some very large ones.

   c. Did you try 1,000,000? What do you notice as you use larger numbers for *n*?

10-166. The Binomial Theorem provides another way to think about the number e. This particular approach turned out to be very useful because later it led to some surprising connections with other areas of mathematics.

The beginning of the binomial expansion for $\left(1+\frac{1}{n}\right)^n$ is written below:

$$\left(1+\tfrac{1}{n}\right)^n = {}_nC_n(1) + {}_nC_{n-1}\left(\tfrac{1}{n}\right) + {}_nC_{n-2}\left(\tfrac{1}{n^2}\right) + {}_nC_{n-3}\left(\tfrac{1}{n^3}\right) + {}_nC_{n-4}\left(\tfrac{1}{n^4}\right) + \ldots$$

The combinations can be written in terms of factorials, and algebra can be used to rewrite, so this expression is equivalent to the following expression.

$$1 + 1 + \frac{1-\frac{1}{n}}{2!} + \frac{\left(1-\frac{1}{n}\right)\left(1-\frac{2}{n}\right)}{3!} + \frac{\left(1-\frac{1}{n}\right)\left(1-\frac{2}{n}\right)\left(1-\frac{3}{n}\right)}{4!} + \ldots$$

a. What happens to each factor in the numerators as the value of n gets very large? If n could be infinitely large, what would each numerator equal? Explain your reasoning.

b. Rewrite the series, changing the numerators to what they would be if n became an infinitely large number.

10-167. Leonard Euler (pronounced as "oiler") was a preeminent mathematician and physicist in the 1700s. Although he was Swiss, he worked mostly in Russia. You can thank Euler for $f(x)$ notation, and for the symbols i, e, and Σ; he popularized the use of π. Among many other discoveries, he found that when n becomes infinitely large:

$$e = \sum_{n=0}^{\infty} \frac{1}{n!} = 1 + 1 + \frac{1}{2!} + \frac{1}{3!} + \frac{1}{4!} + \ldots$$

a. Is this series arithmetic or geometric? Explain your answer.

b. Calculate the sum of the first 5 terms and then the sum of the first 7 terms. What do you notice?

10-168. **Team Challenge:** Investigate the function $f(x) = (1+\frac{1}{x})^x$.

METHODS AND MEANINGS

Compound Interest

The formula for **compound interest** is generally written:

$$A = P\left(1+\tfrac{r}{n}\right)^{nt},$$

where A is the total amount of money at any time, P is the principal or initial value, r is the annual rate of interest, t is the number of years, and n is the number of times per year the interest is compounded.

For example, if you invest \$5,000 for 20 years at an annual interest rate of 4.8%, compounded monthly:

$$A = \$5000\left(1+\tfrac{0.048}{12}\right)^{12\cdot20} = \$5000(1.004)^{240} = \$13,033.50$$

The use of e provides a shortcut for calculation of **continuously compounded interest**. The formula for continuous compounding is

$$A = Pe^{rt},$$

where A is the total amount at any time, P is the original principal, r is the rate of interest, and t is the time period.

10-169. Robin and Teryll each have \$8,000 to invest and they disagree about the best place to start a savings account. Teryll found a savings and loan company that will guarantee a rate of 3.9% compounded monthly for the next 10 years. Robin says her bank is much better because they will give her 4% interest compounded semi-annually for the next ten years. In ten years, which account will end up with the greatest amount and how much difference is there?

10-170. The use of e provides a shortcut for calculation of **continuously compounded interest**. The formula for continuous compounding is $A = Pe^{rt}$, where A is the total amount at any time, P is the original principal, r is the rate of interest, and t is the time period.

    a.   Use this new formula to calculate the amount Tabitha had after investing her $10,000 for one year at 3% annual interest, compounded continuously. How does this compare with her hourly compounding result of $10,304.56?

    b.   Suppose a large investment group invested 10 billion dollars at 8% annual interest. Compare the amount they would have in one year if the interest were compounded continuously with the amount they would earn if the interest were compounded daily.

    c.   Which investors might benefit from continuous compounding, rather than daily compounding?

10-171. Use the Binomial Theorem to write the expansion of each of the following expressions.

    a. $\left(1+\frac{1}{n}\right)^3$ b. $\left(1+\frac{1}{n}\right)^5$

10-172. Atmospheric pressure P (in lbs. per square inch) under typical conditions can be approximately calculated by using the formula below, where h represents the number of feet above sea level.

$$P = 14.7e^{-0.00003h}$$

    a.   What is pressure at sea level?

    b.   Use the formula to calculate the atmospheric pressure in the mile-high city of Denver, Colorado.

    c.   The lowest point in Death Valley is 285 feet below sea level. What is the atmospheric pressure in Death Valley?

10-173. Omar was 8 years old when he received $25,000 dollars from his grandmother's will. His father invested it for him in a fund that earned 6% annual interest compounded quarterly. He was hoping to see the investment double by the time Omar was ready for college. Another fund offered the same interest rate but the interest would compound continuously. This second fund was a little riskier, however.

   a. Write an equation to represent each situation.

   b. Which method of compounding the interest will double his money faster?

   c. Is the difference in doubling time worth the extra risk?

10-174. After graphing $y = 12x^3 + 55x^2 - 27x - 10$ on a graphing calculator, you can easily see that one x-intercept is $(-5, 0)$. Use this information to find all of the x-intercepts.

10-175. Use the pattern for $(a + b)^3$ to expand $(2x - 3)^3$.

10-176. This problem is a checkpoint for rewriting expressions with and solving equations with logarithms. It will be referred to as Checkpoint 10.

In parts (a) through (b), rewrite each expression as a single logarithm. In parts (c) through (f), solve each equation.

   a. $\log_2(30x) - \log_2(6)$

   b. $2\log_3(x) + \log_3(5)$

   c. $\log_7(3x - 2) = 2$

   d. $\log(2x + 1) = -1$

   e. $\log_5(3y) + \log_5(9) = \log_5(405)$

   f. $\log(x) + \log(x + 21) = 2$

Check your answers by referring to the Checkpoint 10 materials located at the back of your book.

Ideally, at this point you are comfortable working with these types of problems and can solve them correctly. If you feel that you need more confidence when solving these types of problems, then review the Checkpoint 10 materials and try the practice problems provided. From this point on, you will be expected to do problems like these correctly and with confidence.

10-177.   The sum of the digits of a two-digit number is 11, and when the digits are reversed the difference between the new number and the original is 27.

   a.   If you use t to represent the tens digit, and u to represent the units digit, how can you represent one of the numbers?

   b.   How can you represent the number with its digits reversed, still using t and u?

   c.   Use the information from the problem and parts (a) and (b) to write two equations that can be used to solve this problem.

   d.   What are the two numbers?

Chapter 10 Closure What have I learned?

Reflection and Synthesis

The activities below offer you a chance to reflect about what you have learned during this chapter. As you work, look for concepts that you feel very comfortable with, ideas that you would like to learn more about, and topics you need more help with. Look for connections between ideas as well as connections with material you learned previously.

①   TEAM BRAINSTORM

What have you studied in this chapter? What ideas were important in what you learned? With your team, brainstorm a list. Be as detailed as you can. To help get you started, a list of Learning Log entries and Math Notes boxes are below.

What topics, ideas, and words that you learned *before* this chapter are connected to the new ideas in this chapter? Again, be as detailed as you can.

Next consider the Standards for Mathematical Practice that follow "③ PORTFOLIO". What Mathematical Practices did you use in this chapter? When did you use them? Give specific examples.

How long can you make your list? Challenge yourselves. Be prepared to share your team's ideas with the class.

Learning Log Entries
- Lesson 10.1.2 – Arithmetic Series
- Lesson 10.2.1 – Geometric Series
- Lesson 10.2.2 – Infinite Geometric Series
- Lesson 10.3.1 – Pascal's Triangle

Math Notes
- Lesson 10.1.1 – Permutations and Combinations
- Lesson 10.1.2 – Series
- Lesson 10.1.3 – Arithmetic Series
- Lesson 10.1.4 – Summation Notation
- Lesson 10.2.2 – Geometric Series
- Lesson 10.3.1 – Binomial Theorem
- Lesson 10.3.2 – Compound Interest

②   MAKING CONNECTIONS

Below is a list of the vocabulary used in this chapter. Make sure that you are familiar with all of these words and know what they mean. Refer to the glossary or index for any words that you do not yet understand.

argument	arithmetic	Binomial Theorem
e	geometric	index
infinite	natural logarithm	Pascal's Triangle
series	sequence	summation notation
sigma		

Make a concept map showing all of the connections you can find among the key words and ideas listed above. To show a connection between two words, draw a line between them and explain the connection. A word can be connected to any other word as long as you can justify the connection. For each key word or idea, provide an example or sketch that shows the idea.

While you are making your map, your team may think of related words or ideas that are not listed here. Be sure to include these ideas on your concept map.

③   PORTFOLIO: EVIDENCE OF MATHEMATICAL PROFICIENCY

This section gives you an opportunity to show growth in your understanding of key mathematical ideas over time as you complete this course.

In this portfolio entry you are going to showcase your current understanding of series. You are also going to showcase your ability to write a meaningful portfolio entry.

Make a list of the big ideas of this chapter. What have you studied in this chapter? What ideas were important in what you learned? Try to keep your list short: limit yourself to the no more than five of the biggest ideas.

a.   Write your own description of each big idea.

b.   For each big idea, provide one or two representative example problems. Solve each problem completely, using multiple representations, if applicable. Include a thorough explanation and justification.

Next, consider the Standards for Mathematical Practice that follow. What Mathematical Practices did you use in this chapter? When did you use them? Give specific examples.

BECOMING MATHEMATICALLY PROFICIENT
The Common Core State Standards for Mathematical Practice

This book focuses on helping you use some very specific Mathematical Practices. The Mathematical Practices describe ways in which mathematically proficient students engage with mathematics everyday.

Make sense of problems and persevere in solving them:

Making sense of problems and persevering in solving them means that you can solve problems that are full of different kinds of mathematics. These types of problems are not routine, simple, or typical. Instead, they combine lots of math ideas and everyday situations. You have to stick with challenging problems, try different strategies, use multiple representations, and use a different method to check your results.

Reason abstractly and quantitatively:

Throughout this course, everyday situations are used to introduce you to new math ideas. Seeing mathematical ideas within a context helps you make sense of the ideas. Once you learn about a math idea in a practical way, you can "**reason abstractly**" by thinking about the concept more generally, representing it with symbols, and manipulating the symbols. **Reasoning quantitatively** is using numbers and symbols to represent an everyday situation, taking into account the units involved, and considering the meaning of the quantities as you compute them.

Construct viable arguments and critique the reasoning of others:

To **construct a viable argument** is to present your solution steps in a logical sequence and to justify your steps with conclusions, relying on number sense, facts and definitions, and previously established results. You communicate clearly, consider the real-life context, and provide clarification when others ask. In this course, you regularly share information, opinions, and expertise with your study team. You **critique the reasoning of others** when you analyze the approach of others, build on each other's ideas, compare the effectiveness of two strategies, and decide what makes sense and under what conditions.

Model with mathematics:

When you **model with mathematics**, you take a complex situation and use mathematics to represent it, often by making assumptions and approximations to simplify the situation. Modeling allows you to analyze and describe the situation and to make predictions. For example, you model when you use multiple representations, including equations, tables, graphs, or diagrams to describe a situation. In situations involving the variability of data, you model when you describe the data with equations. Although a model may not be perfect, it can still be very useful for describing data and making predictions. When you interpret the results, you may need to go back and improve your model by revising your assumptions and approximations.

Core Connections Algebra 2

Use appropriate tools strategically:

To **use appropriate tools strategically** means that you analyze the task and decide which tools may help you model the situation or find a solution. Some of the tools available to you include diagrams, graph paper, calculators, computer software, databases, and websites. You understand the limitations of various tools. A result can be check or estimated by strategically choosing a different tool.

Attend to precision:

To **attend to precision** means that when solving problems, you need to pay close attention to the details. For example, you need to be aware of the units, or how many digits your answer requires, or how to choose a scale and label your graph. You may need to convert the units to be consistent. At times, you need to go back and check whether a numerical solution makes sense in the context of the problem.

You need to **attend to precision** when you communicate your ideas to others. Using the appropriate vocabulary and mathematical language can help make your ideas and reasoning more understandable to others.

Look for and make use of structure:

To **look for and make use of structure** is a guiding principle of this course. When you are involved in analyzing the structure and in the actual development of mathematical concepts, you gain a deeper, more conceptual understanding than when you are simply told what the structure is and how to do problems. You often use this practice to bring closure to an investigation.

There are many concepts that you learn by looking at the underlying structure of a mathematical idea and thinking about how it connects to other ideas you have already learned. For example, you understand the underlying structure of an equation such as $y = a(x - h)^2 + k$ which allows you to graph it without a table.

Look for and express regularity in repeated reasoning:

To **look for and express regularity in repeated reasoning** means that when you are investigating a new mathematical concept, you notice if calculations are repeated in a pattern. Then you look for a way to generalize the method for use in other situations, or you look for shortcuts. For example, the pattern of growth you notice in a geometric sequence results in being able to write a general exponential equation that highlights the growth and starting point.

WHAT HAVE I LEARNED?

Most of the problems in this section represent typical problems found in this chapter. They serve as a gauge for you. You can use them to determine which types of problems you can do well and which types of problems require further study and practice. Even if your teacher does not assign this section, it is a good idea to try these problems and find out for yourself what you know and what you still need to work on.

Solve each problem as completely as you can. The table at the end of the closure section has answers to these problems. It also tells you where you can find additional help and practice with problems like these.

CL 10-178.   Find the sum of each series.

    a. $11+12+13+...+40$ b. $90+84+78+...+24$

CL 10-179.   For the series $3+3.3+3.6+3.9+4.2+...+63$:

    a.   How many terms are there?   b.   What is the sum of the series?

CL 10-180.   From the ground, a rubber ball is thrown 20 feet into the air. If its rebound ratio is $\frac{7}{10}$, how far will it have traveled during the first five bounces?

CL 10-181.   Write each series using summation ($\sum$) notation.

    a. $3+6+9+12+...+30$ b. $-7+-4+-1+2+5+8+11$

CL 10-182.   Consider the series $\sum\limits_{n=0}^{\infty} 4\left(-\frac{2}{3}\right)^{n}$.

    a.   Is it arithmetic or geometric? Explain.

    b.   Does it have a finite sum? Explain.

    c.   If it has a sum, find it.

CL 10-183.   Nitrous oxide, or NO$_x$, is a pollutant created by diesel engines that occurs when nitrogen and oxygen from the atmosphere are combined by the heat of the burning fuel. The EPA and many states limit the amount of NO$_x$ a vehicle is permitted to produce. Assume that diesel cars and trucks on the road produce NO$_x$ according to a normal distribution with a mean of 0.12 g/mile and a standard deviation of 0.04 g/mile. Imagine your state is lowering its limits of NO$_x$ allowed over a 10-year time period.

    a.   If the 2015 limit for NO$_x$ is 0.100 g/mile, what proportion of diesel engines running today meet that standard?

    b.   If the 2020 limit for NO$_x$ is 0.065 g/mile, what proportion of diesel engines running today meet that standard?

    c.   Now think of things the other way. If the 2025 limit for NO$_x$ is 0.030 g/mile, what proportion of diesel engines running today *would not* meet that standard?

CL 10-184.   NBP Model 760 photocopiers print a mean of 76 pages per minute (ppm) with a standard deviation of 11 ppm. NBP Model S22 can scan 50 ppm with a standard deviation of 5 ppm. A software upgrade was tested on both models. After the upgrade, a prototype photocopier makes 90 copies per minute, while a prototype scanner makes 57 scans. Use percentiles to determine on which machine the upgrade had a bigger impact on performance.

CL 10-185.   Part one of the final exam for Algebra 2 contains 10 questions and you get to choose any eight to answer.

    a.   How many different ways could you choose the eight problems?

    b.   If everyone must answer the first two questions, how many ways could you choose the remaining problems?

CL 10-186.   Use the pattern for $(a+b)^4$ to expand $(2m+\frac{1}{m})^4$.

CL 10-187.   What term of $(a-b)^8$ contains a^5 ? What is the whole term?

CL 10-188.   Solve each of the following equations, accurate to the nearest 0.001.

    a. $1.8^x = 10$ b. $\log_2 x = 6$

CL 10-189. Find an equation of the parabola that passes through (2, 11), (–1, –4), and (0, –5).

CL 10-190. Sketch a graph of each of the following functions.

      a. $f(x) = \frac{2}{x-1} + 3$ b. $g(x) = -0.5(x+2)^3 - 3$

      c. $h(x) = |x+5| - 4$ d. $k(x) = 2\sqrt{x+1} + 3$

CL 10-191. Find the equation of the exponential function (with an asymptote of $y = 0$) that passes through the points (–3, 375) and (2, 0.12).

CL 10-192. Check your answers using the table at the end of this section. Which problems do you feel confident about? Which problems were hard? Have you worked on problems like these in math classes you have taken before? Use the table to make a list of topics you need help on and a list of topics you need to practice more.

Answers and Support for Closure Activity #4
What Have I Learned?

Note: MN = Math Note, LL = Learning Log

Problem	Solutions		Need Help?	More Practice
CL 10-178.	a. 765	b. 684	Section 10.1 MN: 10.1.2 and 10.1.3 LL: 10.1.2	Problems 10-17, 10-34, 10-35, 10-49, 10-63, and 10-89
CL 10-179.	a. 201	b. 6633	Lesson 10.1.1 MN: 10.1.2 and 10.1.3 LL: 10.1.2	Problems 10-17, 10-34, 10-35, 10-49, 10-62, and 10-89
CL 10-180.	77.6468 feet (not including the initial toss)		Section 10.2 MN: 10.2.2 LL: 10.2.1	Problems 10-87, 10-96, 10-105, 10-126, 10-147, and 10-156

Problem	Solutions	Need Help?	More Practice
CL 10-181.	a. $\displaystyle\sum_{n=1}^{10}(3n)$ b. $\displaystyle\sum_{n=1}^{7}(3n-10)$	Lesson 10.1.4 MN: 10.1.4	Problems 10-62 and 10-87 part (c)
CL 10-182.	a. Geometric, $r=-\frac{2}{3}$ b. Yes, $|r|<1$ c. $\frac{12}{5}$	Section 10.1 and 10.2 MN: 10.1.4 and 10.2.2 LL: 10.1.2, 10.2.1, and 10.2.2	Problems 10-89, 10-90, 10-117, 10-126, and 10-148
CL 10-183.	a. normalcdf($-10^{\wedge}99$, 0.1, 0.12, 0.04) = 0.309 About thirty one percent would meet the standard. b. normalcdf($-10^{\wedge}99$, 0.065, 0.12, 0.04) = 0.0846 Only about eight percent would meet the standard. c. normalcdf(0.03, $10^{\wedge}99$, 0.12, 0.04) = 0.988 About 99% would not meet the standard.	Lesson 9.3.2 MN: 9.3.2 LL: 9.3.2	Problems 9-88, 9-105, 10-12, 10-41, 10-67, and 10-152
CL 10-184.	Photocopier: normalcdf $(-10^{\wedge}99$, 90, 76, 11) = 89.8 percentile Scanner: normalcdf($-10^{\wedge}99$, 57, 50, 5) = 91.9 percentile The scanner had better performance in relation to its population.	Lesson 9.3.2 MN: 9.3.2 LL: 9.3.2	Problems 9-88, 9-105, 10-12, 10-41, 10-67, and 10-152
CL 10-185.	a. $_{10}C_8 = 45$ b. $_8C_6 = 28$	MN: 10.1.1	Problems 10-20, 10-21, 10-36, 10-37, 10-52, 10-66, 10-91, 10-118, and 10-127

Problem	Solutions	Need Help?	More Practice
CL 10-186.	$16m^4 + 32m^2 + 24 + \frac{8}{m^2} + \frac{1}{m^4}$	Lesson 10.3.1 MN: 10.3.1 LL: 10.3.1	Problems 10-145, 10-146, 10-157, and 10-175
CL 10-187.	$-56a^5b^3$	Lesson 10.3.1 MN: 10.3.1 LL: 10.3.1	Problems 10-146 and 10-155
CL 10-188.	a. $x \approx 3.917$ b. $x = 64$	Lessons 6.2.1 and 6.2.2 Checkpoint 10	Problems CL 6-151, 7-94, 7-149, 10-23, 10-56, 10-95, 10-103, and 10-176
CL 10-189.	$y = 3x^2 + 2x - 5$	Lesson 6.1.5 LL: 6.1.5	Problems CL 6-150, 7-7, 10-154, and 10-163
CL 10-190.	a. b. c. d.	Lesson 2.2.1 MN: 2.2.3 Parent Graph Toolkit	Problems CL 2-171, and 7-58, 8-107, and 10-11
CL 10-191.	$y = 3 \cdot (\frac{1}{5})^x$	Lesson B.2.1, B.2.2, and 6.2.3	Problems CL B-110 and CL 7-175

Chapter 11 Simulating Sampling Variability

In this chapter, you will use computer simulations to model complex probabilities—probabilities that are often too difficult to compute mathematically. Then you will simulate sample-to-sample variability. Your knowledge of sample-to-sample variability will help you place a margin of error on your predictions about certain characteristics of populations and will help you make statistical decisions.

Guiding Question

Mathematically proficient students model with mathematics.

As you work through this chapter, ask yourself:

How can I model this situation with a simulation in order to understand it better and to solve the problem?

Chapter Outline

Section 11.1 You will perform simulations to determine complex probabilities. Then you will use simulations to determine sample-to-sample variability. You will use the variability to put a margin of error on characteristics you predict about a population.

Section 11.2 You will use what you know about sample-to-sample variability and margin of error to conduct a statistical hypothesis test. You will observe the effect of sample size on sample-to-sample variability. Then you will use a hypothesis test to determine whether two results in an experiment are truly different. Finally, you will learn how statistics are used in quality control and process control in manufacturing.

Section 11.3 You will evaluate decisions and strategies based on area or models of probability. You will use probability to solve problems whose solutions are counterintuitive.

11.1.1 How can I estimate complex probabilities?

Simulations of Probability

If you toss a coin ten times, what is the probability of having a run of three or more "heads" in a row?

If an airline "overbooks" a certain flight, what is the chance more passengers show up than the airplane has seats for?

When 67 people get cancer in the 250 homes in a small town, could that be chance alone, or is polluted well water a more likely explanation of the cluster of cancer cases?

When the mathematics becomes too complex to figure out the theoretical probability of certain events, statisticians often use **simulations** instead. Simulations can also be used to check statistical computations, or they can be used in place of a study that is too expensive, time-consuming, or unethical. A simulation is a model—often computer-based—that uses the probabilities of a real-life situation.

All simulations require random numbers. Random numbers have no pattern; they cannot be predicted in any way. Knowing one random number in no way allows you to predict the next random number.

Complex simulations, such as those that model the weather, traffic patterns, cancer radiation therapy, or stock market swings, require tens of billions of random numbers and a large computer that runs for hours or even days. However, many simpler simulations can be done with graphing calculators.

As you work with your team today, consider the following questions:

How can we set up a simulation for this situation?

How many trials are sufficient?

How can we compute the theoretical probability?

11-1.   A GIRL OR ALL BOYS?

Mr. and Mrs. Sittman want to have children and would love to have a girl, but they don't want to have more than four children. They want to figure out the chances of having a girl if they have children until they have a girl, or until they have four children, whichever comes first. Since a coin has a 50% chance of landing on "heads," a coin can be used to model the real-life probability that a girl is born.

a.   Talk with your team about how you can use flipping a coin to determine the probability of a couple having a daughter if they try until the first girl or the fourth child is born, whichever comes first.

b.   Once your class has planned the simulation and found a method for tallying results, run the simulation and tally the results until your team has modeled 25 possible families (25 trials).

c.   Combine your results with those of the rest of the class. According to your class's simulation, what is the couple's probability of having a girl in this situation?

11-2.   In the simulation for problem 11-1, do you think that more trials would lead to a better estimate of the probability? Tossing coins can become tedious, but we can use a calculator or computer to complete many more trials.

a.   Your teacher will show you how to use your calculator to randomly generate a family of four children. You can use "0" to represent a boy, and "1" to represent a girl. Since they will stop having children after their first girl, you can ignore all the digits in the family after the first girl. For example, "0101" would represent a family with one boy and one girl, and you would mark "Girl in Family" on the tally sheet.

b.   Be prepared to share your team results with the rest of the class. Use the class results to estimate the probability of a couple having a girl if they try until they have a girl, or until they have four children, whichever comes first. Do you think this result is a better estimate of the theoretical probability than the result in problem 11-1? Why or why not?

11-3.   For the situation you simulated in problems 11-1 and 11-2, the theoretical probability is not too complicated to work out. Work with your team to calculate the theoretical probability for the problem posed by Mr. and Mrs. Sittman in problem 11-1.

Core Connections Algebra 2

11-4.   According to a mathematical principle known as the **Law of Large Numbers**, the more times you run your simulation, the closer your result will come to the theoretical value. Was this what happened when you compared results from problem 11-1 with problem 11-2? Were you close to the expected theoretical value from problem 11-3?

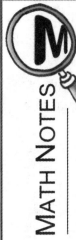

METHODS AND MEANINGS

Area Models for Probability

One way to represent the probabilities that two independent events occur is with an area model. In this type of model, the situation is represented by a square with area of 1. The areas of the parts are the probabilities of the different events that occur.

For example, Mrs. Pimentel goes to a lot of charity events where she needs to dress up. The probabilities she will wear either her red dress or her black dress, with a certain piece of jewelry, are represented by the table at right.

	dress	
	red 0.40	black 0.60
pearls 0.70	0.28	0.42
diamonds 0.20	0.08	0.12
pendant 0.10	0.04	0.06

(jewelry)

Notice that the length and width of the area model table are both 1 (0.40 + 0.60 = 1 and 0.70 + 0.20 + 0.10 = 1). The area of the model is 1. The area of any one of the parts is its length × width. For example, the area of the black-dress-with-diamonds rectangle is $0.60 \cdot 0.20 = 0.12$. The probability that Mrs. Pimentel will wear the black dress and the diamonds is 12%.

A conditional probability means that we know that some event has occurred with certainty, and therefore we look only at that portion of the table. For example, what is the conditional probability Mrs. Pimentel will wear diamonds given that she is wearing the red dress? Since we know with certainty that she is wearing the red dress, we will consider only the red-dress column and ignore the black dress column completely. The conditional probability is calculated using P(diamonds with red dress)/P(red dress). The conditional probability she wears diamonds given that she wears a red dress is $\frac{0.08}{0.28+0.08+0.04} = 0.20$.

11-5.   Consider each of the survey questions below. Decide whether any bias may be influencing the survey results.

   a.   Jolly Juice has twice the Vitamin E of other brands. Which brand of juice is the healthiest?

   b.   Do you think that people who hurt defenseless animals should be punished?

   c.   Do you agree that Hal Poppington is the best man to be elected Mayor?

   d.   What is your favorite kind of juice?

11-6.   In problem 9-8 Katelyn recorded the number of cups of coffee sold at her coffee shop each hour during a 48-hour time period.

Katelyn then sorted the data and made the following histogram:

Cups of Coffee Sold

Cups of Coffee Sold		
1	22	37
5	22	38
7	23	38
12	24	40
12	25	41
12	26	41
12	26	42
12	29	47
14	29	47
16	30	49
17	30	51
19	31	52
20	32	55
21	33	55
21	35	59
22	36	76
checksum 1444		

   a.   Katelyn decides to model her sales with a normal distribution, but Duncan thinks that this is not a good idea. What advice would you give Katelyn about using a normal model?

   b.   Katelyn needs to sell more than 15 cups per hour to make a profit. What percentile is 15 cups per hour? Explain the percentile to Katelyn in terms of profits.

   c.   Duncan thinks Katelyn should expand her business. He estimates that if they hire another server and add more tables and equipment, they will need to sell 48 cups per hour to make a profit. What percentile does 48 cups sold represent? Use the percentile to explain to Duncan whether or not expansion is a good idea.

Core Connections Algebra 2

11-7.   Coach Kenadt has 12 players on his basketball team and needs to select one player to be the team representative to the athletic student council. He wants the selection to be fair, meaning each player has an equal chance of being selected. Rummaging through his gym bag, he finds a single six-sided die and a nickel. How could he use the nickel and die to select the team representative fairly?

11-8.   Eeeeew! Hannah's volleyball teammates left their egg salad sandwiches sitting in their lockers over the weekend. When they got back on Monday, the sandwiches were moldy. *"Perfect!"* said Hannah. *"I can use these sandwiches for my biology project. I'll study how quickly mold grows."*

Using a transparent grid, Hannah estimated that about 12% of the surface of one sandwich had mold on it. She threw the sandwich out. For the rest of the week, Hannah came back when she had time. Each time she measured somebody else's sandwich and threw it out. She collected the following data:

Day 1 (Monday)	Day 2 (Tuesday)	Day 2 (Tuesday)	Day 4 (Thursday)	Day 4 (Thursday)	Day 4 (Thursday)	Day 5 (Friday)
12%	15%	13%	26%	27%	24%	38%

a.   Create a scatterplot and sketch it. Is a linear model reasonable?

b.   Based on the story, what kind of equation do you think will best fit the situation?

c.   Fit an exponential model to the data and write the equation. What percentage of a sandwich did Hannah predict was covered on Wednesday? Consider the precision of Hannah's measurements when deciding how many decimal places to use in your answer.

11-9.   Consider the function $f(x) = e^x$.

a.   What is its inverse function, $f^{-1}(x)$?

b.   Investigate $f(x)$ and $f^{-1}(x)$.

c.   For what integer value of n is the graph of $f^{-1}(x)$ between the graphs of $y = \log_n x$ and $y = \log_{n+1} x$?

d.   For what values of x is the graph of $f^{-1}(x)$ above each of the graphs in your answer to part (c)? For what x-values is it below?

11-10. Natural logs and exponential functions with base e are often used in formulas. But many problems can be solved equally well using either a base-10 logarithm or a base-e logarithm. Solve each of the following problems, first using the $\boxed{\text{LOG}}$ key (base 10) and then using the $\boxed{\text{LN}}$ key (base e) on your calculator.

    a. $10,000(1.08)^x = 20,000$

    b. $30,000(0.8)^x = 15,000$

    c.   Interpret the answer for part (a) if the equation represents an amount of money invested at 8% annual interest.

    d.   Interpret the answer for part (b) if the equation represents the price paid for a car that depreciates at 20% per year.

11-11. Find the sum of the integers $-10 + -9 + -8 + ... + 40$.

11-12. Compute each complex product.

    a. $(1+i)^2$ b. $(1+i)^3$

11-13. 75% of the homes in a small town in England have large backyards, and 80% have garages. Assume that having a garage is independent of whether you have a large backyard.

    a.   What is the probability a home has neither a garage nor a large backyard? Decide what the two variables in this situation are and make an area model to help answer the question. (See the Math Notes box in this lesson.)

    b.   Given that a house has a garage, what is the conditional probability it has a large backyard?

                                                       Core Connections Algebra 2

11.1.2 How many in a streak?

••

More Simulations of Probability

The serious study of probability started
when two mathematicians, Blaise Pascal and
Pierre de Fermat, became interested in
determining probabilities for casino games,
particularly dice games. Roulette is one of
the more straightforward casino games to
analyze, and it provides a good opportunity
for examining streaks.

In American roulette the bettor places a bet, then
the croupier (game manager) spins the wheel and
drops the ball. Everyone waits for the ball to land in one of 38 slots. The 38 slots on the
wheel are numbered $00, 0, 1, 2, 3, \ldots, 36$. Eighteen of the slots are colored red and
eighteen are black; 0 and 00 are green.

Before the ball is dropped, players make bets by placing their chips on the roulette layout
(the region that has the numbers and their colors printed on it). One of the most popular
bets is that the ball will drop into a red or a black slot on the wheel.

11-14.   Players who watch play, and then make a bet are called "lurkers." A commonly
held belief among "lurkers" is that once they see the ball land on red three times
in a row, they should join the game and bet a lot on the black (or vice versa).
What do you think? Discuss this with your team. Be prepared to share your
ideas with the rest of the class.

11-15.   The new owner of the One-Eyed Jack Casino wanted to test the two roulette
wheels that were included in the purchase. There were rumors that some of the
games were rigged under the old ownership. He decided to watch each of the
wheels for 200 spins and record whether red or black came up. He chose to
ignore the green slots; if green came up, he just spun again.

Problem continues on next page →

11-15.   *Problem continued from previous page.*

Roulette Wheel I: RBRRRRBBRBRBRBRRRRBBRBRBBBBBBBBBBRBRBRBBBR
BBBRRBBRBRBBBBBRBBBRBBBRRBRBRBRRRRRBBRBRB
RBRRRBRRRRBBRRRRBRRRRBRRRRBBBRBRBBRRRBRR
RBRRBBRBBBRBBBBBRBBBRRBBBRBBRBBRRRRRRBRRRB
RRRBRRBRRRBRRBBBBBRBBBBRRBRRRRRRBBRBRRRBB

Roulette Wheel II: RBRBRRRBRRRRBBRBRRRBRRBBBRBBRBRBRBRRRRBB
RRBBRRBBBRBBBBRRBBBBRRRBBBRBBBBRRRBRBRBBBB
RBRRBBBRBBBRRRRBBRBBBBRBBBBBRRBRBBBRBBBRRRB
RBBBRBBRRRBBBRRRRBBBBRBRBBBBBRBRRBBRRRRBRB
RBRRBRBBRRBRRRBRRRBBBBBRBBBBRRBBRBBBRBBR

Discussion Points

How many streaks are likely in 200 spins?

How long will streaks be?

How can we set up a computer simulation for a roulette wheel?

What do the results of the simulation tell us about the casino owner's results?

Your Task: Run a simulation of 200 spins of a roulette wheel. Use the results of your simulation to justify whether either wheel is rigged. If a wheel were rigged, would that be advantageous to the One-Eyed Jack Casino? Write up a brief report explaining your results and what they imply about his roulette wheels.

Further Guidance

11-16.   You will investigate how many streaks of red and black numbers occur randomly when the game is played 200 times.

a.   Use the results to make a conjecture: which roulette wheel, if either, is rigged in some way? Explain why you think so.

b.   Work with a partner to set up and run a simulation of 200 spins of a roulette wheel. Record the color of each spin—red or black—in order.

c.   How many streaks of five or more reds or five or more blacks did you get? Compare with your team and other classmates.

d.   Which wheel might have been rigged?

e.   Would it be to the advantage of the owner of the One-Eyed Jack Casino to leave it that way?

f.   Write up your results in a report to the casino owner.

Further Guidance
section ends here.

11-17.   Katelyn is going to be babysitting her nephew a lot this summer. She has the great idea that one way to entertain him is to walk to McBurger's for a Kids' Meal for lunch. The Kids' Meal comes packed randomly with one of six equally-likely action figures. Katelyn is worried that her nephew will be disappointed unless he gets all six figures. She wants to know how many meals she can expect to buy before he will get all six figures.

a.   Model the action figures with the digits 1 through 6. Simulate a large number of meals (such as 200) and put the results into a list. How many meals did you have to buy in order to get all six action figures?

b.   Run your simulation ten more times, each time generating a new list of about 200 meals. Keep track of how many Kid's Meals it takes to get all six action figures. Calculate your **wait time,** or the average number of meals it took to get all six figures.

c.   Combine your results with those of your team. On average, how many Kid's Meals do you think you need to buy in order to get all six action figures?

d.   Estimate a range for the number of meals you might need to buy. What is the most you need to buy? The least? Do you think it possible that you may have to buy 50 meals to get all six action figures? 100 meals?

11-18.   Myriah hates doing the dishes, but her parents insist that she must help out and take a turn sometimes. Since Myriah wants to leave whether or not she will have to do the dishes to chance, her mom proposes that they roll two dice. If the sum of the dice is 6 or less, Myriah will do the dishes. If the sum is 7 or more, one of her parents will do the dishes.

How many days each week can Myriah expect to have to do the dishes? Create a simulation of rolling the two dice (generate two random integers between 1 and 6) and record the sum. Run the simulation 30 times to determine how often Myriah can expect to do the dishes.

11-19.   Calculate the theoretical probability that Myriah will have to wash the dishes. Then determine the number of days per week that she can expect to wash the dishes.

11-20. The term "curving" is often misused as it applies to test scores. Many believe it refers to adding points or otherwise adjusting test scores such that the highest paper is 100% or the average score is raised to some passing level. To curve is actually to model test scores with the normal distribution (normal "curve") and then use percentiles to assign letter grades.

a. A "curve" sometimes used is shown below:

Grade	D	C	B	A
Number of Standard Deviations Above or Below Mean	−2	−1	+1	+2
Minimum Percentile	2nd	16th	84th	98th

Using this curve, what percentage of students would earn each letter grade?

b. The following statistics are from problem 9-98, the test scores on Mrs. Abraha's Chapter 3 test in Geometry. The mean was 76.5, and the standard deviation was 17.4.

If Mrs. Abraha used the curve in part (a), the minimum score for a B would be one standard deviation above the mean, or 93.9. What would be the minimum test scores for the other letter grades on Mrs. Abraha's test?

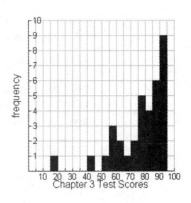

c. Shown at right is a histogram of the scores from Mrs. Abraha's Chapter 3 test in Geometry. Is using the curve from part (a) reasonable to assign letter grades? What advice would you give students who want the test "curved"?

11-21. Using the given population and assuming your math class is a sample from that population, come up with a research question that could be asked to determine parameters from the given population. Write each survey question and what you are hoping to show from each question. Examples are given for each population.

a. Population: Students at my school

Example:

I would ask my math class this survey question: *If the school library were open at 7:15 a.m., would you use it at least once per week?*

The research question I am trying to answer is: *How many students at our school would take advantage of extended library hours?*

Problem continues on next page →

Core Connections Algebra 2

11-21.   *Problem continued from previous page.*

    b.   Population: All high school math students in the U.S.

Example:

I would ask my math class this survey question:

The main reason I'm taking this class is:
1) It is a graduation requirement.   *2) It is a college prerequisite.*
3) My parents are making me.   *4) I'm interested in math.*
5) For some other reason.

The research question I am trying to answer is: *Why do high school students take math?*

    c.   Population: U.S. teenagers

Example:

I would ask my math class this survey question: *How far is it from where you live to school or work?*

The research question I am trying to answer is: *What is the average commute distance to school or work for teenagers?*

11-22.   Solve each system of equations below.

    a. $x - 2y = 7$
          $2x + y = 3$

    b. $\frac{x+4y}{3} - \frac{6y-x}{4} = -3$
          $\frac{x}{10} + 5y = 2$

11-23.   Find the infinite sum (if possible).

    a. $6 + 3 + \frac{3}{2} + \ldots$

    b. $\sum\limits_{k=1}^{\infty} (\frac{1}{3})^k$

11-24.   Eddie told Allison, *"I'll bet if I flip three coins, I can get exactly two heads."*
Allison replied, *"I'll bet I can get exactly two heads if I flip four coins!"*
Eddie scoffed, *"Well, so what? That's easier."*
Allison argued, *"No, it's not. It's harder."*

Who is correct? Show all of your work and be prepared to defend your conclusion.

11-25.   Given $\ln 2 \approx 0.69315$ and $\ln 3 \approx 1.0986$, why is $\ln 2 < 1$ and $\ln 3 > 1$? For what value of x does $\ln x = 1$?

11-26.   Use the values for $\ln 2$ and $\ln 3$ given in problem 11-25 to evaluate each of the following expressions. Do not use a calculator.

a. $\ln 6$ b. $\ln 12$ c. $\ln 16$ d. $\ln \frac{1}{3}$

11.1.3 How much do samples vary?

Simulating Sampling Variability

In Chapter 9 you developed the idea that if a sample is selected randomly, taking care to avoid bias, we can be confident that the sample represents the whole population. Making inferences from samples about whole populations is at the heart of statistics.

Your friend Ramien says that you have to have the latest, hottest πPhone—everybody else already has it! What proportion of young people have the πPhone? We cannot possibly ask everybody in the United States who is between the ages of 12 and 20, but we can take a random sample of this population and calculate the proportion that have the phone.

If in a random sample of 1000 members of our population, 250 have the πPhone, it still does not mean that exactly $\frac{1}{4}$ of all people between the ages of 12 and 20 in the U.S. have the πPhone. The proportion of young people with the phone will naturally vary from sample to sample—some samples of young people will have more phones, some will have less.

If we knew how much the proportion naturally varied from sample-to-sample, we could establish a range of estimates for the proportion of phones in the teen population. This **margin of error** is frequently reported in statistical studies. You might read in a newspaper that the percentage of teens with πPhones is 23% with a margin of error of 3%. This means that statisticians can be reasonably certain, based on their small sample, that between 20% and 26% of all teens own the πPhone.

As you work with your team on today's investigation, keep the following discussion questions in mind:

Why do we give a margin of error?

How certain are statisticians when they give a margin of error?

How do statisticians decide on a margin of error?

11-27.   WERE THERE ENOUGH BLUE ONES?

Abigail is eagerly looking forward to Friday,
when each student in her fifth grade class has
been promised a bag of candy-coated chocolates
as a reward for figuring out the percentages of the
different colors. Abigail loves the blue ones.

What proportion of candy-coated chocolates are blue? We
cannot just open one bag and count, because the number of blue
candies will vary naturally from bag to bag.

Since we cannot count every candy in the world, we can take a
sample. We are assuming a bag of candy-coated chocolates makes a reasonable
sample that represents the whole population. We will investigate how much the
proportion of blue candies naturally varies from bag to bag.

a.   Get a sample from your teacher. Calculate the proportion of blue candies
      in your sample. Write your answer as a decimal and share it with the
      class.

b.   Use your calculator to make a histogram of all the proportions of blue
      candies your classmates found in each of their samples. A histogram that
      shows the results of taking many samples is called a **sampling
      distribution**. Sketch the histogram.

c.   What is the mean proportion for the whole class? This gives an estimate
      of the proportion of blue candies in the population.

d.   We are interested in typical results, not the extreme ones. We will call the
      middle 90% typical. Between what upper and lower bounds are the
      middle 90% of the blue proportions? That is, 90% of the time, we expect
      the proportion of blue candies in the sample to be between ____ and ____.

e.   Tell Abigail your prediction of the proportion of blue candies in the whole
      population and give the **margin of error**. The margin of error is half the
      spread between the upper and lower bounds.

11-28.   HOW MANY GAMES IN A WORLD SERIES?

In baseball's World Series, the first team to win four games wins the championship. The series might last four, five, six, or seven games. A fan who buys tickets would like to know how many games, on average, he can expect a championship series to last. Assume the two teams are equally matched, and set aside such potentially confounding factors as the advantage of playing at home. We want to know the expected value for the number of games that will be played in the World Series.

a.   Simulate a World Series on your calculator or computer. Let a "1" represent Team 1 winning a game, and a "2" represent Team 2 winning. You will simulate seven "games," but as soon as one team wins four games the World Series is over and you have to ignore any results that follow that. See below for an example.

Record how many games it took to win the series. In the example at right, it took 5 games.

first two games won by Team 1
third game won by Team 2
Team 1 wins Series

randInt(1,2,7)
{1 1 2 1 1 1 2}

ignore

Repeat the simulation at least 25 times.
Each time, record the number of games it took to win the World Series. You do not care *which team* won, you only care *how long* the series took.

b.   Based on your simulation, what is the average number of games a World Series lasts?

11-29.   Sports announcers frequently get excited when basketball players make several free throw shots in a row. They say things like "He's on a hot streak tonight!" or "He's really in the zone—what an amazing performance!" Are these "hot" streaks really special, or are they just a natural run to be expected by probability? Assume a basketball player has a 50% free throw average, and a typical game has 20 free throw attempts. Use your calculator to set up a simulation for 20 free throws.

a.   Run the simulation 25 times, and each time record the length of the longest streak.

b.   How long would a streak have to be before you considered it unusual?

11-30. A music company wants to know the music preference of people in Cleveland. Their surveyor asks people who are walking out of a business office building, "What is your favorite type of music?" What kind of problems may arise that will not produce accurate results? (List as many problems as you can.)

11-31. Solve the following systems of equations and describe the shapes of the intersections.

a. $z^2 = x^2 + y^2$
    $z = x + 2$

b. $z^2 = x^2 + y^2$
    $z = 7$

11-32. For the sequence $0.52, 0.55, 0.58, ..., 2.02$:

a. How many terms are there?

b. What is the sum of the associated series?

11-33. What do you notice about the two problems below when you simplify them?

a. $\frac{x^{1/2}}{x^{-3/2}}$

b. $\sqrt{x} \div (\frac{1}{\sqrt{x}})^3$

11-34. Given the points A (3, 2) and B (–21, 0), determine each of the following.

a. The slope of the line $\overrightarrow{AB}$.

b. The length of $\overline{AB}$.

c. The midpoint of $\overline{AB}$.

d. An equation of $\overrightarrow{AB}$.

11-35.   Solve each ratio problem below for x.

   a.   Forty-two percent of x is 112.

   b.   Forty-two is x percent of 112.

   c.   Twenty-seven is x percent of 100.

   d.   Twenty-seven percent of 500 is x.

11-36.   In the casino game of roulette, some players think that when the ball lands on red several times in a row that it will be more likely to land on black on the next spin. You can calculate probabilities to demonstrate that this is not the case. In other words, the outcome of one spin of a roulette wheel does not have any effect on the outcome of the next one.

   a.   Make an area model for two spins of the wheel. Remember that there are 18 red numbers, 18 black numbers, and two greens.

   b.   What is the probability that the ball will land on red twice in a row?

   c.   Based on your diagram, what is the probability that the ball will land on red on the second spin?

   d.   Calculate the conditional probability that the first spin was red given that the second spin is red.

   e.   How do your answers to parts (c) and (d) compare to the simple probability of the ball landing on red for any single spin? If they are all the same, you have demonstrated that the probability of the ball landing on red is independent of where it landed before.

11.2.1 Can I make a decision based on my sample?

Statistical Test Using Sampling Variability

In Lesson 11.1.3 you used a sample to determine what the population value is within a margin of error, and simulation to predict the sample-to-sample variability. In future courses, you will use mathematical theory (based on the normal distribution) to predict the population and margin of error from a sample.

Today, you will take what you know about sample-to-sample variability and margin of error and conduct a **hypothesis test**. A claim will be made about the population, and we will use a sample to test whether there is convincing evidence for the claim.

Then you will consider how a difference in sample size can affect how much the means of the samples may vary.

As you work, think about the following questions:

How large should the sample be?

How could the size of the sample affect our conclusions?

Do we have convincing evidence?

11-37. The principal of Algieres High School cancelled the Winter Formal dance because he believed that students preferred an all-school trip to an amusement park during spring break. However, he told the student council that if they could convince him that more than 50% of the school preferred the Winter Formal, he would reinstate it.

The student council decided that they should select a random sample of students to respond to a survey, but they disagreed about how large the sample should be. Some thought they should ask at least 100 students, but others thought that 25 would be enough. For convenience, they decided to randomly survey 25 students. It turned out that 60% preferred to keep the dance.

Unfortunately, the principal was not convinced. He said that because of natural sample-to-sample variability, the true proportion of dance supporters might not be more than 50%.

Problem continues on next page →

11-37.   *Problem continued from previous page.*

a.   To investigate the sample-to-sample variability of a survey that concludes 60% of students support the dance, work with a partner to set up a calculator or computer simulation. You could generate a sample of 25 random numbers between 1 and 100. Numbers from 1 to 60 can represent a student who supports the dance, while the numbers from 61 to 100 represent students who do not support the dance.

Because of natural sample-to-sample variability, the proportion of students who support the dance in your random sample is probably not exactly 0.60. What proportion of students in your sample supported the dance?

b.   Each team member should repeat the simulation with 5 more trials and record the proportion of dance supporters each time.

c.   If you were to combine your proportions with those of your classmates, what do you suppose the mean of all the samples would be close to? Why?

d.   For the whole class, what are the lower and upper 5% bounds of your sample-to-sample variability?

e.   Predict the proportion of all the students at Algieres High that support the dance and give the margin of error.

11-38.   In the previous problem, a claim was made about the student population: more than 50% support the dance. To test that claim (to find evidence to support the claim), a sample was taken from the student population, and the sample-to-sample variability was considered. This procedure is called a **hypothesis test**.

Based on your results for problem 11-37, does the principal have convincing evidence that more than 50% of all the students support the dance?

11-39.   When the student council at Algieres High presented their results, the principal was not convinced that at least 50% supported the dance. However, the council is still determined to persuade him otherwise, so they have called an emergency meeting. They have agreed that they should survey a larger sample of 100 students.

a. Why would the student council want to survey more students?

b. Do you think the margin of error for a sample of 100 students will be larger or smaller than for the samples of 25? Discuss this with your team.

c. With a partner, set up and run another simulation for 100 students. Assume that the student council finds the same 60% support for the dance in this larger sample. Record the results for 5 trials.

d. Share your results from part (c) with the rest of the class and use the data to compute the lower and upper 5% bounds for the class data. Report the margin of error.

e. Do you think this new evidence will convince the principal? Explain how you will make the case for or against the student council.

11-40.   LEARNING LOG

Create a Learning Log entry titled "Sample-to-Sample Variability" and label it with today's date. Discuss the pros and cons of larger or smaller samples. Explain why the margin of error might lead the principal in problem 11-37 to reject the first study even though he was convinced it was not biased and it reported that more than 50% of the students said they supported the dance.

MATH NOTES

METHODS AND MEANINGS

Sample-to-Sample Variability

We take samples to learn about a population when it is too time-consuming, expensive, or impractical to study the whole. Even if we are very careful to avoid bias so that our sample represents the whole population, statistics (measurements) vary naturally from sample to sample. To make an inference about the population, we need to quantify this **sample-to-sample variability**. With this knowledge, we can state a margin of error for our prediction of the true parameters of the whole population.

In Lesson 11.1.3, Abigail wanted an estimate of the proportion of blue candy-coated chocolates in the population of all candies. One sample (one bag) was not very much information due to natural sample-to-sample variability. Since taking many samples is often not practical, computer simulations, like the one conducted in this lesson, are one way to estimate the sample-to-sample variability. In future courses, you will learn theoretical ways to predict sample-to-sample variability based on the normal distribution.

11-41. It's bad enough when Myriah has to do the dishes. But Myriah really hates doing the dishes several days in a row! Myriah and her mom have agreed to roll two dice. When the sum of the dice is 6 or less, Myriah has to do the dishes. If the sum is 7 or more, one of her parents does the dishes. Myriah wants to know how many times in the next two months she will end up doing the dishes 3 or more days in a row.

a. Run a simulation of rolling the two dice and record the sum of each roll to simulate the 60 days (2 months).

b. How often can Myriah expect to have to do the dishes 3 or more days in a row during two months?

11-42. The Bright Idea Lighting Company wants to determine what proportion of LED flashlights that come off of its assembly line are defective. It takes many samples of 100 flashlights over the week and determines the proportion that are defective in each sample. The results of their tests as shown below:

Proportion of defective flashlights in 100 samples.				
0.09	0.05	0.05	0.05	0.09
0.07	0.06	0.10	0.07	0.09
0.08	0.09	0.05	0.05	0.08
0.07	0.07	0.08	0.08	0.09
0.10	0.08	0.11	0.08	0.09
0.09	0.13	0.08	0.09	0.09
0.07	0.06	0.06	0.08	0.08
0.06	0.10	0.11	0.09	0.09
0.05	0.07	0.05	0.09	0.10
0.04	0.07	0.09	0.08	0.06
0.08	0.09	0.06	0.06	0.07
0.08	0.08	0.08	0.09	0.09
0.10	0.07	0.09	0.08	0.12
0.12	0.09	0.06	0.05	0.02
0.11	0.05	0.05	0.05	0.06
0.08	0.10	0.08	0.10	0.06
0.06	0.07	0.08	0.11	0.09
0.09	0.08	0.07	0.07	0.05
0.10	0.07	0.11	0.06	0.06
0.10	0.08	0.10	0.10	0.07

checksum 7.83

a. What is the mean proportion of defective flashlights (as a percent)?

b. What are the upper and lower 5% bounds of the sample-to-sample variability?

c. Predict the proportion of defective flashlights (in percent) in the whole population and give the margin of error.

11-43. Avra, Evan, and Tam were working on a survey. They each polled 25 people over the weekend to determine if the subject of a large new mural downtown should be wildlife, sports, or black history. Avra forgot about her homework until the last minute, so she quickly surveyed her family and any relatives she could reach on the phone. Evan talked to some of the people in the stands at his baseball game Saturday, and Tam questioned people leaving a local church. Each got very different results. Explain why.

11-44.   For the sequence: $7, -2, -11, -20, \ldots$

        a.   Find $t(40)$, the 40th term.

        b.   Find $S(40)$, the sum of the first 40 terms.

11-45.   If $p = \ln 2$ and $q = \ln 3$, solve for x in terms of p and/or q.

        a. $e^x = 2^{10}$ b. $4e^x = 27$

11-46.   Solve the system at right.

$$\frac{z+y}{4} + \frac{z-y}{2} = 1$$
$$\frac{3z-y}{4} + \frac{4z+2y}{11} = 3$$

11-47.   Harold sorted his jellybeans into two jars. He likes the purple ones best and the black ones next best, so these are both in one jar. His next favorites are yellow, orange, and white, and these are in another jar. He gave all the rest to his little sister. Harold allows himself to eat only one jellybean from *each* jar per day. He wears a blindfold when he selects his jellybeans so he cannot choose his favorites first.

        Make an area model that represents the probabilities. What is the probability that Harold gets one black jellybean and one orange jellybean if the first jar has 60% black and 40% purple jellybeans, and the second jar has 30% yellow, 50% orange, and 20% white jellybeans?

11-48.   Where do the graphs of $x^2 - y = 4$ and $y = 2x - 1$ intersect?

11-49.   Logarithms are used to measure the "loudness" of sound. Decibels (dB) are logarithmic units used to describe a ratio of two levels of intensity or pressure. The difference between two levels of sound pressure (P_1 and P_2) is defined as $10 \log(\frac{P_1}{P_2})$ dB. Usually, when decibels are used to describe just one sound, it is assumed that that sound is being compared to a reference level of 20 micropascals.

        a.   How many decibels correspond to doubling the pressure of a sound?

        b.   What is the sound pressure of a noise described as 60 dB?

        c.   What does 0 decibels mean?

        d.   How many times more pressure is in a sound of 40 dB than of 20 dB?

11.2.2 Did my experiment show results?

±10%

Variability in Experimental Results

Today you will use what you know about sample-to-sample variability to determine whether two results in an experiment are truly different.

11-50.   ENDANGERED FROGS

The female red-eyed poison-dart frog visits numerous bromeliads ("air plants") where pools of water have collected in the leaves. In each pool, she lays a single egg that grows into a tadpole. The tadpoles feed on mosquito larvae in the pools, but local health officials have been killing the mosquito larvae. Environmentalists are concerned because they are unsure whether the tadpoles will adapt to eat some other food source.

Luis led a team of environmental scientists to the Costa Rican rain forest. They tagged 100 female tadpoles and determined the number that grew to adulthood. Mosquito larvae were placed in 50 bromeliads, and the other 50 bromeliads were treated so that mosquitoes could not live there.

36 of the 50 tadpoles (72%) fed with mosquitoes survived, while 29 of the 50 (58%) non-mosquito-fed tadpoles survived. The difference in the proportion that survived is $0.72 - 0.58 = 0.14$. Investigate whether this difference of 0.14 in the proportion of tadpoles that survived can be explained by natural sample-to-sample variability, or if there is a true difference between the two groups.

First, explore the sample-to-sample variability using a computer simulation.

a.   72% of the mosquito-fed tadpoles survived. For the simulation, the numbers 1 to 72 can represent the mosquito-fed tadpoles that survived. The numbers 73 to 100 will represent a tadpole that died. Simulate one sample of 50 mosquito-fed tadpoles. What proportion of your sample survived?

b.   58% of the non-mosquito-fed tadpoles survived. Simulate one sample of 50 non-mosquito-fed tadpoles. What proportion of your sample survived?

c.   What is the *difference* between these two proportions (mosquito-fed proportion that survived minus non-mosquito-fed proportion that survived)?

Problem continues on next page. →

11-50.   *Problem continued from previous page.*

    d.   The difference of proportions in your random sample that survived is likely to be higher or lower than 0.14, or even negative, because of natural sample-to-sample variability. What does a positive difference mean? What would a negative difference mean?

    e.   If we take repeated random samples by repeating the simulation, we can estimate the sample-to-sample variability, and then the margin of error. Below are the results of 100 trials. The table shows the differences in the proportion that survived (mosquito-fed proportion that survived minus non-mosquito-fed proportion survived).

Proportion of mosquito-fed survivors minus proportion of non-mosquito-fed survivors. Simulation mean = 0.14				
0.10	0.33	0.13	0.13	0.10
0.05	0.10	0.02	−0.05	0.14
0.21	0.12	0.22	0.22	0.17
0.13	0.24	−0.07	0.23	0.14
0.16	0.30	0.12	0.21	0.11
0.17	0.19	0.14	0.13	0.09
0.05	0.10	0.23	0.29	0.30
0.26	0.08	0.07	0.30	0.05
0.12	−0.04	0.16	0.03	0.13
0.26	0.16	0.08	0.14	0.07
0.27	0.19	−0.01	0.19	0.16
0.06	0.17	0.18	0.06	0.13
0.15	0.11	0.07	0.05	0.15
0.18	0.24	−0.02	0.10	0.16
0.19	0.18	0.36	0.20	0.06
0.22	0.17	0.16	0.26	−0.04
0.13	0.05	0.05	0.15	0.19
0.13	0.18	0.10	0.13	0.10
0.16	0.21	0.17	0.09	0.03
0.13	0.13	0.12	0.15	0.23

checksum 14.1

Find an upper and lower bound on the middle 90% of the proportions and the margin of error.

    f.   You have found the sample-to-sample variability. You are ready to make a prediction for the entire population. Report your prediction for the difference between the proportion of mosquito-fed tadpoles that survived and the proportion of non-mosquito-fed tadpoles that survived.

    g.   What does a difference of zero mean in the context of this problem?

    h.   Are you convinced (do you have evidence) there is a true difference in the tadpoles that ate mosquitoes and those that did not? Explain why or why not.

11-51.   LEARNING LOG

Create a Learning Log explaining the steps you would take
to determine whether two results in an experiment are truly
different. You can use Endangered Frogs as an example or
create an example of your own. Title this entry "Comparing
Experimental Results" and label it with today's date.

METHODS AND MEANINGS

MATH NOTES

Margin of Error

Using a statistic from a representative random sample to make an
inference about a population parameter is an important application of
statistics, but because of natural sample-to-sample variability you
cannot say for certain what the true value for the population is based on
a statistic. But you can have confidence that the true value lies within
an interval. The **margin of error** is half width of this interval.

To compute a margin of error, a computer simulation can be used to estimate
sample-to-sample variability. Then the middle 90% (or 95% or 99%) of the data is
used to predict the interval in which we are confident the true value lies. By sorting
the simulated samples from lowest to highest and determining where the lowest 5%
and upper 5% of the data begin, we can find the margin of error. The margin of
error is half this range. The larger the margin of error, the less confidence we have
in our prediction.

For example, data from 100 simulated samples from a population in which 48%
support the president might look like this:

43% 44% 44% 45% 45% 45%...(88 more samples)...50% 51% 51% 52% 52% 54%

The lowest five samples (lowest 5% of 100 samples) are at 45% support and the
upper five samples are at 51% support. The range is 6%, and therefore the margin
of error is ± 3%. We would report that 48% ± 3% of the voters support the
president.

11-52.   A survey of 80 seniors at Algieres High School found that 65% had been
          accepted to a four-year university. A computer simulation was conducted and
          the proportions sorted to determine the sample-to-sample variability:

Proportion of students accepted to a four-year university (sorted). Simulation mean 0.65.				
0.51	0.60	0.63	0.66	0.69
0.52	0.61	0.63	0.66	0.70
0.54	0.61	0.63	0.66	0.70
0.54	0.61	0.63	0.67	0.71
0.56	0.61	0.63	0.67	0.71
0.56	0.61	0.64	0.67	0.71
0.56	0.62	0.64	0.67	0.71
0.57	0.62	0.64	0.67	0.71
0.57	0.62	0.64	0.67	0.71
0.58	0.62	0.65	0.67	0.72
0.58	0.62	0.65	0.67	0.73
0.59	0.62	0.65	0.67	0.73
0.59	0.62	0.65	0.68	0.73
0.59	0.62	0.65	0.68	0.73
0.59	0.62	0.65	0.68	0.74
0.59	0.62	0.65	0.68	0.74
0.59	0.63	0.65	0.68	0.75
0.59	0.63	0.65	0.68	0.76
0.60	0.63	0.65	0.69	0.76
0.60	0.63	0.66	0.69	0.77

checksum 64.64

a.   Use the technique of problem 11-27 to find the upper and lower 5%
      bounds of the sample-to-sample variability.

b.   Predict the proportion of the seniors at Algieres High that have been
      accepted to four-year universities and give the margin of error.

11-53.   A consumer magazine randomly selects 250 of its
          readers and asks whether their luggage was lost on
          their last airplane flight. Seven out of the 250 lost
          their luggage. The consumer magazine conducted a
          simulation to determine the sample-to-sample
          variability and concluded that about 3% ± 1.7% of all passengers lose their
          luggage. Make a conjecture about what the number of passengers who lose
          their luggage might be if the magazine had surveyed 1000 readers instead.

11-54.   Daylight Saving Time was adopted in the U.S. in 1918. During the oil crisis of the 1970s, the Department of Transportation found that daylight saving time decreased national energy usage by about 1 percent compared with standard time. Since then, energy use in the U.S. has changed and daylight saving time has been extended. In 2007 a group of researchers found that daylight saving time decreased national energy usage by 0.2% with a margin or error of 1.5%. If a 1% decrease in energy use will save the state of Indiana $9 million, what conclusion(s) can you draw from the 2007 study in relation to the state of Indiana?

11-55.   A team of 8 students has finished an investigation on the many uses of parabolas. They must select a single group member to present their findings to the class. They have only a single coin to make chance selections, but they can flip it as many times as necessary to select a student fairly.

   a.   Using a single coin, find a fair way to select the presenter.

   b.   What is the smallest number of coin tosses needed to select a presenter fairly? Describe the method.

   c.   Two of the group members realize they won't be in class the day of the presentation because they are playing in a baseball tournament. Can a presenter still be chosen fairly with a single coin? Explain why or why not?

11-56.   Change each equation to graphing form. Sketch the graph and label each vertex and axis of symmetry.

   a. $y = 2x^2 + 7x - 7$ b. $y = 3x^2 - x - 8$

11-57.   Sketch the graph of $g(x) = (x-2)^2 - 1$.

   a.   On the same set of axes (in a different color) sketch the graph of $|g(x)|$, which is $|g(x)| = |(x-2)^2 - 1|$.

   b.   On a new set of axes, sketch the graph of $g(|x|)$, which is $g(|x|) = (|x|-2)^2 - 1$.

   c.   Describe how each of the graphs in parts (a) and (b) are related to the original graph of $g(x)$.

11-58.   In the summer of 1994, a couple was going through their attic and found a
           $1000 bond issued by the State of Nevada in 1865. It read, "Pay to the Bearer"
           (whoever has possession). States issue bonds when they need to borrow money.
           In 1865, Nevada was a new state and in great need of cash, so it issued this bond
           at an interest rate of 24% compounded annually.

           a.   Do you think it would have been possible to cash in this bond?

           b.   If $1000 were invested in 1865 at an interest rate of 24% compounded
                annually, how much would the investment be worth in 1994?

           c.   What is the place value of the first digit in the answer to part (b)?

           d.   Would the amount be significantly different if was compounded
                continuously instead?

11-59.   Rewrite each equation as an equivalent equation using $\log_{10}$. You do not need
           to find a numerical answer. These are sometimes known as **change of base**
           problems.

           a. $\log_2(3) = x$ b. $\log_5(8) = x$ c. $\log_7(12) = x$ d. $\log_a(b) = x$

11-60.   In a certain town, 45% of the population has dimples and
           70% has a widow's peak (a hairline above the forehead
           that makes a "V" shape). Assuming that these physical
           traits are independently distributed, what is the
           probability that a randomly selected person has both
           dimples and a widow's peak? What is the probability
           that he or she will have neither? Use a generic area
           model or a tree diagram to represent this situation.

11.2.3 Should I reject for poor quality?

Quality Control

When companies accept items for shipment or distribution, they often do not test every single item for quality. In many processes, testing every item would be far too time-consuming and expensive. For example, when testing 2-liter soda bottles for bursting strength, sometimes testing destroys the item. If companies tested every item, there would be nothing left to ship. Instead, quality control testing is done on a small sample of items. If the sample does not meet quality standards, the entire batch is thrown out or recycled.

11-61. Your task is to assure quality control for the P.C.I. (Probability Cubes Incorporated) dice company. The quality of their product is critical for the success of P.C.I. We plan to take 10 dice out of each case and test to see whether they fall within company specifications. If the dice fail to fall within the acceptable range, the entire case will be thrown out.

First we need to determine the acceptable range for well-functioning dice. We will use a simulation.

a. Work with a partner to set up a simulation for rolling ten dice. Record the mean of the ten dice.

b. Have each person in your team run five simulations of the rolling of a perfectly manufactured set of ten dice and record the mean for each simulated sample.

c. Combine your results with those of your classmates. Make a histogram of the sampling distribution. What is the mean of the sampling distribution?

d. Find the upper 5% and lower 5% bounds for the class as you did in previous lessons.

11-62. Consider the bounds you found in problem 11-61 to be the upper and lower bounds of a normal manufacturing process of ten dice. A set of ten dice that does not fall within this range will be considered defective and the entire case will be thrown out.

Problem continues on next page →

11-62.   *Problem continued from previous page.*

a.   Your teacher will have one or more samples of ten
      dice from P.C.I., each from a different case that was
      "manufactured" early this morning. Roll the sample
      of ten dice once and calculate the mean roll. Did
      your batch fall within the quality control bounds? If
      not, P.C.I. will need to discard the entire case they came from.

b.   Repeat part (a) for another sample of dice if you have one.
      Was this sample of dice within your quality control bounds?

11-63.   How many cases of dice were rejected by the quality control engineers in your
          class? What percent of the cases were rejected?

Statistical Hypothesis Tests

MATH NOTES

         You have looked at two different types of **statistical hypothesis
tests**. In Lesson 11.2.1, you took a sample and compared the sample
statistic to a **claim** about the population. Specifically, you compared the
survey results of 60% to the principal's claim that the true value of the
population was 50% or less. By simulating the sample-to-sample
variability, you created a margin of error. If the claim was within the
margin of error, you concluded that the claim was plausible. If the claim
was not within the margin of error, you concluded that the claim was not
plausible.

In the experiment with frog tadpoles, you performed a different kind of statistical
test. You had two samples, and you calculated the *difference* between those two
samples. Then you looked at the sample-to-sample variability of the differences
between the two samples. A margin of error was created for the true difference
between the two populations. If a difference of zero was within that margin of
error, you concluded that it was plausible that there was no difference between
the two populations; you could *not* conclude that the two populations were in fact
different. On the other hand, if a difference of zero was not within the margin of
error, you could conclude that it was plausible that there was actually a true
difference between the two populations.

There are many other kinds of hypothesis tests you will learn about in future
Statistics courses.

11-64. A copy machine company advertises that its copiers will make at least 25,000 copies before requiring maintenance. A consumer research group tested the claim by collecting data from users of the particular copy machine in 30 different regions of the country. The means for each of the 30 regions are listed in the table below.

24928	24574	24652	24758	24691
24893	25024	24767	24791	24609
25249	24914	24895	24656	24883
24551	24928	25025	24798	25041
24782	25020	24618	24904	24764
24705	24889	24656	24600	24735

checksum 744300

Find the upper and lower 5% bounds of the sample-to-sample variability and predict the number of copies that can be made before a machine requires maintenance. Do you think the consumer research group will support the company's claim?

11-65.   Students in Miss Hampton's science class tested the
effectiveness of detergent in getting dishes clean. They started
by weighing each plate. Then they created a gooey paste of
hard-to-clean foods (spaghetti sauce, mustard,
mashed potatoes, peanut butter, and grape jelly)
and smeared 250 clean dinner plates with a
measured amount of the food paste. They weighed
each plate and randomly placed them into
commercial dishwashers. Half the dishwashers had
detergent in them, and half had only clean water. After
cleaning the dishes, they weighed each plate to determine the
portion of food paste that remained. 84% of the food was
removed from dishes cleaned with detergent, while only 72%
of the food was removed from dishes cleaned without
detergent. Does using detergent really help get dishes cleaner?

a.   What is the difference in the proportions (detergent minus plain water)?
Express your answer as a decimal.

b.   Mrs. Hampton's class ran a computer simulation and determined the
sample-to-sample variability of the *difference* between the proportion of
food removed by the detergent compared to plain water. They concluded
that the *difference* in the true proportion of food removed was
0.12 ± 0.085.

Is a difference of zero a plausible result considering their margin of error?
What does a difference of zero mean in the context of this problem?

c.   Are you convinced that there is a true difference between cleaning with
detergent and cleaning with plain water?

11-66.   As part of a lesson in survey design, Janette asks her study team of four students
the following question: *"Given the association between movie violence and
crime, what kind of movie would you rather watch: romantic comedy or
action?"* All four indicate they would rather watch a romantic comedy. She
states in her conclusion, *"It is obvious romantic comedies are the best."*

a.   If the population of movie goers is actually equally split between those
who prefer romantic comedies versus action movies, what is the chance of
finding a group of 4 who unanimously prefer one genre over the other? Is
it plausible?

b.   Write a few sentences commenting on the validity of Janette's methods
and her conclusion.

Core Connections Algebra 2

11-67.   The Algiers High School booster club is planning a fund-raiser to collect money for a new synthetic turf field and stadium lights. The football field is $100 \times 53\frac{1}{3}$ yards. They cover it completely with playing cards (2.5×3.5 inches) face down. All the cards are aligned in the same direction as the football field (long side of the card along the long side of the field). There will be exactly one joker card placed at random among the face-down cards on the field.

Contestants pay five dollars for every card they wish to turn over. Whoever finds the joker wins one million dollars.

a.   What is the probability that the first contestant finds the joker?

b.   The playing cards used to cover the field cost $0.99 per pack (52 cards per pack). What is the largest amount of money the boosters could lose in this fundraiser?

c.   What is the maximum amount of money the boosters could make?

d.   What is a reasonable expected profit for the booster club? That is, if this fundraiser were done many, many times, what would be the average profit?

e.   A state Mega Millions lottery advertises odds of 176 million to one. If the state lottery were played like the booster club fundraiser, how many football fields covered with non-joker playing cards would be needed?

11-68.   What is the solution for the system of equations at right?

$$\frac{7}{13}x + \frac{4}{15}y = 0$$
$$\frac{5}{8}x + \frac{12}{7}y = 0$$

11-69.   Let $p = 2 + 5i$ and $q = 3 - 4i$.
Calculate the following values and simplify to $a + bi$ form.

a. $p + q$ b. $p - q$ c. $p \cdot q$ d. $\frac{p}{q}$

11-70.   Solve and graph each inequality.

a. $|7 - y| \le 3$ b. $3|2m + 1| - 1 > 8$

11-71. The graphs of $f(x) = 2x^2 + 5x - 3$ and
$g(x) = x^2 + 4x + 3$ are shown at right.
Use the graphs to solve:

a. $f(x) = g(x)$

b. $f(x) > g(x)$

11.2.4 Is the process out of control?

±10%

Statistical Process Control

In Lesson 11.2.3 you checked the quality of an item after it was manufactured to verify that it was within the natural sample-to-sample manufacturing specifications. Today we will explore whether the manufacturing process remains constant over time.

Natural variation occurs in all manufacturing processes, no matter how precise, computerized, or state-of-the-art. For example, a manufacturer of ball bearings for precision aircraft parts needs to be sure the ball bearings are always the correct size. If they are slightly too large or too small, they may cause an airplane crash!

Each ball bearing is a slightly different size than the next one due to small variations in the metals being used, impurities in raw materials, wear of the machinery, temperature, and humidity, among other possibilities. Since variation is always present, engineers must control the manufacturing process so that the final product remains useful. The ball bearing cannot be manufactured to an exact size each and every time, but it can be manufactured to fall within a specification, say 50mm +/– 0.2mm.

Checking quality over a time period is called **statistical process control**. The process needs to remain stable over time so that the output or product of that process remains of high quality.

In Lesson 11.2.3 you verified the quality of an item (the set of dice) *after* it was manufactured. If the quality was poor, large quantities of the item had to be discarded or recycled at great expense. A fundamental tenet of manufacturing is that it is far less expensive to control the manufacturing *process*—to catch and fix problems early—than to wait to test the quality of the finished product when it can no longer be fixed.

11-72.   *x*-BAR CONTROL CHART

The Brrrr! Ice Company must keep the size of the
ice cubes it makes within certain specifications for
the ice cubes to be useful for restaurants. Brrr! Ice
keeps track of the process of making ice cubes by
taking a sample of 10 ice cubes every hour and then
plotting the mean size over time. Some of their data
from yesterday is below.

Hour	1	2	3	4	5	6	7	8	9	10
mean cube size (mm)	273.1	262.7	264.1	206.9	295.4	238.6	197.8	277.2	284.5	256.6

Hour	11	12	13	14	15	16	17	18	19	20	
mean cube size (mm)	220.3	303.1	278.9	306.3	263.3	208.9	253.3	213.7	216.4	263.3	*checksum 5084.4*

a.   Create a scatterplot with mean cube size as the
dependent variable and time as the independent
variable. Use the option on your calculator or
computer to connect the dots as shown in the
display at right.

b.   The process data is useful only if we know what
size ice cubes are acceptable. These specifications
are called the upper control limit (UCL) and lower
control limit (LCL). The Brrrr! Ice Company will
tolerate ice cubes that are between 250mm +/–
100mm. Add the control limits to your scatterplot.
Your graph will look something like the one shown
at right.

This kind of chart is called an ***x*-bar process control chart** because it plots
the mean ($\bar{x}$) data from the manufacturing process. Since all of the means
are within the process control limits, this manufacturing process is said to
be **in control**.

11-73. AN OUT-OF-CONTROL PROCESS

The mean ice cube size for today's data at Brrr! Ice is below.

hour	1	2	3	4	5	6	7	8	9	10
mean cube size (mm)	242.5	277.1	250.0	234.2	229.7	243.6	282.8	303.0	247.7	217.0

hour	11	12	13	14	15	16	17	18	19	20	
mean cube size (mm)	278.6	244.2	195.4	224.3	382.1	242.4	226.5	284.4	239.1	288.2	*checksum 5132.8*

a. Create an x-bar process control chart.

b. At which hour did the process go **out of control**? Consider the context and make conjectures about what might have happened during the manufacturing process this hour to make the process go out of control.

11-74. The mean ice cube size for yet another day at Brrr! Ice is below.

hour	1	2	3	4	5	6	7	8	9	10
mean cube size (mm)	275.4	213.8	182.6	250.1	228.7	275.3	220.1	166.0	258.5	240.9

hour	11	12	13	14	15	16	17	18	19	20	
mean cube size (mm)	255.3	309.1	270.0	255.7	306.8	338.2	336.6	311.3	332.5		*checksum 5026.9*

a. Create an x-bar process control chart.

b. What do you notice about the process control chart that might concern you as a quality control engineer at Brrr! Ice? Why would the engineers stop the process after the 19th hour?

c. Even though a process is entirely within the process control limits, a process is considered out of control if nine consecutive points lie above or below the centerline of the process control limits. What size of ice cube is in the center between the UCL and the LCL?

d. Add the centerline to your graph and determine whether this process is out of control.

e. Make a conjecture in the context of the problem as to what in the manufacturing process may cause a "nine points loss of control."

11-75.   The principal at Algieres High School believes that over 20% of students are text-messaging at least once a week during class. He believes this is an impediment to effective learning. Students claim that the actual percentage is much lower and that stricter rules are not necessary. Mrs. Rahil secretly observed her homeroom class very carefully for a week; only 13% of students actually text-messaged during class. Assuming her homeroom is representative of the whole school, Mrs. Rahil's class did a computer simulation and determined a margin of error of 10%. Is it plausible that the principal is correct and 20% of the whole school is text-messaging?

11-76.   MINIATURE GOLF

Olivia loves playing putt-putt golf. In putt-putt golf you do not swing at a golf ball, but rather you only putt the golf ball (tap the ball with a club so that it rolls into a hole). Olivia experimented with her new club to determine whether or not she played better with it. Each time before she putted a golf ball, Olivia flipped a coin to determine whether she would use her new club or the old one. She experimented on 80 putts. With the new club, Olivia made 25% of the 40 putts, while with the old one, she made only 15% of the 40 putts. Using the steps below, help Olivia decide whether or not her new golf club is really better, or if this difference can be explained by sample-to-sample variability.

a.   What is the difference in the proportions (new club minus old club)? Express your answer as a decimal.

b.   Olivia needs a computer simulation to determine the sample-to-sample variability:

   i.   Out of the 80 putts, how many went into the hole?

   ii.   A model of this situation needs to represent 80 putts. What will the numbers 1 to 16 represent? What will the numbers 17 to 80 represent?

   iii.   Conduct one simulation of 80 putts. What proportion of the putts in your simulation went into the hole? What proportion did not go into the hole? What is the *difference* in the proportion (proportion that went into the hole minus proportion that did not go in)?

Problem continues on next page →

11-76.   *Problem continued from previous page.*

Olivia ran the simulation 50 times and calculated the *difference* in the proportion of putts that went into the hole and those that did not go into the hole for each simulation. From her results, she predicted the true *difference* in proportion of all her putts was 0.10 ± 0.146.

c.   What does a difference of zero mean in the context of this problem? Is a difference of zero a plausible result considering your margin of error?

d.   Are you convinced that there is a true difference between the new club and the old club?

11-77.   Because of natural variability in manufacturing, a 12-ounce can of soda does not usually hold exactly 12 ounces of soda. A can is permitted to hold a little more or a little less. The specifications for the soda-filling machine are that it needs to fill each can with 12 ± 0.25 ounces of soda. If a can of soda is filled with 11.97 ounces of soda, is the filling machine operating within specifications?

11-78.   Every hour, Katie's Konfections weighs a sample of chocolates from their manufacturing process. For each of the process control charts below, describe whether the process is in control, and if not, what in the manufacturing process could have led to the out-of-control state.

11-79.   Graph each equation below.

a. $x^2 + (y-3)^2 = 9$

b. $(x-5)^2 + (y-1)^2 = 4$

11-80.   Solve each equation below for x. Show all of your work. (Your answers will contain the variables a, b, and/or c.)

      a. $cx - a = b$ b. $\frac{x}{a} - b = c$ c. $(x-a)(x-b) = 0$

      d. $ax^2 - acx = 0$ e. $\frac{x}{a+b} = \frac{1}{c}$ f. $\frac{1}{x} + a = b$

11-81.   Solve the equations below.

      a. $\frac{3x}{x+2} + \frac{7}{x-2} = 3$ b. $\frac{x-7}{x-5} = \frac{6}{x}$

11-82.   Solve the equations below.

      a. $(x+2)^2 - (x-2)^2 = 8$ b. $(x+2)^2 + (x-2)^2 = (2x)^2$

11-83.   Kendra has programmed her cell phone to randomly show one of six photos when she turns it on. Two of the photos are of her parents, one is of her niece, and three are of her boyfriend, Bruce. Today, she will need to turn her phone on twice: once before school and again after school.

      a.   Create an area model to represent this situation.

      b.   Given that the before-school photo was of her boyfriend, what is the conditional probability the after-school photo will also be of her boyfriend?

      c.   What is the probability that neither photo will be of her niece?

      d.   Given that neither photo was of her niece, what is the conditional probability that the before-school photo was of her boyfriend?

11.3.1 When is probability counterintuitive?

Analyzing Decisions and Strategies

In today's problems you will have the opportunity to see how probability can play an important role in decision-making. In *Midnight Mystery,* the results of your investigation will shed light on the accusation that one of the Measleys is guilty of the curling trophy prank, and in *Testing for AIDS,* your results can be used in an argument about mandatory testing. There are many other similar applications. As you work through this lesson, discuss the following questions:

How can we find the probability?

What model should we use?

How should we set up the model?

Which probabilities do we need to compute?

11-84. SHIFTY SHAUNA

Shauna has a bad relationship with the truth—she doesn't usually tell it! In fact, whenever Shauna is asked a question, she rolls a die. If it comes up 6, she tells the truth. Otherwise, she lies.

a. If Shauna flips a fair coin and you ask her how it came out, what is the probability that she says "heads" and is telling the truth? Use an area model to solve this problem and carefully record your work. Be ready to share your solution method with the class.

b. Suppose Shauna flips a fair coin and you ask her whether it came up heads or tails. What is the probability that she says "heads"? (Hint: The answer is not $\frac{1}{12}$!)

11-85. MIDNIGHT MYSTERY

Each year, the students at Haardvarks School randomly select a student to play a prank. Late last night, Groundskeeper Lily Smilch saw a student steal the school's National Curling Championship trophy from the trophy case. All Lily can tell the headmaster about the crime is that the student who stole the trophy looked like he or she had red hair.

Problem continues on next page →

11-85. *Problem continued from previous page.*

Unfortunately, of the 100 students at Haardvarks, the only ones with red hair are your friend Don Measley and his siblings. Groundskeeper Smilch insists that one of the five Measleys committed the crime and should be punished. Don is incensed: *"We Measleys would never play such a stupid prank! Groundskeeper Smilch claims to have seen someone with red hair, but it was so dark at the time and Smilch's eyes are so bad, there is no way she could have identified the color of someone's hair!"*

The Headmaster isn't convinced, so he walks around with Lily at night and points to students one by one, asking her whether each one has red hair. Lily is right about the hair color 4 out of every 5 times.

This looks like bad news for Don, but Professor McMonacle agrees to take up his defense. *"I think,"* McMonacle says, *"that the thief probably wasn't one of the Measleys."*

Your Task: Develop the basis for McMonacle's argument as follows:

a. Model the probabilities in this situation with an area model. The two chance events in your model should be "The thief is/is not a redhead" and "Lily is/is not correct about the thief's hair color."

b. If you performed this experiment with 100 students, how many times would you expect Lily to say the student had red hair and be correct about it?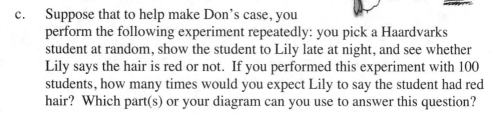

c. Suppose that to help make Don's case, you perform the following experiment repeatedly: you pick a Haardvarks student at random, show the student to Lily late at night, and see whether Lily says the hair is red or not. If you performed this experiment with 100 students, how many times would you expect Lily to say the student had red hair? Which part(s) or your diagram can you use to answer this question?

d. If you performed this experiment with 100 students, what percentage of the students Lily *said* had red hair would *actually* have red hair?

e. How can you use these calculations to defend the Measleys? Is it likely that a Measley was the thief?

f. Have you *proven* that none of the Measleys stole the Curling Trophy?

11-86.   TESTING FOR AIDS

An understanding of probability is valuable in relation to important policy issues that are often decided for political reasons. As the issues get more complicated, knowledge of probability and statistics could make a big difference in the decisions each of us will help to make. For example, with the growing number of AIDS cases, some people have called for mandatory testing of healthcare professionals (doctors, dentists) for the HIV virus, with public disclosure of the results. Others argue that mandatory testing jeopardizes the lives and livelihood of many people who do not have the disease and is therefore an unwarranted and unjust invasion of their privacy. Furthermore, they argue that if results are not ever made public for anybody, more people who are not required to test (like health technicians) will volunteer for testing, increasing the likelihood of identifying and helping people who do have the disease.

In order to explore these issues further we will consider a hypothetical situation. Suppose that the currently used test for HIV is 99% accurate, and suppose that in the population to be tested (in this case it is doctors, dentists, and other health practitioners) 100 out of 100,000 people actually are HIV positive. The question is: what is the probability that a health practitioner would be identified as having the AIDS virus who actually did not?

a.   Make a model for this situation.

b.   How does the number of people who are HIV positive compare with the number of people who will be told they are HIV positive but really are not?

c.   If a randomly tested health practitioner's test comes back positive, what is the probability that he is *not* actually HIV positive? (This is called a **false positive**.) In other words, if you are told that you are sick, what is the conditional probability that you are not sick?

d.   Write up your statistical conclusions about mandatory testing of health practitioners. How might your statistics change if the study was about subjects in the general population who volunteered for testing?

e.   Are the test results mathematically independent of the fact that the person tested does or does not have aids? How could you check this? Explain.

11-87.   A never-ending game?

Jack and Jill are playing a game in which Jack has 2 pennies and Jill has
4 pennies. A coin is tossed. If it lands on heads Jill has to give a penny to Jack.
If it lands on tails, Jack gives a penny to Jill. The game is won when one of
them has all of the pennies. They think that they can keep playing all day since
the coin has an equal chance of landing on heads or tails, so they will just keep
passing coins back and forth.

Simulate the coin tosses on your calculator and keep track of the pennies with
pencil and paper. Can they keep playing all day, or does one player have a
better chance of winning the game?

11-88.   Any system that is responsible for detecting relatively rare events is going to
have problems with false positives. You saw this in problem 11-86 regarding
testing for HIV. Consider other cases such as burglar alarms, smoke detectors,
red light cameras and drug testing for athletes. All of these systems have proven
accuracy and all have a persistent problem of false positives (false alarms).

Consider a hypothetical situation. Suppose that rare event A occurs with a
frequency of 1/1000. Suppose that a detection system for event A responsible
for sounding an alarm is 96% accurate. The question is: if the alarm is
sounding, what is the probability that event A has not occurred (false alarm)?

a.   Make a model for this situation.

b.   If the alarm has been activated, what is the probability that it is false?

c.   Are the test results mathematically independent of whether event A occurs
or not? How could you check this? Explain.

11-89.   Find the equation of the line passing through the point $(-2, 5)$ that is
perpendicular to the line $y = -5x + 2$.

11-90.   Solve the system of equations at right. $x^2 + y^2 = 16$

$$y = x^2 - 4$$

11-91. Multiply and simplify each expression.

    a. $(3 + 2i)(4 + i)$ b. $(2 + 3i)(2 - 3i)$

    c. $(5 - 2i)(5 + 2i)$ d. $(a + bi)(a - bi)$

11-92. Graph at least one full cycle of each graph.

    a. $y = 2 \sin x$ b. $y = \cos(2x)$

    c. $y = -1 + 2\cos(x)$ d. $y = -1 + 2\sin(x + \frac{\pi}{2})$

11-93. Each of the following sums is the beginning of an arithmetic series. Find the nth term of each series, for the specified value of n.

    a. $(-2) + (-5) + (-8) + ..., \; n = 12$ b. $9 + 15 + 21 + ..., \; n = 20$

11-94. This problem is a checkpoint for solving rational equations. It will be referred to as Checkpoint 11.

Solve each of the following rational equations.

    a. $\frac{x}{3} = \frac{4}{x}$ b. $\frac{x}{x-1} = \frac{4}{x}$ c. $\frac{1}{x} + \frac{1}{3x} = 6$ d. $\frac{1}{x} + \frac{1}{x+1} = 3$

Check your answers by referring to the Checkpoint 11 materials located at the back of your book.

Ideally, at this point you are comfortable working with these types of problems and can solve them correctly. If you feel that you need more confidence when solving these types of problems, then review the Checkpoint 11 materials and try the practice problems provided. From this point on, you will be expected to do problems like these correctly and with confidence.

11-95. Sketch a graph, $f(x)$, that has the number and types of roots described for each situation below.

    a.   5 real roots   b.   3 real and 2 complex roots

    c.   4 complex roots   d.   4 complex and 2 real roots

                                                         Core Connections Algebra 2

Chapter 11 Closure What have I learned?

Reflection and Synthesis

The activities below offer you a chance to reflect
about what you have learned during this chapter. As
you work, look for concepts that you feel very
comfortable with, ideas that you would like to learn
more about, and topics you need more help with.
Look for connections between ideas as well as
connections with material you learned previously.

①   TEAM BRAINSTORM

What have you studied in this chapter? What ideas were important in what you
learned? With your team, brainstorm a list. Be as detailed as you can. To help
get you started, a list of Learning Log entries and Math Notes boxes are below.

What topics, ideas, and words that you learned *before* this chapter are connected
to the new ideas in this chapter? Again, be as detailed as you can.

How long can you make your list? Challenge yourselves. Be prepared to share
your team's ideas with the class.

Learning Log Entries

- Lesson 11.2.1 – Sample-to-Sample Variability
- Lesson 11.2.2 – Comparing Experimental Results

Math Notes

- Lesson 11.1.1 – Area Models for Probabilities
- Lesson 11.2.1 – Sample-To-Sample Variability
- Lesson 11.2.2 – Margin of Error
- Lesson 11.2.3 – Statistical Hypothesis Tests

②   MAKING CONNECTIONS

Below is a list of the vocabulary used in this chapter. Make sure that you are familiar with all of these words and know what they mean. Refer to the glossary or index for any words that you do not yet understand.

area model	claim	conditional probability
hypothesis test	in/out of control	Law of Large Numbers
margin of error	population	process control
quality control	random number	sample-to-sample variability
sampling distribution	simulation	streak
upper/lower bound	upper/lower control limit	x-bar chart

Make a concept map showing all of the connections you can find among the key words and ideas listed above. To show a connection between two words, draw a line between them and explain the connection. A word can be connected to any other word as long as you can justify the connection.

While you are making your map, your team may think of related words or ideas that are not listed here. Be sure to include these ideas on your concept map.

③   PORTFOLIO: EVIDENCE OF MATHEMATICAL PROFICIENCY

This section gives you an opportunity to show growth in your understanding of key mathematical ideas over time as you complete this course.

You now have enough mathematical knowledge to analyze the results of a survey. Obtain the questions you created and refined in Chapter 9 (problems 9-1, 9-6, 9-21, and 9-33) for your own survey. In your portfolio, explain why you chose the wording of your questions the way you did. Consider everything you know about biased questions. For what population are your survey results valid? How will you sample? Refine your questions again if you choose. Explain the difference between open and closed questions.

Then conduct your survey as instructed by your teacher. Analyze the results, and make a conclusion about the population you defined. Include a margin of error.

Activity continues on next page →

③ *Activity continued from previous page.*

Your teacher may assign the following portfolio entry:

AIDS IN SOUTH AFRICA

In this investigation, you will showcase your understanding of estimating sample-to-sample variability and conducting a hypothesis test.

A drug manufacturer claims that only 13% of the population of South Africa is living with HIV/AIDS. As a United Nations World Health Organization researcher, you collect evidence to test this claim. You use statistical techniques to sample 125 random residents of South Africa and find that 20 of them have HIV/AIDS.

a.   Simulate one sample of 125 residents by randomly selecting 125 integers between 1 and 100. Carefully explain what the random numbers represent and why you picked 125 of them. What proportion of the 125 people in your simulated sample is living with HIV/AIDS? How do you know?

b.   Obtain the results of 100 simulations from your teacher. Without actually making the computation, what do you suppose the mean of the 100 proportions would be close to? Why? What is the margin of error?

c.   Are you able to support the claim of the drug manufacturer?

d.   Is margin of error you obtained reasonable for this study? Why or why not?

e.   What could be done to make the margin of error smaller? Why does that make sense?

④   WHAT HAVE I LEARNED?

Most of the problems in this section represent typical problems found in this chapter. They serve as a gauge for you. You can use them to determine which types of problems you can do well and which types of problems require further study and practice. Even if your teacher does not assign this section, it is a good idea to try these problems and find out for yourself what you know and what you still need to work on.

Solve each problem as completely as you can. The table at the end of the closure section has answers to these problems. It also tells you where you can find additional help and practice with problems like these.

CL 11-96.   If 75 percent of people do not believe in ghosts, design a simulation that would estimate the probability of randomly selecting a group of 5 non-believers:

a.   Using two coins.

b.   Using a calculator.

CL 11-97.   Mr. Knolsen takes pride in his difficult chemistry tests, 60 multiple-choice questions with 4 possible answers for each question. He tells the students to study hard because the mean score is 15 correct, but just 20 correct is all you need to earn an A. Mr. Knolsen admits that only about 10% of the students earn an A on the test. Jeff is wondering the value of Mr. Knolsen's pep talk so he runs a simulation of 100 students taking Mr. Knolsen's exam who blindly guess the answers for each question.

Questions correct in a simulation of 100 tests (the data is sorted)				
8	11	14	16	18
8	11	14	16	19
8	11	14	16	19
9	12	14	16	19
9	12	14	16	19
10	12	14	16	19
10	12	14	16	19
10	12	15	16	19
10	13	15	16	19
10	13	15	17	19
11	13	15	17	20
11	13	15	17	20
11	13	15	17	20
11	13	16	17	20
11	13	16	18	20
11	13	16	18	21
11	13	16	18	22
11	13	16	18	22
11	13	16	18	22
11	14	16	18	24

checksum 1489

a.   What is the mean number of questions answered correctly by the simulated students? As a percent?

b.   What percentage of the simulated students earned an A?

c.   Compare Jeff's simulated students to Mr. Knolsen's claims about his actual students.

d.   What advice would you give Jeff about preparing for Mr. Knolsen's famous chemistry tests?

CL 11-98.   A survey of 1024 people found 580 of them eat chicken soup when they have a cold or flu and concluded that a majority of the population believes that chicken soup helps relieve cold and flu symptoms. A computer simulation found the margin of error to be 3%. Does the conclusion seem reasonable? Why?

CL 11-99.   A company makes metal plates on which they put a special coating. Flaws appear in the finish of these metal plates and the company wants to establish a quality control system. A machine scans each plate after it is finished and reports the number of flaws. The data they collected for 50 samples are shown below.

7	10	9	3	13	7	5	8	8	10
13	9	21	10	6	8	3	12	7	11
5	10	6	13	3	2	7	4	11	8
1	7	5	2	0	11	3	4	3	1
4	14	7	12	6	1	10	6	2	12

checksum 361

Discuss the quality control bounds for this company with your team. Should you reject plates that have too few flaws? What upper and lower bounds make sense?

CL 11-100.   Students at Algieres High think they are safer drivers than average teenagers. In a random sample of 120 students at Algieres High, 18 students said that they got into a car accident when they were 16 years old.

a.   What percent of 16-year-olds in this sample got into a car accident?

b.   Set up a simulation of the sample-to-sample variability. Explain exactly what you would type into your calculator to do this simulation. After doing the simulation once, what would the numbers in your calculator screen represent?

c.   Chase ran the simulation 100 times and obtained the following proportions of 16-year-olds that got into a car accident.

Problem continues on next page →

CL 11-100. *Problem continued from previous page.*

Proportion of 16-year-old students in a car accident. Simulation mean = 0.15				
0.19	0.14	0.13	0.12	0.20
0.13	0.17	0.15	0.16	0.14
0.12	0.13	0.14	0.12	0.17
0.11	0.13	0.16	0.18	0.20
0.10	0.17	0.15	0.17	0.19
0.14	0.19	0.11	0.15	0.10
0.12	0.14	0.19	0.09	0.13
0.18	0.20	0.14	0.11	0.17
0.20	0.15	0.20	0.18	0.15
0.11	0.16	0.12	0.20	0.14
0.17	0.10	0.18	0.17	0.19
0.18	0.11	0.11	0.14	0.13
0.15	0.13	0.18	0.17	0.28
0.14	0.15	0.13	0.11	0.13
0.11	0.11	0.15	0.15	0.12
0.20	0.15	0.22	0.17	0.11
0.15	0.18	0.12	0.26	0.15
0.13	0.11	0.13	0.15	0.16
0.14	0.15	0.23	0.15	0.08
0.19	0.15	0.15	0.18	0.10

checksum 15.17

Consider the lower and upper 5% bounds to determine the margin of error for the proportion of students who got into an accident at Algieres High.

d. According to the U.S. Census Bureau, 21% of 16-year-olds nationwide get into a car accident. But in the sample at Algiers High, only 15% got into a car accident. Can students at Algieres make the claim that they are safer drivers?

CL 11-101. Jenn and Ryan needed to save money for their trip to the Galapagos Islands. They currently have $3000. They figure they will need $4000 for the trip.

a. They can put the $3000 into a CD account that earns interest compounded continuously. What annual interest rate will the account need so that they have $4000 in the account in ten years?

b. Instead, they can put the money in a savings account that earns 2.75% interest annually, compounded quarterly. In how many years will they have $4000?

CL 11-102. Find the infinite sum (if possible).

      a. $8 - 6 + \frac{9}{2} - \frac{27}{8} + \ldots$ b. $\displaystyle\sum_{k=0}^{\infty} \frac{1}{8}(2)^k$

CL 11-103. For the sequence: $150, 100, 50, 0, \ldots$

      a.   Find $t(10)$, the 10th term.

      b.   Find $S(10)$, the sum of the first 10 terms.

CL 11-104. For each equation, state the amplitude, period, vertical shift, and horizontal shift, and sketch two cycles of the graph.

      a. $y = 3\cos(2x)$ b. $y = \cos 2(x + \frac{\pi}{4})$

CL 11-105. Bias is present in the following observational studies.

      a.   Explain why the question is biased:

           A political pollster seeking information on public attitudes toward funding of pornographic art by the National Endowment for the Arts (NEA) asks an SRS of 2000 U.S. adults, "Instead of supporting government censorship of artistic expression, are you in favor of continuing federal funding for artists whose work may be controversial?" Eight-five percent of those surveyed answered "yes."

      b.   Explain why the sample is biased:

           A flour company in Minneapolis wants to know what percentage of local households bake at least twice a week. A company representative calls 500 households during the daytime and finds that 50% of them bake at least twice a week.

      c.   What is a possible lurking variable?

           Dentists would like to determine if eating an apple a day keeps cavities away. Fifty patients who say they routinely eat an apple a day, and 50 patients who say they eat less than one apple a week, will have their dental records checked. The dentists will compare the number of cavities in the two groups.

CL 11-106.   Check your answers using the table at the end of this section. Which
             problems do you feel confident about? Which problems were hard? Have
             you worked on problems like these in math classes you have taken before?
             Use the table to make a list of topics you need help on and a list of topics
             you need to practice more.

Answers and Support for Closure Activity #4
What Have I Learned?

Note: MN = Math Note, LL = Learning Log

Problem	Solutions	Need Help?	More Practice
CL 11-96.	a. There are 4 equally likely outcomes when you toss two coins HH HT TH TT. Assign one of the outcomes to represent a ghost-believer. The other three outcomes represent the 75% chance of a non-believer being selected. Toss the coins in sets of 5 representing the selection of 5 people in a group. Divide the number of groups without a ghost believer by the total number of groups.	Lesson 11.1.1	Problems 11-7, 11-18, 11-28, 11-29, 11-41, and 11-55
	b. Assign numbers 1 – 25 to represent selecting a believer and 26 – 100 to selecting a non-believer. Using randInt(1,100,5) generate sets of 5 numbers representing the selection of 5 people in a group. Divide the number of groups without a ghost believer by the total number of groups.		
CL 11-97	a. $1489/100 = 14.89$, $14.89/60 = 24.82\%$ b. $10/100 = 10\%$ c. They are nearly identical. d. If the real students are preparing for the exam, it doesn't help because students blindly guessing would perform just as well.	Lessons 11.1.3 and 11.2.1. MN: 11.2.1, 11.2.2, and 11.2.3 LN: 11.2.1	Problems 11-42, 11-52, 11-53, 11-54, 11-64, 11-65, 11-75, 11-76, and 11-77

Problem	Solutions	Need Help?	More Practice
CL 11-98.	Yes, $580/1024 = 0.566$. Adding and subtracting the margin of error, we can be reasonably sure the population proportion is between 0.536 and 0.596, which is greater than 0.500 (a majority).	Lesson 11.2.1 MN: 11.2.1, 11.2.2, and 11.2.3 LL: 11.2.1	Problems 11-64, 11-65, 11-75, 11-76, and 11-77
CL 11-99.	Students should reject the upper 10% of the data. Flaws should be ≤ 12.	Lesson 11.2.1 MN: 11.2.1, 11.2.2, and 11.2.3 LL: 11.2.1	Problems 11-64, 11-65, 11-75, 11-76, and 11-77
CL 11-100.	a. 15% b. [MATH] PRB randInt(1,100,120) [STO▶] [2nd] [L1]. That stores 120 students in List1. The numbers 1 to 15 represent a student who had an accident when they were 16 years old, while the numbers 16 to 100 represent a student who did not have an accident. c. $15\% \pm 5\%$ d. Yes. 21% is outside of the interval of the margin of error. There is convincing evidence that the rate of accidents at Algieres is lower than the nationwide rate.	Lesson 11.2.1 MN: 11.2.1, 11.2.2, and 11.2.3 LL: 11.2.1	Problems 11-64, 11-65, 11-75, 11-76, and 11-77
CL 11-101.	a. $4000 = 3000 \cdot e^{r \cdot 10}$; $r = 2.87\%$. b. $4000 = 3000(1.006875)^q$ $q = 42.0$ quarters $= 10.5$ years	Lesson 10.3.2 MN: 10.3.2	Problems 10-170, 10-172, 10-173, 11-10, and 11-58
CL 11-102.	a. $\frac{32}{7}$ b. No sum, $r > 1$.	Lessons 10.1.4 and 10.2.2 MN: 10.1.2, 10.1.4, 10.2.1, and 10.2.2 LL: 10.2.1 and 10.2.2	Problems 11-11, 11-23, 11-32, 11-44, and 11-93

Problem	Solutions	Need Help?	More Practice
CL 11-103.	a. −300 b. −750	Lesson 10.1.3 MN: 10.1.3	Problems 11-11, 11-23, 11-32, 11-44, and 11-93
CL 11-104.	a. amplitude: 3 period: π vertical shift: 0 horizontal shift: 0 b. amplitude: 1 period: π vertical shift: 0 horizontal shift: $-\frac{\pi}{4}$	Lessons 7.2.1, 7.2.2, and 7.2.3 MN: 7.2.4 LL: 7.2.4	Problems CL 8-188, CL 8-189, 9-69, 9-82, 10-94, and 11-92
CL 11-105.	a. Before asking the question, the person conducting the survey is connecting funding decisions to censorship. b. People at home during the day are more likely to have time to bake than the genreral population. c. Possibly healthy habits. Healthy habits might increase the nunber of apples you eat and also decrease the number of cavities you have. The apples are not preventing the cavities, the healthy habits are.	Lessons 9.1.1, 9.1.2, and 9.1.3 LL: 9.1.3	Problems 9-50, 9-75, CL 9-112, 11-5, 11-21, 11-30, 11-43, and 11-66

Chapter 12   Analytic Trigonometry

In Chapter 7 you began your study of trigonometric functions when you learned about radians and how to transform the graphs of $y = \sin(x)$, $y = \cos(x)$, and $y = \tan(x)$. In this chapter, you will continue your study of trigonometry with the investigation of solutions to trigonometric equations. You will learn about three new trigonometric ratios (secant, cosecant, and cotangent) and their corresponding functions.

By the end of this chapter, you will be able to solve a wide variety of trigonometric equations. You will make statements, based on the unit circle and the graph, about how many solutions there are and why.

Guiding Question

Mathematically proficient students reason abstractly and quantitatively.

As you work through this chapter, ask yourself:

How can I rewrite this in another useful form?

Chapter Outline

Section 12.1 In this section, you will solve trigonometric equations. You will learn about inverse and reciprocal trigonometric functions. You will understand solutions to trigonometric equations in multiple representations: algebraically, from the graphs of the functions, and based on the unit circle. You will also learn how to determine the number of solutions for a trigonometric equation.

Section 12.2 Here, you will identify trigonometric identities (statements that are always true). These identities will allow you to rewrite trigonometric equations, which will enable you to solve a broader range of equations.

12.1.1 When is it true?

Analyzing Trigonometric Equations

True?
When?

Throughout your study of algebra, you have encountered algebraic statements that are always true, sometimes true, or never true. In Chapter 7, you learned about the trigonometric functions $y = \sin(x)$, $y = \cos(x)$, and $y = \tan(x)$. You learned how to represent these functions in a table, on a graph, and with a unit circle. In this chapter, you will expand your understanding of trigonometric functions and develop strategies to determine when trigonometric equations are true. All answers in this chapter should be given in radians unless otherwise stated in the problem.

12-1.   How can you tell which values of x make an algebraic statement true? For each of the following statements, work with your team to decide if it is always true, sometimes true, or never true. If it is always true, justify how you know; if it is sometimes true, give the exact values of x that make it true; and if it is never true, explain why it is never true.

    a. $5(x-7) = 5x - 35$ b. $2x^2 = 50$

    c. $4x - (3x + 2) = x - 7$ d. $\frac{2}{3}(x-9) = \frac{3}{4}(2x+5)$

12-2.   **WHEN IS IT TRUE?**

Your teacher will assign your team one of the following equations. Your task is to decide if the equation is always true, sometimes true, or never true, and to justify your decision using as many representations as you can.

- If the equation is always true, explain how you know. Then look for ways you could change the equation so that it would never be true.

- If the equation is sometimes true, find the exact values of x that make it true. Then decide how you could change the equation so that it would never be true.

- If the equation is never true, explain how you know. Then decide how you could change the equation so that it would sometimes be true.

    a. $\sin(x) = \frac{1}{2}$ b. $\cos(x) = 2$

    c. $\sin(x) = \cos(\frac{\pi}{2} - x)$ d. $\sin(x) = \sin(\frac{\pi}{2} - x)$

    e. $\tan(x) = 0$ f. $2\sin(x) = \sqrt{3}$

    g. $\sin(x) = \frac{3}{2}$ h. $\cos(x) = \sin(\frac{\pi}{2} - x)$

12-3.   Organize your work from problem 12-2 into a poster that will serve as a visual aid for a presentation. Be sure to include all of your justifications and reasoning. Use colors, arrows, and other math tools to help make your thinking clear. When you have prepared your poster and presentation, go back to problem 12-2 and evaluate the equations your team did not work on.

12-4.   With your team, discuss the meaning of solutions. Record what you know about the solutions of an equation that are:

a.   Always true.   b.   Sometimes true.   c.   Never true.

12-5.   Decide if each of the following statements are always true, sometimes true, or never true. If a statement is always true, justify how you know; if it is sometimes true, give the exact values of x that make it true; and if it is never true, explain why it is never true.

a. $3x - 2 - 4(x+1) = -x - 6$ b. $3x - 5 = 2(x+1) + x$

c. $\sin(x) = \cos\left(\frac{\pi}{2} - x\right)$ d. $\tan(x) = 1$

12-6.   Factor each of the following expressions.

a. $x^2 - 4$ b. $y^2 - 81$

c. $1 - x^2$ d. $1 - \sin^2(x)$

12-7.   Solve for x in each of the following triangles. What methods can be used for finding unknown parts of triangles?

a.

b.

c.

12-8.   Show that $\sin(2x) = 2\sin(x)$ only if x is an integer multiple of π.

Core Connections Algebra 2

12-9.   Given the function $f(x) = 2 + \sqrt{2x - 4}$, find:

   a.   The domain and range.

   b.   The inverse equation.

   c.   The domain and range of the inverse.

12-10.   Consider the function $f(x) = 3 \sin (x + \frac{\pi}{2}) - 4$.

   a.   How is its graph different from $f(x) = \sin(x)$?

   b.   Sketch the graph.

12-11.   Every hour, Miguel's Microchips measures the signal strength of a chip from their manufacturing process. For each of the process control charts below, say whether the process is in control, and if not, what in the manufacturing process could have led to the out-of-control state.

12-12.   If you remember what $n!$ means, you can do some messy calculations quickly or compute problems that are too large for your calculator's memory. For instance, if you wanted to calculate $\frac{9!}{6!}$, you could use the $n!$ button on your calculator and find that $9! = 362{,}880$ and $6! = 720$, so $\frac{9!}{6!} = \frac{362{,}880}{720} = 504$. You could also use a simplification technique. Since $9! = 9 \cdot 8 \cdot 7 \cdot 6 \cdot 5 \cdot 4 \cdot 3 \cdot 2 \cdot 1!$ and $6! = 6 \cdot 5 \cdot 4 \cdot 3 \cdot 2 \cdot 1$, you can rewrite $\frac{9!}{6!} = \frac{9 \cdot 8 \cdot 7 \cdot 6 \cdot 5 \cdot 4 \cdot 3 \cdot 2 \cdot 1}{6 \cdot 5 \cdot 4 \cdot 3 \cdot 2 \cdot 1} = 9 \cdot 8 \cdot 7 = 504$.

   Use this simplification technique to simplify each of the following problems before computing the result.

   a. $\frac{10!}{8!}$ b. $\frac{20!}{18!2!}$ c. $\frac{7!}{4!3!}$ d. $\frac{75!}{72!}$

12-13.   If the pep squad has 12 members, in how many ways can five students:

   a.   Line up for a picture in the school newspaper?

   b.   Be chosen to visit the rival school before the big game?

12-14.   List three possible values for h that will make the equation $\cos(x - h) = \sin(x)$ true.

12-15.   If $\pi \le \theta \le \frac{3\pi}{2}$, what must be true about the sign of:

    a. $\sin(\theta)$ b. $\cos(\theta)$ c. $\tan(\theta)$ d. $\frac{1}{\cos(\theta)}$

12-16.   Find all values of a for which the equation $ax^2 + 5x + 6 = 0$ has a solution that is a real number. Express a in terms of one or more inequalities.

12-17.   Using a graph of $f(x) = \cos(x)$ for reference, graph $f(x) = |\cos(x)|$.

12-18.   Factor and reduce the rational expression $\frac{5x+10}{x^2+6x+8}$. Justify each step.

12-19.   Solve each equation.

    a. $\sqrt{x+7} + 5 = x$ b. $\frac{a}{a^2-36} + \frac{2}{a-6} = \frac{1}{a+6}$

12-20.   Change the angle measures below from radians to degrees or degrees to radians.

    a. $108°$ b. $320°$ c. $\frac{7\pi}{9}$

    d. $\frac{19\pi}{12}$ e. $\frac{17\pi}{2}$ f. $260°$

12-21.   A jar contains five red, four white, and three blue balls. If three balls are randomly selected, find the probability of choosing:

    a.   Two red and one white.   b.   Three white.

    c.   One of each color.   d.   All the same color.

    e.   One red and two white.   f.   Two of one color and one of another.

12-22.   Expand.

    a. $(a+b)^3$ b. $(2m+5)^3$

12.1.2 How many solutions are there?

True? When?

Solutions to Trigonometric Equations

In Lesson 12.1.1, you recognized that an equation could be always true, sometimes true, or never true. In the next few lessons you will focus on trigonometric equations that are sometimes true as you learn how to solve them and how to determine the number of solutions they have.

12-23. When is the equation $\cos(x) = \frac{1}{2}$ true?

    a.   What do the solutions to this equation represent?

    b.   Solve the equation graphically. How many solutions can you find on the graph?

    c.   Draw a unit circle showing the solutions to $\cos(x) = \frac{1}{2}$. How many solutions do you see?

12-24. Just as taking the square root ($\sqrt{}$) can be used to undo a square when solving an equation algebraically, there is an undo (inverse) operation for cosine.

    a.   With your team, see if you can find the undo operation for cosine on your calculator. What does it look like? How can you be sure that it is undoing cosine?

    b.   Use the undo operation for cosine on your calculator to solve the equation $\cos(x) = \frac{1}{2}$. Show where the solution given by the calculator can be seen on the graph and on the unit circle.

12-25. With your team, decide how many solutions there are to the equation $\cos(x) = \frac{1}{2}$. Justify your decision using as many representations as you can. How can you write all of them?

12-26. How do all of the solutions to $\cos(x) = \frac{1}{2}$ relate to the one given by $\cos^{-1}(\frac{1}{2})$ on your calculator?

12-27. Find all of the solutions for each equation below. You may use your calculator, but you must represent your solutions graphically and on a unit circle. After you have found all of the solutions, identify which ones lie in the domain $0 \le x \le 2\pi$. Then work with your team to write a summary statement about your solutions.

a. $2\cos(x) + 1 = 0$

b. $\tan(x) = 1$

12-28. Jeremy used the $\sin^{-1}$ button on his calculator to solve a trigonometric equation and got the solution $37°$. He knows that there must be more than one solution. What are the rest of the solutions to Jeremy's equation? Explain how you found them. Use a unit circle and a graph in your explanation.

12-29. For each of the following equations, find the solutions that lie in the domain $0 \le x \le 2\pi$.

a. $2\sin(x) - 1 = 0$

b. $2\cos(x) = -\sqrt{3}$

c. $2\sin(x) = \sqrt{2}$

d. $\cos(x) = 1$

12-30. Salina, Tamara, and Uma are working on their homework together. Salina tells her friends that she got $\theta = 52°$ for the inverse cosine problem she is working on and asks if they got the same answer. Tamara says she got $\theta = 128°$, and Uma volunteers her answer of $\theta = 308°$. Is it possible that these are all solutions to the same problem? Justify your answer.

12-31. Graph $f(x) = 1 + \tan\left(x - \frac{\pi}{4}\right)$.

12-32. What is the inverse of $f(x) = -x + 6$? Justify your answer.

12-33. Simplify, then add $\frac{x-2}{x+2} + \frac{2x-6}{x^2-x-6}$. Justify each step.

12-34. Josephina thinks that she has discovered a new pattern, shown at right.

$$\frac{x-1}{x-1} = 1$$

$$\frac{x^2-1}{x-1} = x+1$$

a. Check her equations by multiplying. Does her pattern work?

$$\frac{x^3-1}{x-1} = x^2+x+1$$

b. Based on her pattern, what does $\frac{x^5-1}{x-1}$ equal? Is it true? Justify your answer.

$$\frac{x^4-1}{x-1} = x^3+x^2+x+1$$

c. Make a conjecture about how to represent the result for $\frac{x^n-1}{x-1}$. You will need "…" in the middle of your expression.

12-35. A number of states are considering legislation that calls for people to get mandatory drug testing in order to qualify for public assistance money. Some argue that mandatory testing of welfare recipients would jeopardize the livelihood of many people who do not have substance abuse problems and is therefore an unwarranted invasion of their privacy.

Consider a hypothetical situation. Suppose that the currently used test for illegal drugs is 99% accurate, and suppose that in the population to be tested (in this case it is the population of people on public assistance of a given state) 2,300 out of 100,000 people are substance abusers. The question is: what is the probability of a "false negative"? That is, the probability that the test identifies a person on public assistance as using drugs when they actually do not use drugs?

a. Make a model for this situation.

b. How does the proportion of people who are using drugs compare with the proportion of people who will be told they are using drugs but really are not?

c. If a randomly tested recipient's test comes back positive, what is the probability that he or she is *not* actually using drugs?

d. Write up your statistical conclusions.

e. Are the test results mathematically independent of using or not using drugs? How could you check this? Explain.

12-36.   If five cards are dealt from a shuffled deck of playing cards:

   a.   What is the probability of getting a five-card hand that is all red?

   b.   Express your solution to part (a) in the form: $\frac{aC_b}{dC_e}$.

   c.   What is the probability of getting a five-card hand that is all clubs?

   d.   Express your solution to part (c) in the form $\frac{aC_b}{dC_e}$.

   e.   What is the probability of getting 5 cards from any one suit?

12-37.   Three light bulbs are chosen at random from 15 bulbs, of which five are defective. What is the probability that:

   a.   None of the three are defective?

   b.   Exactly two are defective?

12.1.3 Is it a function?

True?
When?

Inverses of Trigonometric Functions

In Lesson 12.1.2, you learned how to use the inverse trigonometric functions to undo operations and solve trigonometric equations. You also learned that the keys for the inverse trigonometric functions on your calculator give you only one of the possible solutions to these equations. In this lesson, you will investigate the inverse trigonometric functions more thoroughly. You will determine whether the inverses are also functions.

12-38.　Obtain the Lesson 12.1.3 Resource Page from your teacher.

　　　a.　Make a careful graph of $y = \sin(x)$. Is it a function? What are its domain and range?

　　　b.　Graph the line $y = x$.

　　　c.　Reflect the graph of $y = \sin(x)$ across the line $y = x$ to make a graph of its inverse, $x = \sin(y)$. Is it a function? What are its domain and range?

　　　d:　Discuss with your team the restriction you would need to make on the domain of $y = \sin(x)$ so that its inverse is a function.

12-39.　Now graph $y = \sin^{-1}(x)$ on your graphing calculator. How is the result different from the graph that you made? Does it make sense in terms of your answer to part (d) in the problem above? Highlight the portion of your graph that represents the inverse function and label it with its domain and range. Also highlight the portion of the unit circle (provided on the resource page) that shows the restriction on the domain of $y = \sin(x)$ required to make its inverse a function.

12-40.　Consider the equation $\sin(x) = -\frac{\sqrt{3}}{2}$.

　　　a.　How many solutions does the equation have?

　　　b.　Without using a calculator, find the solutions and show them on the unit circle.

　　　c.　Which solution do you predict your calculator will give? How do you know? Once you have made your prediction, use your calculator to solve $\sin(x) = -\frac{\sqrt{3}}{2}$. Were you correct? (Note that this solution can be written as $\sin^{-1}(-\frac{\sqrt{3}}{2})$.)

12-41. Obtain two more copies of the Lesson 12.1.3 Resource Page from your teacher. Sketch $y = \cos(x)$ and $y = \tan(x)$ on separate axes and label the domain and range of each.

   a. Reflect each graph across the line $y = x$ to generate graphs of the inverse relations.

   b. Find the domain and range of the relations $x = \cos(y)$ and $x = \tan(y)$.

   c. Use your graphing calculator to graph the functions $y = \cos^{-1}(x)$ and $y = \tan^{-1}(x)$. Highlight the portion of your graph that represents the inverse function. Find the domain and range for each function. Then highlight a portion of the unit circle (provided on the resource pages) that shows the domain restrictions required to make the inverses of $y = \cos(x)$ and $y = \tan(x)$ functions.

12-42. For each of the following problems, find all of the solutions without using a calculator. Draw a graph or unit circle to support your answers. Then predict the solution that your calculator will give and use your calculator to check your prediction.

   a. $2\cos(x) - 1 = 0$ b. $\tan(x) = \sqrt{3}$

   c. $2\sin(x) = \sqrt{3}$ d. $4\sin^2(x) - 3 = 0$

Review & Preview

12-43. Solve each equation for $0° \le \theta \le 360°$, or if you prefer, $0 \le \theta \le 2\pi$. You may need your calculator, but remember that it only gives *one* answer.

   a. $\sin(\theta) = 0.5$ b. $\cos(\theta) = -0.5$

   c. $4\tan(\theta) - 4 = 0$ d. $3\sin^2(\theta) = 1$

12-44. State the domain and range for each graph below. Then state whether or not it is a function.

a.

b.

c.

d.

12-45. Solve each equation. Check for extraneous solutions.

a. $\sqrt{x+7} = x+1$

b. $\frac{2}{x+3} - \frac{1}{x} = \frac{-6}{x^2+3x}$

12-46. Graph.

a. $(-2, 3, -2)$

b. $3x - 2y - 3z = -6$

12-47. Solve each system.

a. $\frac{x}{2} + \frac{y}{4} = 4$

   $\frac{x}{4} - \frac{3y}{8} = -2$

b. $x + 2y + z = -1$

   $4x - y - z = -1$

   $-3y = 2z$

12-48. Governments and security companies are coming to rely more heavily on facial recognition software to locate persons of interest.

Consider a hypothetical situation. Suppose that facial recognition software can accurately identify a person 99.9% of the time, and suppose the suspect is among 200,000 facial images available to a government agency. When the software makes a positive identification, what is the probability that it is not the suspect?

a. Make a model for this situation.

b. If a person has been identified as the suspect, what is the probability that he or she is *not* actually the suspect?

12-49. A pizza parlor has 12 toppings other than cheese. How many different pizzas can be created with five *or fewer* toppings? List all subproblems and calculate the solution.

12-50. Find $(2x^5 - 6x^4 - 2x^2 + 7x - 4) \div (x - 3)$.

12-51. A glass factory makes a continuous ribbon of glass by pouring a continuous stream of hot liquid silicon on a lake of molten tin. The liquid silicon spreads out evenly on the tin and then cools into glass. It is a process that must continue uninterrupted 24 hours a day, so adjustments to equipment and materials are ongoing. Assume that inspectors work eight-hour shifts, watching the glass ribbon as it flows from the lake of tin, marking and counting the number of defects on the new glass. The number of defects identified by the inspectors for a 24-hour period is shown below:

Hour	1	2	3	4	5	6	7	8	9	10	11	12
Defects	43	40	42	40	38	39	36	38	44	41	45	42

Hour	13	14	15	16	17	18	19	20	21	22	23	24
Defects	40	37	39	39	43	40	42	42	38	41	38	37

a. Create an x-bar process control chart with a UCL of 45 and an LCL of 35.

b. What do you notice about the process control chart that might concern you as a quality control engineer?

12-52. Hector missed the beginning of this lesson, and he is confused about domains for inverse functions. Explain why restrictions are needed. Describe specifically the restrictions that each trigonometric function (sine, cosine, and tangent) requires in order to find its inverse function.

12-53. For each of the following problems, find all of the solutions without using a calculator. Use a graph or unit circle to support your answers. Then predict the solution that your calculator will give and use your calculator to check your prediction.

a. $4\sin(x) + 2 = 0$

b. $2\cos(x) = \sqrt{3}$

c. $\tan(x) + 1 = 0$

d. $4\cos^2(x) - 4 = 0$

12-54. Explain each transformation below in terms of the parent graph $f(\theta) = \tan\theta$.

    a. $f(\theta) = \tan\theta + 1$ b. $f(\theta) = \tan(\theta + \frac{\pi}{4})$

    c. $f(\theta) = -\tan(\theta)$ d. $f(\theta) = 4\tan\theta$

12-55. Quickly sketch each of the following functions.

    a. $f(x) = (x-1)^2(x-3)^3(x-5)^2$

    b. $g(x) = -(x-1)^2(x-3)^3(x-5)^2$

    c.   Express $g(x)$ in terms of $f(x)$.

12-56. Rewrite each sum below as a single expression.

    a. $\frac{1}{2} + \frac{1}{3}$ b. $\frac{3}{2x} + \frac{4}{x^2}$

    c. $\frac{x}{x+1} + \frac{3}{x-1}$ d. $\frac{\sin\theta}{\cos\theta} + \frac{1}{\sin\theta}$

12-57. Rewrite $f(x) = 2x^2 - 4x + 1$ in graphing form. State its domain, range, vertex and line of symmetry. Include a labeled sketch as part of your solution.

12-58. Solve the following equations. Round to three decimal places. Be sure to check your answers.

    a. $7 = 4.2^x$ b. $3x^5 = 126$ c. $14 = 2 \cdot 4^x - 10$

12-59. Expand.

    a. $(a+b)^4$ b. $(3m-2)^4$

12-60. Another pizza parlor had a super special. The parlor had a rack of small pizzas, each with three or four different toppings. The price was really low because an employee forgot to indicate on the boxes what toppings were on each pizza. Eight toppings were available, and one pizza was made for each of the possible combinations of three or four toppings.

    a.   How many pizzas were on the rack?

    b.   What was the probability of getting a pizza that had mushrooms on it?

12.1.4 What is the reciprocal?

Reciprocal Trigonometric Functions

In this lesson, you will investigate the reciprocal trigonometric functions and their graphs.

12-61.   Your team will investigate the graph of the reciprocal of $y = \sin(x)$.
Obtain a Lesson 12.1.4A Resource Page from your teacher.

a.   Using values on the x-axis as your inputs, complete the table on your resource page and make a careful graph of $y = \sin(x)$.

b.   Now you will use the values in your table to help you make a graph of the reciprocal of $y = \sin(x)$, which can be written as $y = \frac{1}{\sin(x)}$. Label the third column in your table $\frac{1}{\sin(x)}$. To find the values that go in this column, calculate the reciprocal of each value for $\sin(x)$.

c.   Where are the outputs for $\sin(0)$, $\sin(\frac{\pi}{2})$, and $\sin(\pi)$ located on the graph? What is true about the reciprocal function at these locations in your table? How would they appear on your graph?

d.   Now, using a colored pencil, graph $y = \frac{1}{\sin(x)}$ carefully.

e.   This ratio that is the reciprocal of sine is named **cosecant**. The cosecant function can be abbreviated by $f(x) = \csc(x)$. Label your graph with its name, "Cosecant."

12-62.   Is $y = \csc(x)$ a function?

a.   What are its domain and range?

b.   What are the intercepts?

c.   Are there asymptotes? If so, what are their equations?

d.   Describe the relationship between the sine and cosecant graphs.

12-63.   Use your graph to solve each of the following equations in the domain $0 \le x \le 2\pi$. What do you notice about each of the solutions?

a. $\sin(x) = \frac{1}{2}$

b. $\csc(x) = 2$

c. $\sin(x) = 1$

d. $\csc(x) = 1$

e. $\sin(x) = \frac{\sqrt{3}}{2}$

f. $\csc(x) = \frac{2}{\sqrt{3}}$

12-64.   Is there an inverse cosecant button on your calculator? How could
you use your calculator to solve $\csc(x) = 3.5$?

12-65.   Obtain the Lesson 12.1.4C and Lesson 12.1.4D Resource Pages from your
teacher. Use the same process as you did in problem 12-61 to create graphs of
the reciprocal of the cosine function (named **secant** and abbreviated
$f(x) = \sec(x)$) and the reciprocal of the tangent function (named **cotangent** and
abbreviated $f(x) = \cot(x)$). What are the domains and ranges for these
functions?

12-66.   For each of the following equations, work with your team to decide if it is
always true, sometimes true, or never true. If it is always true, explain how you
know; if it is sometimes true, give the exact values of x that make it true; and if
it is never true, explain why it is never true. Hint: Use what you have learned
above and the idea of rewriting to get started.

a. $\sin^2(x)\csc(x) = \frac{\sqrt{3}}{2}$

b. $\sec^2(x) = \frac{2}{\cos(x)}$

c. $\tan(x)\sec(x)\sin(x) = 0$

d. $\sec^2(x)\cos(x) = 0$

e. $\cos(x)\sec(x) = 1$

$\mathbf{M}$ETHODS AND $\mathbf{M}$EANINGS

MATH NOTES

Inverses of Trigonometric Functions

To find the inverse function for a trigonometric function, the domain of the original function has to be restricted. For each function, the restriction is different.

For sine, restricting the domain to $-\frac{\pi}{2} \leq x \leq \frac{\pi}{2}$ leads to the inverse function, $y = \sin^{-1} x$ with domain $-1 \leq x \leq 1$ and range $-\frac{\pi}{2} \leq y \leq \frac{\pi}{2}$.

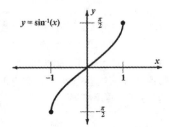

For cosine, restricting the domain to $0 \leq x \leq \pi$ gives a good piece of the graph close to the origin, and gives an inverse function $y = \cos^{-1} x$, with domain $-1 \leq x \leq 1$ and range $0 \leq y \leq \pi$.

For tangent, the restriction is $-\frac{\pi}{2} < x < \frac{\pi}{2}$, so the domain for the inverse tangent $y = \tan^{-1} x$ is all real numbers and the range is $-\frac{\pi}{2} < y < \frac{\pi}{2}$.

636   *Core Connections Algebra 2*

12-67.   Using the triangle on the right, find:

a. $\sin A$ b. $\sec A$

c. $\csc B$ d. $\tan B$

12-68.   Solve each equation below for x if $-2\pi \le x \le 2\pi$.

a. $4\sin^2(x) = 1$ b. $3\tan^2(x) = 1$

12-69.   Solve $2\sin(x)\cos(x) - \sin(x) = 0$ in the domain $0 \le x \le 2\pi$. Give answers in degrees or radians.

12-70.   Solve for x in the figure at right.

12-71.   If the cost of a CD now averages \$15.95 and in 4 years will be \$21.95, what are the annual multiplier and the annual percent increase?

12-72.   Multiply the expressions in parts (a) through (d).

a. $(a+b)(a^2 - ab + b^2)$ b. $(x-2)(x^2 + 2x + 4)$

c. $(y+5)(y^2 - 5y + 25)$ d. $(x-y)(x^2 + xy + y^2)$

e.   What did you notice about these products?

f.   Make up another multiplication problem that follows the same pattern.

12-73. Parts (a) through (d) of problem 12-72 represent a general pattern known as the **sum and difference of cubes**. Use this pattern to factor each of the following polynomials.

a. $x^3 + y^3$ b. $x^3 - 27$ c. $8x^3 - y^3$ d. $x^3 + 1$

e. Make up another problem involving the sum or difference of cubes and show how to factor it.

12-74. Find the equation of a cubic function that has $y = x^3$ as its parent graph, a locator point at $(-6,-10)$, and passes through the origin.

12-75. From the 13 spades in a deck of cards, four are selected. Find the probability that:

a. Exactly one card is a "face" card (Jack, Queen, or King).

b. The four cards can be rearranged to form a sequence $(A, 2, 3, 4; 2, 3, 4, 5; \dots; J, Q, K, A)$.

12-76. Using the triangle on the right, find:

a. $\sec B$ b. $\tan A$

c. $\cot A$ d. $\csc A$

12-77. Find all solutions to $2 \sin(x) \cos(x) + \cos(x) = 0$. Give your answers in degrees or radians.

12-78. If $f(x) = 2x^2 - 3$ and $g(x) = x + 1$, find $f(g(x))$.

12-79. Use the sum or difference of cubes and what you already know about factoring to factor the following expressions as completely as possible.

a. $x^5 + 8x^2y^3$

b. $8y^6 - 125x^3$

c. $x^6 - y^6$ (Note: This is tricky. If you start it as the difference of two cubes, you will not be able to factor it completely. Think of it as the difference of two squares and then factor the factors as the sum and difference of two cubes.)

12-80. Write an equation for the curve at right. Then sketch the graph of the inverse of this function and write its equation.

12-81. An exponential function has an asymptote at $y = 5$ and passes through the points $(2, 5.64)$ and $(-1, 15)$. Find the equation of the function.

12-82. What is the fifth term of each expansion?

a. $(a+b)^9$

b. $(2x+y)^8$

12-83. Write a quadratic equation with roots $x = 3 \pm 5i$.

12-84. Sure Shot Jane can hit the bull's eye with a bow and arrow 90% of the time. If she shoots five arrows, what is the probability that three or more arrows hit the bull's eye?

12.2.1 How can I rewrite it?

Trigonometric Identities

To solve many trigonometric equations, it is first necessary to rewrite the equation in a simpler form. In this lesson, you will solve trigonometric equations graphically and will develop methods for rewriting those equations so that you can solve them algebraically.

12-85. Consider the equation $2 \sin(x) \cos(x) = \frac{1}{2}$ for the domain $0 \le x \le 2\pi$.

    a. Do you have tools to solve this equation algebraically?

    b. Use your graphing calculator to graph $y = 2 \sin(x) \cos(x)$ and $y = \frac{1}{2}$ in the domain $0 \le x \le 2\pi$. Copy the graph onto your paper and use it to approximate the solutions to $2 \sin(x) \cos(x) = \frac{1}{2}$. How many solutions are there in this domain?

    c. Crystal was working on this problem and noticed that the graph of $y = 2 \sin(x) \cos(x)$ looked just like the graph of a regular cyclic function. She thought it must be possible to write a different equivalent equation for this graph. Work with your team to write a cyclic equation for this graph. Is there more than one? If so, which is the simplest?

    d. Using your equivalent equation from part (c), rewrite the equation $2 \sin(x) \cos(x) = \frac{1}{2}$ and solve it algebraically. How do your solutions compare to those you approximated from your graph?

    e. Write an algebraic statement showing that these two expressions are equivalent. This is called the **Double Angle Identity** for sine.

12-86.   DISCOVERING IDENTITIES GRAPHICALLY

The graphs of some other trigonometric functions can be used to rewrite the functions and create new identities. Use a method similar to the method used in problem 12-85 to rewrite each of the following equations. Then use your result to write a new identity.

$y = \cos(-x)$ $y = \sin(-x)$

$y = \cos(\frac{\pi}{2} - x)$ $y = \sin(\frac{\pi}{2} - x)$

$y = \sin^2(x)$ $y = \cos^2(x)$

$y = \cos^2(x) - \sin^2(x)$ $y = \cos^2(x) + \sin^2(x)$

12-87.   Obtain the Lesson 12.2.1 Resource Page from your teacher. This resource page will be referred to as your Identity Toolkit. Record each identity you have discovered along with its justification.

12-88.   Use your new identities to help you rewrite and solve the following equations in the given domains.

   a. $2\cos(\frac{\pi}{2} - x) = 1$ for all x b. $\cos^2(x) - \sin^2(x) = \frac{\sqrt{3}}{2}$ for $0 \le x \le 2\pi$

12-89.   One of the identities in problem 12-86 you initially worked with in Chapter 7. Recall that $\cos^2(x) + \sin^2(x) = 1$ is called the **Pythagorean Identity**. It is one of the most useful identities you will learn.

   a.   Work with your team to explore the following question: Why is $\cos^2(x) + \sin^2(x) = 1$ called the Pythagorean Identity? Does it have anything to do with the Pythagorean Theorem? Be prepared to share your ideas with the class.

   b.   Two more very useful identities can come directly from the Pythagorean Identity. To discover the first related identity, divide both sides of the equation by $\cos^2(x)$. For the second related identity, divide both sides of the equation by $\sin^2(x)$. Add these two new identities to your Identity Toolkit (Lesson 12.2.1 Resource Page).

12-90. Rewrite each of the following expressions in a simpler form.

a. $\cos^2(\theta - \pi) + \sin^2(\theta - \pi)$ b. $\cos^2(2w) - \sin^2(2w)$ c. $\frac{\sin\theta}{\cos\theta}$

12-91. An isosceles triangle has sides with lengths 10, 10, and 5 cm. What are the measures of the angles in the triangle?

12-92. Solve for x in *degrees*.

a. $2\sin(x) = 1$ b. $\cos^2(x) + 4\cos(x) + 4 = 0$

12-93. Divide $(6x^3 - 5x^2 + 5x - 2)$ by $(2x - 1)$.

12-94. Divide $(x^4 - 7x^2 + 3x + 18)$ by $(x + 2)$.

12-95. Mr. Dobson is planning to give a quiz to his class tomorrow. Unfortunately for his students, Mr. Dobson is notorious for writing quizzes that seem to have no relevance to the subject. With this in mind, his students know that their efforts will be purely guesswork. If the quiz contains ten questions that the students will have to match with ten given answers, what is the probability that Rodney Random will get all ten questions matched correctly?

12-96. Which is greater: $(5-2)!$ or $(5-3)!$? Justify your answer.

12-97. If $f(x) = x^2 + 7x$, calculate the value of:

a. $f(2)$ b. $f(-3)$ c. $f(i)$

d. $f(-3.5 + 1.5i)$ e. x if $f(x) = 0$.

12-98.   Each labeled point on the graph below is either a maximum or a minimum.

   a.   Find the period and amplitude of the graph.

   b.   Find an equation for the graph.

   c.   Use one of the labeled points to check your equation.

(15,23)

(81,−17)

12-99.   Rewrite the Pythagorean Identity as many ways as you can. One way to change the identity is to solve the equation for one trigonometric function. Another way is to use factoring. Try several different ways.

12-100. If $\pi \le \theta \le \frac{3\pi}{2}$ and $\sin\theta = -\frac{3}{5}$, find $\cos\theta$. Use what you know about the Pythagorean Identity and the unit circle to get started.

12-101. Rewrite each of the following expressions in terms of either $\sin(\theta)$ or $\cos(\theta)$.

   a. $\tan(\theta)$ b. $\csc(\theta)$ c. $\cot(\theta)$ d. $\sec(\theta)$

12-102. Given the points $(2, 9)$ and $(4, 324)$:

   a.   Write the equation of a line that passes through them.

   b.   Write the equation of an exponential function with an asymptote at $y = 0$ that passes through them.

12-103. Without graphing, determine where the graphs of $f(x) = 2x^2 - 3x + 1$ and $g(x) = 4x - 2$ intersect.

12-104. Simplify each rational expression below.

   a. $\dfrac{\frac{x+1}{2x}}{\frac{x^2-1}{x}}$ b. $\dfrac{\frac{4}{x+3}}{\frac{1}{x}+3}$

12-105.   Find $m\angle C$ in each triangle below.

a.

b.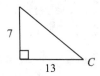

12-106.   For the function $f(x) = 5x^2 + 4x + 20$, find the roots and the vertex of the graph. Then rewrite the equation in graphing form.

12-107.   Hospital records show that 10% of all the cases of a certain disease are fatal. If five patients suffer from this disease, find the probability that:

a.   All will recover.

b.   At least three will die.

12.2.2 How can I prove it?

Proving Trigonometric Identities

In Lesson 12.2.1 you investigated trigonometric identities by graphing trigonometric functions and determining what other trigonometric functions were equivalent. Now you will learn how to use your algebra skills to prove trigonometric identities.

12-108. Polly Parabola has a cousin named Thomas Trig. The Functions of America and Professional Parabola Productions companies have enjoyed such huge success that Thomas has decided to open a company called Identity Island. However, to do this, he needs some help and has sent your team the following memo.

> *Dear Study Team,*
>
> *My goal for Identity Island is to be able to offer a wide selection of trigonometric identities to interested customers. I found a list of identities on the Internet, but I know that lots of information on the Internet is false! I cannot afford to be embarrassed in front of my potential customers by offering identities that are not true.*
>
> *I need your help. I need a solid algebraic proof on file for each identity that we offer. Please submit a report by the end of the day that demonstrates each of the identities algebraically.*
>
> *I have the utmost faith in your team's abilities. Thank you for your time!*
>
> *Sincerely,*
>
> *Thomas Trig*

Your Task: Work with your team to demonstrate algebraically if each of the identities below is always true, never true, or sometimes true. To prove some of the identities, you will need to refer to the identities that you developed in Lesson 12.2.1.

a. $\cot(x) + \tan(x) = \sec(x)\csc(x)$

b. $(1 - \sin x)(1 + \sin x) = \frac{1}{1 + \tan^2(x)}$

c. $\frac{1}{\sec^2(x)} + \frac{1}{\csc^2(x)} = 1$

d. $\sec^2(x) - \csc^2(x) = \tan^2(x) - \cot^2(x)$

e. $\frac{\sec(x)}{\tan(x) + \cot(x)} = \sin(x)$

f. $\sin^2(x)\cot^2(x) + \cos^2(x)\tan^2(x) = 1$

g. $\frac{\csc^2(x) - 1}{\csc^2(x)} = \cos^2(x)$

h. $\frac{\sin x}{\cos x} + \frac{\cos x}{\sin x} = 2$

12-109.   A 125-foot redwood tree is leaning 20° off vertical. How long will its shadow be when the angle the sunlight makes with the ground is 68°?

12-110.   Divide each of the following polynomials, $P(x)$, by $D(x)$ to find the quotient $Q(x)$ and then rewrite the polynomial in the form $P(x) = D(x) \cdot Q(x) + R$, where R is the remainder.

a. $P(x) = 2x^4 - x^2 + 3x + 5$

   $D(x) = x - 1$

b. $P(x) = x^5 - 2x^3 + 1$

   $D(x) = x - 3$

12-111.   Without using a calculator, solve each equation below in the domain $0 \le x \le 2\pi$.

a. $\sin(x) = -1$

b. $2\cos(x) - 1 = 0$

c. $\tan(x) = 1$

d. $2\sin(x) = 4\sin(x) + 1$

12-112.   Solve for x.

a.

b.

12-113.   Andrea has just purchased a five-digit combination lock that allows her to set up her own combination. She can use the numbers 0 through 9 for her combination, and she must use five digits.

a.   How many five-digit combinations can she make so that no digit is repeated?

b.   How many five-digit combinations are possible if she *can* repeat the digits, but cannot use the same digit twice in a row?

12-114.   Use the Pythagorean Identity to find the missing coordinate of this point on the unit circle: $(?, \frac{4}{5})$.

12-115. Change the equation $x^2 + 8x + y^2 - 12y = 12$ to graphing form and sketch a graph.

12-116. At the Bright Idea Lighting Company 10 flashlights are sampled each hour to determine whether the manufacturing process is in control. The UCL is 0.10 defective, and the LCL is 0.05 defective.

   a.   Create a process control chart for the following hours.

Hour	1	2	3	4	5	6	7	8	9	10	11	12	13
proportion defective	0.06	0.08	0.09	0.06	0.05	0.08	0.08	0.07	0.11	0.10	0.05	0.07	0.04

hour	14	15	16	17	18	19	20	21	22	23	24	25	
proportion defective	0.08	0.08	0.09	0.08	0.09	0.09	0.08	0.09	0.10	0.06	0.05	0.05	*checksum* 1.88

   b.   As a quality control engineer for Bright Idea, what do you report about the process control?

12-117. Simplify each expression.

   a. $\dfrac{2x^2 - 5x - 3}{3x^2 - 11x + 6}$

   b. $\dfrac{x^3 - 8}{4x^3 - 3x^2 - 10x}$

12-118. Prove that each of the following equations is an identity. In other words, prove that they are each true for all values for which the functions are defined.

   a. $(\sin\theta + \cos\theta)^2 = 1 + 2\sin\theta\cos\theta$

   b. $\tan\theta + \cot\theta = \sec\theta\csc\theta$

   c. $(\tan\theta\cos\theta)(\sin^2\theta + \frac{1}{\sec^2\theta}) = \sin\theta$

12-119. Solve $\frac{2 + \sin^2\theta}{3} = \frac{3}{4}$ in the domain $0 \le \theta \le 2\pi$. Show your solutions on a unit circle.

12-120. If the side lengths of $\triangle ABC$ are $a = 9$, $b = 10$, and $c = 5$, calculate the measure of the largest angle.

12-121. Write an equation for the curve shown at right. Is it a function? Justify your answer.

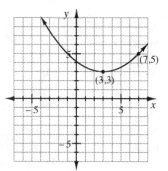

12-122. Solve for x, correct to three decimal places.

a. $27 = 6^x$

b. $27 = \dfrac{1}{6^x}$

c. $27 = \dfrac{1}{(\frac{1}{6})^x}$

d. Show that $\dfrac{1}{(\frac{1}{6})^x} = 6^x$.

12-123. Solve each system of equations. Explain the graphical implications of your answer.

a. $3x - 2y = -10$
$4x + y = 49$

b. $7x - 2y = 11$
$14x - 4y = 3$

12-124. Here is another way to think about the question: *"What is 0! ?"*

a. How many ways are there to choose all five items from a group of five items? What happens when you substitute into the factorial formula to compute $_5C_5$? Since you know (logically) what the result has to be, use this to explain what 0! must be equal to.

b. On the other hand, how many ways are there to choose *nothing* from a group of five items? And what happens when you try to use the factorial formula to compute $_5C_0$?

12-125. The area of $\triangle ABC$ is 24 square inches. If $\overline{AB} \perp \overline{BC}$ and $BC = 8$ inches, find AC.

12-126. Find a polynomial function of degree three with roots $x = 3, 1 \pm i$. Express your answer in standard form.

12.2.3 What about sums and differences?

Angle Sum and Difference Identities

In this lesson you will use your knowledge of relationships in the unit circle to develop four new identities called the Angle Sum and Difference Identities.

12-127.   Danny and Damian were working on finding identities. They thought it would be useful to look at the sums and differences of angles. They started with a unit circle and created the angles α and β as shown at right. They recognized that they had formed a triangle, $\triangle POQ$.

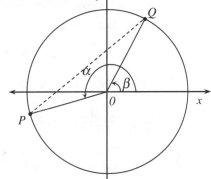

a.   Write the measure of the obtuse angle in $\triangle POQ$ in terms of α and β.

b.   Danny and Damian each realized that they could calculate the length of side PQ of their triangle, but they wanted to use two different methods. What are the two methods they could have been thinking of?

c.   Danny wanted to use the idea of distance between points P and Q to calculate the length. In order to do that, he needed to label the coordinates of points P and Q. Based on angles α and β, represent the coordinates of each point using trigonometric functions.

d.   Use your answer from part (c) to write an expression for the distance between points P and Q.

e.   Damian realized that since this is a unit circle, the lengths of OP and OQ are both one unit, so he wanted to use the Law of Cosines. Use the Law of Cosines to write an expression for the length of side PQ.

f.   Since the expressions you wrote for parts (d) and (e) both represent the length of PQ, what equation can you write? Simplify your equation to write a formula for $\cos(\alpha - \beta)$. This is called the **Angle Difference Identity** for cosine. Add this to your Identity Toolkit (Lesson 12.2.1 Resource Page).

12-128.   Danny and Damian were so pleased with this result that they wanted to keep going. They wanted to know how they could rewrite $\cos(\alpha + \beta)$. As they were thinking about this, Damian had a realization. *"I know how we could figure it out!"* he exclaimed. *"We could use the identity we already found to rewrite it as* $\cos(\alpha - (-\beta))$, *since that's the same thing as* $\cos(\alpha + \beta)$." Work with your team to use this idea to find the **Angle Sum Identity** for cosine.

12-129.   *"So now we have the sum and difference formulas for cosine, but what about for sine?"* Damian asked. Danny pondered this for a while and then remembered an identity he thought they could use to figure these out. *"Don't we have an identity that relates sine to cosine?"* he asked.

a.   Which identity is Danny thinking of?

b.   Danny and Damian realized that they could use this to rewrite $\sin(\alpha + \beta)$. Work with your team to rewrite $\sin(\alpha + \beta)$ and find the **Angle Sum Identity** for sine.

c.   Now work with your team to develop the **Angle Difference Identity** for the sine. Be prepared to share your strategies with the class.

METHODS AND MEANINGS

Trigonometric Identities

Identities are equations that are true for all values for which the functions are defined.

$$\cos(-x) = \cos(x) \qquad \sin(-x) = -\sin(x)$$

Reciprocal Trigonometric Functions:

$$\csc(x) = \frac{1}{\sin(x)} \qquad \sec(x) = \frac{1}{\cos(x)} \qquad \cot(x) = \frac{1}{\tan(x)}$$

Pythagorean Identities:

$$\sin^2(x) + \cos^2(x) = 1 \qquad \tan^2(x) + 1 = \sec^2 x \qquad 1 + \cot^2(x) = \csc^2(x)$$

Cofunction Identities:

$$\sin(x) = \cos\left(\tfrac{\pi}{2} - x\right) \qquad \cos(x) = \sin\left(\tfrac{\pi}{2} - x\right) \qquad \sec(x) = \csc\left(\tfrac{\pi}{2} - x\right)$$

$$\csc(x) = \sec\left(\tfrac{\pi}{2} - x\right) \qquad \tan(x) = \cot\left(\tfrac{\pi}{2} - x\right) \qquad \cot(x) = \tan\left(\tfrac{\pi}{2} - x\right)$$

Angle Sum and Difference Identities:

$$\sin(x+y) = \sin(x)\cos(y) + \cos(x)\sin(y)$$

$$\sin(x-y) = \sin(x)\cos(y) - \cos(x)\sin(y)$$

$$\cos(x+y) = \cos(x)\cos(y) - \sin(x)\sin(y)$$

$$\cos(x-y) = \cos(x)\cos(y) + \sin(x)\sin(y)$$

Double Angle Identities:

$$\sin(2x) = 2\sin(x)\cos(x)$$

$$\cos(2x) = \cos^2(x) - \sin^2(x)$$

12-130. Write $\frac{\pi}{12}$ as the difference of two special angles. Then use the appropriate angle difference formula to find the exact sine and cosine of $\frac{\pi}{12}$.

12-131. Write each angle as the sum or difference of two special angles and then find the exact sine or cosine.

a. $\sin\frac{7\pi}{12}$

b. $\cos\frac{11\pi}{12}$

12-132. Show how to derive the double angle formulas for $\sin(2x)$ and $\cos(2x)$ by substituting x for both α and β in the formulas for $\sin(\alpha + \beta)$ and $\cos(\alpha + \beta)$, then simplifying.

12-133. Consider the function $f(x) = \cos(x + \frac{\pi}{2})$.

   a. Make a complete graph of $f(x)$.

   b. Write a simpler trig function that is represented by the same graph.

   c. Now use the angle sum identity to expand and simplify $\cos(x + \frac{\pi}{2})$.

   d. Does your work in part (c) agree with your graphical results from parts (a) and (b)? Explain.

12-134. Express $\frac{\cos x}{1 - \tan x} - \frac{\sin x}{\cot x - 1}$ in terms of $\sin x$ and $\cos x$ and then simplify.

12-135. Latisha had graphed the polynomial $y = x^3 - 5x^2 + 8x - 6$ during class and remembered that it had one real root at $x = 3$. Explain how you could use division to find the other roots, and then find them.

12-136. Without using a calculator, solve these two problems from a college entrance exam.

   a. If $x^{-4/3} + 1 = 17$, find $x^{-1/3}$.

   b. If $\log(A) = a$, find $\log(\frac{A}{100})$.

12-137. In a certain family, the probability of any one child having dark hair is $\frac{3}{4}$. If the family has three children, what is the probability that exactly one has dark hair?

Chapter 12 Closure   What have I learned?

Reflection and Synthesis

The activities below offer you a chance to reflect about what you have learned during this chapter. As you work, look for concepts that you feel very comfortable with, ideas that you would like to learn more about, and topics you need more help with. Look for connections between ideas as well as connections with material you learned previously.

①   TEAM BRAINSTORM

What have you studied in this chapter? What ideas were important in what you learned? With your team, brainstorm a list. Be as detailed as you can. To help get you started, a list of Math Notes boxes are below. (There were no Learning Log entries in this chapter.)

What topics, ideas, and words that you learned *before* this chapter are connected to the new ideas in this chapter? Again, be as detailed as you can.

How long can you make your list? Challenge yourselves. Be prepared to share your team's ideas with the class.

Math Notes

- Lesson 12.1.4 – Inverses of Trigonometric Functions
- Lesson 12.2.3 – Trigonometric Identities

②   **MAKING CONNECTIONS**

Below is a list of the vocabulary used in this chapter. Make sure that you are familiar with all of these words and know what they mean. Refer to the glossary or index for any words that you do not yet understand.

$\cos^{-1}$	cosecant	cotangent
identity	inverse	reciprocal
secant	$\sin^{-1}$	solution
$\tan^{-1}$		

Make a concept map showing all of the connections you can find among the key words and ideas listed above. To show a connection between two words, draw a line between them and explain the connection. A word can be connected to any other word as long as you can justify the connection. For each key word or idea, provide an example or sketch that shows the idea.

While you are making your map, your team may think of related words or ideas that are not listed here. Be sure to include these ideas on your concept map.

③   **PORTFOLIO: EVIDENCE OF MATHEMATICAL PROFICIENCY**

This section gives you an opportunity to show growth in your understanding of key mathematical ideas over time as you complete this course.

In this portfolio entry you are going to showcase your current understanding of Analytic Trigonometry. You are also going to showcase your ability to write a meaningful portfolio entry.

Make a list of the big ideas of this chapter. What have you studied in this chapter? What ideas were important in what you learned? Try to keep your list short: limit yourself to no more than five of the biggest ideas.

a.   Write your own description of each big idea.

b.   For each big idea, provide one or two representative example problems. Solve each problem completely, using multiple representations, if applicable. Include a thorough explanation and justification.

④

Most of the problems in this section represent typical problems found in this chapter. They serve as a gauge for you. You can use them to determine which types of problems you can do well and which types of problems require further study and practice. Even if your teacher does not assign this section, it is a good idea to try these problems and find out for yourself what you know and what you still need to work on.

Solve each problem as completely as you can. The table at the end of the closure section has answers to these problems. It also tells you where you can find additional help and practice with problems like these.

CL 12-138.   Decide if each of the following statements is sometimes true, always true, or never true. If it is sometimes true, give the values for x that make it true; if it is always true or never true, explain how you know.

a. $\cos(x) = \frac{3}{4}$

b. $2\tan(x) = 0$

c. $\sin(x) = \frac{5}{2}$

d. $\sin(x) = \cos\left(\frac{\pi}{2} - x\right)$

CL 12-139.   Solve each of the following equations in the domain $0 \le x < 2\pi$.

a. $2\cos(x) = 1$

b. $4\tan(x) + 4 = 0$

c. $2\sin^2(x) - \sin(x) - 1 = 0$

d. $\csc(x) = -2$

CL 12-140.   An angle θ on the unit circle has a cosine of $\frac{1}{3}$. Find the exact coordinates of point Q by using the Pythagorean Identity.

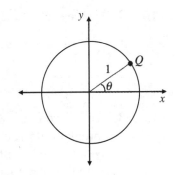

CL 12-141. Solve each of the following equations in the domain $0 \le x \le 2\pi$.

  a. $\cot(x) = 1.2$

  b. $\cos(x) = -1$

  c. $\frac{1}{4}\csc(x) = \sin(x)$

  d. $\cos(2x) = \frac{1}{2}$

CL 12-142. Using radian measure, represent all possible solutions to each equation.

  a. $\tan(x) = \sqrt{3}$

  b. $\cos(x) = -\frac{\sqrt{2}}{2}$

  c. $\sin(x) = \frac{\sqrt{3}}{2}$

  d. $\cot(x) = -1$

CL 12-143. Graph each of the following functions.

  a. $y = 3\sin 2(x - \frac{\pi}{4}) + 1$

  b. $f(x) = -2\cos(x + \frac{\pi}{12}) - 1$

CL 12-144. Find the roots of the function $f(x) = x^4 + x^3 + 2x - 4$.

CL 12-145. Find the vertex of the parabola given by each quadratic equation below.

  a. $f(x) = x^2 + 8x + 12$

  b. $g(x) = x^2 - 2x + 3$

CL 12-146. Write a possible equation for the graph at right.

CL 12-147. Solve each of the following equations.

  a. $5^x = 72$

  b. $2^{3x} = 7$

  c. $3^{(2x+4)} = 17$

CL 12-148. Check your answers using the table at the end of this section. Which problems do you feel confident about? Which problems were hard? Have you worked on problems like these in math classes you have taken before? Use the table to make a list of topics you need help on and a list of topics you need to practice more.

Answers and Support for Closure Activity #4
What Have I Learned?

Note: MN = Math Note, LL = Learning Log

Problem	Solutions	Need Help?	More Practice
CL 12-138.	a. True when $x \approx 0.72 + 2\pi n$ radians or when $x \approx 5.56 + 2\pi n$ radians. b. True for $x = \pi n$ radians. c. Never true. The range of sine is $-1 \le y \le 1$. d. Always true.	Lesson 12.1.1	Problems 12-2, 12-5, 12-14, 12-23, and 12-66
CL 12-139.	a. $x = \frac{\pi}{3}, \frac{5\pi}{3}$ b. $x = \frac{3\pi}{4}, \frac{7\pi}{4}$ c. $x = \frac{7\pi}{6}, \frac{11\pi}{6}, \frac{\pi}{2}$ d. $x = \frac{7\pi}{6}, \frac{11\pi}{6}$	Lessons 12.1.2, 12.1.4, and 12.2.1 MN: 12.1.4	Problems 12-29, 12-43, 12-53, 12-63, 12-68, 12-69, 12-77, 12-111, and 12-119
CL 12-140.	$\left(\frac{1}{3}, \frac{\sqrt{8}}{3} \right)$	Lesson 7.1.4 and problem 12-94	Problems 7-53, 7-64, 7-89, 12-90 part (a), 12-100, and 12-114
CL 12-141.	a. $x \approx 0.69$ radians or $x \approx 3.84$ radians b. $x = \pi$ c. $x = \frac{\pi}{6}, \frac{5\pi}{6}, \frac{7\pi}{6}, \frac{11\pi}{6}$ d. $x = \frac{\pi}{6}, \frac{5\pi}{6}, \frac{7\pi}{6}, \frac{11\pi}{6}$	Lessons 12.1.2 and 12.1.4 MN: 12.1.4 and 12.2.3	Problems 12-63, 12-64, 12-68, 12-69, 12-77, 12-111, and 12-119
CL 12-142.	a. $x = \frac{\pi}{3} + \pi n$ b. $x = \frac{3\pi}{4} + 2\pi n, \frac{5\pi}{4} + 2\pi n$ c. $x = \frac{\pi}{3} + 2\pi n, \frac{2\pi}{3} + 2\pi n$ d. $x = -\frac{\pi}{4} + \pi n$ or $x = \frac{3\pi}{4} + \pi n$	Lesson 12.1.2 MN: 12.1.4	Problems 12-27, 12-40, 12-42, 12-53, 12-63, 12-68, and 12-77

Problem	Solutions	Need Help?	More Practice
CL 12-143.	a. b.	Chapter 7 MN: 7.2.4 LL: 7.2.4	Problems 12-10, 12-31, 12-54, 12-98, and 12-133
CL 12-144.	$x = 1, -2, \pm\sqrt{2}i$	Lesson 8.3.2 MN: 8.3.2	Problems 12-83, 12-106, 12-126, and 12-135
CL 12-145.	a. $(-4, -4)$ b. $(1, 2)$	Lesson 2.1.4 MN: 2.1.3 and 2.1.4 LL: 2.1.5 and 2.2.2	Problems 11-56, 12-57, and 12-106
CL 12-146.	$y = -x^2(x-2)^2(x+2)^2$	Section 8.1 and Lesson 8.3.3	Problems 10-38, 10-39, 10-57, 10-151, 12-126, and 12-135
CL 12-147.	a. $x \approx 2.657$ b. $x \approx 0.936$ c. $x \approx -0.711$	Lesson 6.2.1	Problems 10-56, 10-162, CL 10-188, 12-58, and 12-122

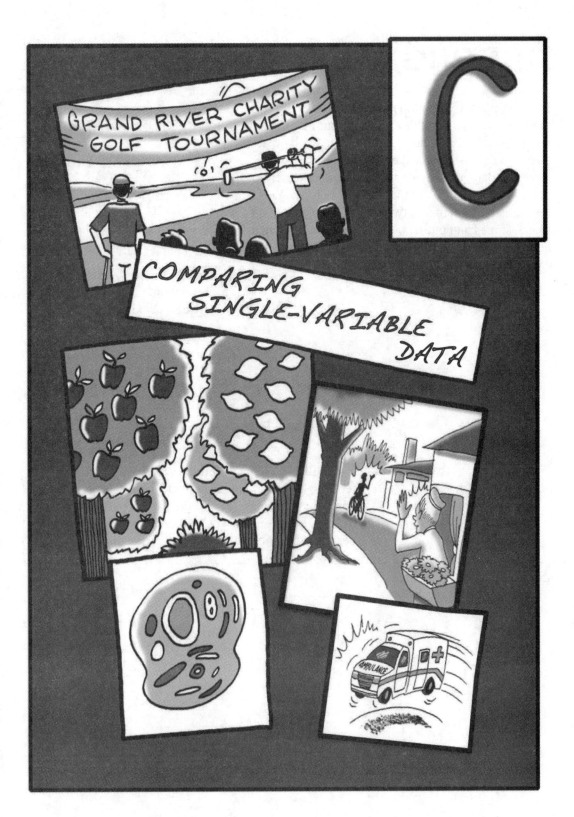

GRAND RIVER CHARITY GOLF TOURNAMENT

COMPARING SINGLE-VARIABLE DATA

C

Appendix C Comparing Single-Variable Data

In this appendix you will learn how to compare data that only has one variable. You will start by modeling a golf game and comparing your results with other teams. You will review the ways to graphically represent data, and decide whether to use scatterplots or two histograms to compare two variables. You will use statistics to compare two sets of data: center, shape, spread and outliers. Finally, you will learn a new way to describe the variability (the spread) in data called the standard deviation.

Guiding Question

Mathematically proficient students make sense of problems and persevere in solving them.

As you work through this chapter, ask yourself:

Am I taking advantage of everything I know to really engage with the mathematics and understand the problems I am solving?

Chapter Outline

Section C.1 You will review the differences between graphical representations of single-variable data. Then you will compare the center, shape, spread, and outliers of two distributions. Finally you will develop a new way to describe the spread called standard deviation.

C.1.1 How do I represent consistency?

Investigating Data Representations

The field of Statistics is the application of probability theory to make sense of large quantities of data. The study of Statistics allows people to make decisions and predictions from the natural variability in data.

A **statistic** (with a lower-case "s") is a numerical fact or calculation that is formed from a large quantity of data. A "mean" or a "correlation coefficient," for example, is a statistic.

In this section you will continue your study of Statistics from previous courses by modeling a golf tournament.

C-1.   FORTY HOLES OF GOLF

The Hookenslise Corporation is having its annual charity fundraising event. In order to encourage donors to attend, the Hookenslise organizes a fun game called "Forty Holes of Golf" and gives away prizes.

Each team plays forty holes of golf. There is a prize for the team that is consistently closest to the hole. Your teacher has set up a "hole." Your team will "swing" forty pennies toward the "hole." You will then represent your data on a graph and with numerical statistics. Analyzing the statistics will help you decide which team was the most consistently close to the hole.

Your Task:

- Your teacher will give you ten pennies. Have one team member stand 200 cm from the "hole." That team member will toss all ten pennies. No "do-overs" and no practice shots are allowed. Then record the distance from the center of each penny to the "hole" (to the nearest centimeter), even if the penny rolled far away.

- Repeat with different team members until 40 pennies have been tossed. Do not take turns tossing pennies – each team member should toss all their pennies, one at a time. Then the next team member can take their turn.

- When directed by the teacher, return to your table or desks. Decide how you want to represent your data on your poster: dot plot, boxplot, circle graph ("pie chart"), scatterplot, histogram, or bar graph. Create a poster. Leave room for the task below.

Problem continues on next page →

C-1.   *Problem continued from previous page.*

- Decide the five most important facts you wish to report about your team's golf shots and add them to your poster.

- Record your team's data in a safe place. You will need it for Lesson C.1.2.

- Your teacher will direct you on how to compare your team's results with the other teams. Which team was most consistently close to the hole?

C-2.   LEARNING LOG

You had your choice of six graphical representations of data: dot plot, boxplot, circle graph ("pie chart"), scatterplot, histogram, or bar graph. Discuss with your team how to choose among them. Give examples. Consider the following discussion points.

Discussion Points

What is the difference between single-variable data and two-variable data?

What is the difference between numerical and categorical data?

Do a lot of data values repeat?

What are the advantages?

Record your conclusions in your Learning Log. Be sure to include examples. Title this entry "Representing Data Graphically" and include today's date.

METHODS AND MEANINGS

Interquartile Range and Boxplots

Quartiles are points that divide a data set into four equal parts (and thus, the use of the prefix "quar" as in "quarter"). One of these points is the **median**. The **first quartile (Q1)** is the median of the lower half, and the **third quartile (Q3)** is the median of the upper half.

To find quartiles, the data set must be placed in order from smallest to largest. Note that if there are an odd number of data values, the median is not included in either half of the data set.

Suppose you have the data set: 22, 43, 14, 7, 2, 32, 9, 36, and 12.

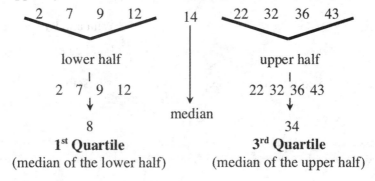

The **interquartile rage (IQR)** is the difference between the third and first quartiles. It is used to measure the spread (the variability) of the middle fifty percent of the data. The interquartile range is $34 - 8 = 26$.

A **boxplot** (also known as a box-and-whisker plot) displays a five-number summary of data: minimum, first quartile, median, third quartile, and maximum. The box contains "the middle half" of the data and visually displays how large the IQR is. The right segment represents the top 25% of the data and the left segment represents the bottom 25% of the data. A boxplot makes it easy to see where the data are spread out and where they are concentrated. The wider the box, the more the data are spread out.

C-3.   A sample of 23 newborns at the Dallas University Health
        Center had the following lengths in centimeters. The
        measurements have been sorted from lowest to highest.

        46.4, 46.9, 47.7, 48.1, 48.5, 48.5, 48.8, 49.0, 49.3, 50.0, 50.1,
        50.4, 50.6, 51.1, 51.4, 51.8, 52.4, 52.5, 53.2, 53.8, 54.4, 55.1, 55.9

        Find the **five number summary** of the lengths of the newborns. A five number
        summary includes the minimum, first quartile, median, third quartile, and
        maximum. Do not use a calculator. If you need help, see the Math Notes box
        in this lesson.

C-4.   For each function, find the inverse function.

        a. $f(x) = \frac{x}{3} - 2$ b. $g(x) = \frac{1}{2}x + 5$

C-5.   Solve the equations and inequalities below, if possible.

        a. $\sqrt{x-1} + 13 = 13$ b. $6|x| > 18$ c. $|3x - 2| \le 2$

        d. $\frac{4}{5} - \frac{2x}{3} = \frac{3}{10}$ e. $(4x - 2)^2 \le 100$ f. $(x - 1)^3 = 8$

C-6.   Ten minutes after he left his home, Gerald was
        40 miles from his grandmother's house. Then,
        22 minutes after he left, he was 34 miles from her
        house. If he was traveling toward his
        grandmother's home at a constant rate and
        reached her house after 90 minutes, how far away
        from her house does he live?

C-7.   Write the inequality represented
        by the graph at right.

C-8.   Kiesha graphed $y = x(6 - x)$ in a standard calculator viewing window.

   a.   What is the best name for her graph?

   b.   Jamal has bet Kiesha that with his graphing calculator he can make the graph look like a horizontal line without changing, adding, or deleting functions. Kiesha doesn't think he can do this, but Jamal is sure he can. What strategy does Jamal have in mind?

C-9.   In the diagram at right, the point (x, y) is the same distance from $(-3, 4)$ as it is from $(2, -1)$. There are many possibilities for (x, y). Algebraically, what do they have in common?

   a.   What is the distance from (x, y) to $(-3, 4)$?

   b.   What is the distance from (x, y) to $(2, -1)$?

   c.   Write the equation that states that the two expressions in (a) and (b) are equal and simplify.

   d.   What is the specific name of the geometric object represented by your equation from part (c)?

C-10.   Find the real solutions to the equations below using any method of your choice.

   a. $2x^2 = 2 - 3x$ b. $(2x - 3)^2 + 4 = 0$

C-11.   The GPAs of a sample of 26 community college applicants were selected and listed in ascending order below. Do not use a calculator for this problem.

1.58	1.87	2.32	2.44	2.46	2.46	2.50	2.63	2.69
2.72	2.78	2.81	2.83	2.99	3.10	3.16	3.30	3.42
3.46	3.49	3.54	3.67	3.75	3.87	3.89	4.29	

   a.   Find the five-number summary of the GPAs of these applicants.

   b.   On grid paper, create a combination histogram and boxplot. Use an interval of 0.5 on the x-axis. (A combination histogram and boxplot starts with a histogram. Then place a boxplot on top of the histogram. Refer to the Math Notes box for this lesson, if needed. Use the same x-axis scale for both the histogram and the boxplot.)

Combination Histogram and Boxplot

Problem continues on next page →

C-11.   *Problem continued from previous page.*

   c.   Describe the center, shape, spread, and outliers. To review descriptions of "shape," see the Math Notes box in Lesson C.1.2. To describe "spread" use the IQR, reviewed in the Math Notes box in this lesson.

C-12.   Fully investigate the function $g(x) = \sqrt{x-3} + 1$.

C-13.   Find an equation that represents the number of tiles in the tile pattern at right.

Figure 0   Figure 1   Figure 2

C-14.   Write and solve an equation to solve the problem below. State your solution as a sentence.

Shu Min currently has 1980 digital songs, and downloads 30 more songs each month. Her older brother, Wei, currently has 2590 songs but he only downloads 20 more songs each month. The computer they share can only hold 5000 songs. After how many months will their computer be full?

C-15.   Solve the inequalities and equations below, if possible. Represent your solution on a number line.

   a. $|x| + 3 < 5$ b. $5(2x+1) \geq 30$ c. $\frac{1}{x} - \frac{5}{2} = \frac{3}{2}$

   d. $-5 - x > 3 - x$ e. $3\sqrt{4-x} + 1 = 13$ f. $|x+1| \leq 4$

C-16.   In one of the games at the County Fair, people pay to shoot a paint pistol at the target shown at right. The center has a radius of one inch. Each concentric circle has a radius one inch larger than the preceding circle. Assuming the paint pellet hits the target randomly, what is the probability that it hits:

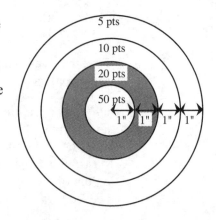

   a.   The 50-point ring?

   b.   The 20-point ring?

C-17.   Frank says that $\frac{a}{x+b} = \frac{a}{x} + \frac{a}{b}$, while Fred does not think that the two expressions are equivalent. Who is correct? Justify your answer.

C-18.   Where do the graphs below intersect?
You should be able to do these without a graphing calculator.

a. $2x + y = 10$ b. $2x + y = 10$
     $x + y = 25$ $x^2 + y^2 = 25$

C-19.   Given the quadratic function $f(x) = -2(x-2)^2 + 6$:

a.   Without drawing a graph, tell the coordinates of the vertex and tell if the vertex represents the maximum or minimum value of the function.

b.   Use your graphing shortcuts to draw a graph and verify your answer to part (a).

C.1.2 How can I compare results?

Comparing Data

In Lesson C.1.1 you tried to decide which team was close to the hole most consistently. Comparing sets of data is an essential part of the study of Statistics. Data is often not meaningful unless it is compared to other data. What does your batting average or free throw average mean if you are the only person who has one? If there are no other SAT scores to compare to then what does your score matter?

C-20.   As the Managing Grower at All-Organic Orchards, you know the farmer's market will only accept fruit that is above average size for your orchard. However, they do not define how to calculate "average," with a mean or with a median. You want to sell as much fruit as possible for premium prices at the farmer's market.

Weight of Apples

a.   Your apple crop is represented by the histogram and boxplot at right. To get the maximum amount of fruit to the market, should you use the mean or the median for the "average"?

b.   Your lemon crop is represented by the histogram at right. Why do you suppose the right "whisker" is missing? Which average, mean or median, should you use?

Weight of Lemons

c.   Why might the farmers at other orchards feel like you were being deceptive by reporting the mean for your fruit?

d.   To best represent numerically the center, or the "typical" value, of a large quantity of data, when would you use the mean and when would you use the median?

C-21. Home sales in Fancyville and Smallville are shown in the tables below. Calculate the mean and median sales price in each town and compare Fancyville to Smallville. In which town does the "typical" home cost less?

Fancyville Home Sales (in thousands of dollars)						
230	270	150	305	240	280	1100
340	160	320	440	2800	250	210

Smallville Home Sales (in thousands of dollars)						
255	289	275	247	299	281	272

C-22. Cyrus had an idea, *"To compare sales in Fancyville to Smallville, let's make a scatterplot with Fancyville on the x-axis and Smallville on the y-axis. Then we can draw a line of best fit and see if there is an association."* Ramien responded that it was a great idea! What is wrong with Cyrus and Ramien's plan?

C-23. CREATING HISTOGRAMS AND BOXPLOTS ON THE CALCULATOR

The difference between life and death is often just minutes when it comes to stopping bleeding. Two emergency procedures are being compared for their speed in stopping bleeding at the scenes of accidents. The time from when 911 was called to the time that paramedics reported the bleeding stopped was recorded for each procedure. The data is shown below (in minutes).

Procedure C-2: 7, 6, 7, 4, 24, 8, 10, 3, 3, 5, 4, 17, 6, 5, 19, 29, 5, 6, 10, 4
checksum 182

Procedure C-7: 11, 13, 8, 9, 12, 10, 10, 9, 12, 7, 10, 6, 14, 11, 11
checksum 153

Your teacher will show you how to make a combination histogram and modified boxplot on your graphing calculator. (A **modified boxplot** displays the outliers separately from the boxplot.) You will need to choose an appropriate interval for each of the bins ("bars") on your histogram. This interval is called the **bin width**. A very rough approximation of the number of bins your histogram should have is the square root of the number of values in the largest data set.

Obtain the Lesson C.1.2A Resource Page from your teacher. Make a sketch of the combination histogram and boxplot for each emergency procedure. Compare and contrast the two procedures. Which one would you recommend? Why?

C-24.   CENTER, SHAPE, SPREAD, AND OUTLIERS

It takes several statistics to get a meaningful
description of single-variable data like the
sales prices of houses in Fancyville and
Smallville – comparing the medians alone
does not tell a useful story about the
difference in prices. Statisticians like to
report the **center**, **shape**, **spread**, and **outliers**
of single-variable data.

Your teacher will give you the data from a previous "Forty Holes of Golf"
fundraiser on the Lesson C.1.2B Resource Page. Compare the center, shape,
spread, and outliers of your team's performance to the data on the resource page.

C-25.   LEARNING LOG

To compare two collections of single-variable data,
statisticians often compare the center, shape, spread, and
outliers. Discuss with your team how to describe the four
statistics. Give examples. Consider the following Discussion Points:

Discussion Points

When do we use a histogram and when do we use a scatterplot?

How does the shape determine which statistics we will use?

Is there another statistic we can use instead?

What is spread? What is an outlier?

Record your descriptions of center, shape, spread, and outliers in your Learning
Log. Be sure to include examples. Title this entry "Describing Single-Variable
Data" and include today's date.

ETHODS AND MEANINGS

Describing Shape (of a Data Distribution)

MATH NOTES

Statisticians use the words below to describe the shape of a data distribution.

uniform and symmetric

double-peaked and symmetric

single-peaked and symmetric

single-peaked and skewed

Outliers are any data values that are far away from the bulk of the data distribution. In the example at right, data values in the right-most bin are outliers. Outliers are marked on a modified boxplot with a dot.

C-26. The auto repair shop is concerned about the reliability of its lathe, which is lathe is a rotating piece of equipment used in restoring parts. The shop's owner measured the rotations per minute (RPM) at various times over the course of a month. These were his measurements:

250, 251, 253, 253, 253, 254, 257, 257, 259, 259, 261, 263, 265, 270, 291 RPM

a. On grid paper, draw a combination histogram and boxplot. Do not use a calculator.

b. Describe center, shape, spread, and outliers, similar to the way you did in problem C-11.

c. When reporting the center of this data, or the "typical RPM," which would be more appropriate, the mean or the median? Why?

C-27.   Find an equation for each sequence.

a.

n	$t(n)$
1	7
2	4
3	1

b.

Year	Cost
2	$2000
3	$6000
4	$1800

C-28.   Given the quadratic function $f(x) = x^2 - 3$, find the new expression for each part below and describe the transformation.

a. $f(x) - 2$ b. $-2 \cdot f(x)$

c. $f(x - 2)$ d. $f(-2x)$

C-29.   For the quadratic function $f(x) = 2(x+1)^2 - 5$:

a.   Identify the vertex and tell if it is a maximum or minimum point on the graph.

b.   What is the value of the function at that minimum or maximum point?

C-30.   Aura currently pays $800 each month to rent her apartment. Due to inflation, however, her rent is increasing by $50 each year. Meanwhile, her monthly take-home pay is $1500 and she predicts that her monthly pay will only increase by $15 each year. Assuming that her rent and take-home pay will continue to grow linearly, will her rent ever equal her take-home pay? If so, when? And how much will rent be that year?

C-31.   Rewrite each of the expressions below with no parentheses and no fractions. Negative exponents are acceptable in your answer.

a. $(5a^{-2}b^3)^8 \cdot (5ab^{-2})^{-6}$ b. $\dfrac{15x^{-5}y^2}{(3x^2)^2 \cdot y^{-3}}$

C-32.   On Friday, Randy Random went to DJ's to get a cone.

a.   If he made a random selection, what is the probability that he got *all* three scoops the same?

b.   What is the probability that he got all three different?

C-33.   Find the distance between each pair of points.

     a.   (2, 3) and (4, 7)   b.   (2, 3) and (x, y)

C-34.   The function $f(x) = 200(0.7)^x + 72$, where x is the time in minutes, could represent the temperature over time of a hot cup of tea placed on the kitchen counter. What does the 72 represent in the context of this situation? What does the 0.7 represent?

C-35.   The Dallas University Health Center is running a clinical trial comparing two medicines to treat fibromyalgia. They need to compare the ages of the two groups receiving the medicines. The ages follow:

Group 7A: 72, 71, 59, 62, 48, 70, 57, 48, 68, 68, 57, 49, 53, 72, 60
checksum 914

Group 7B: 64, 29, 75, 55, 85, 51, 74, 34, 80, 28, 49, 79, 68, 45, 94, 32
checksum 942

     a.   Use your calculator to make a sketch of the combination histogram and boxplot for each treatment group. Sketch the graphs. Compare and contrast the distributions of ages between the two groups, using the center, shape, spread, and outliers of the two groups.

     b.   When reporting the typical age in each group, which is a more appropriate measure of center, the mean or the median? Explain.

C-36.   For the function $f(x) = 7x - 2$:

     a.   Find the inverse function.

     b.   Show that your inverse function is correct. Choose an input number for the function and calculate the output. Use this output as the input for the inverse function. Is your final output the same as your original input?

C-37.   Solve the following inequalities for x. Graph your solutions on a number line.

     a. $3x - 5 \le 7 + 2x$ b. $|x| - 3 < 7$

     c. $5(2 - x) + 6 > 16$ d. $|x + 2| > 3$

C-38.   Complete the square to convert $y = 2x^2 + 4x + 6$ into graphing form.

C-39.   Solve each of the following equations or systems.

   a. $x^2 - 1 = 15$ b. $y = 3x - 2$
                                                  $y = 4x + 3$

   c. $x^2 - 2x - 8 = 0$ d. $2x^2 = -x + 7$

C-40.   Graph and shade the solution for the system of inequalities below.

$$y \le 4 + \tfrac{3}{4}x$$
$$y > -\tfrac{1}{2}x + 1$$

C-41.   Your teacher has decided that one person in your class will get an extra 50
        points of credit. The lucky person has been narrowed down, so now it is
        between you and Newton. The teacher says, *"I'm thinking of a number
        between 0 and 10. Whoever can choose the number closest to it gets the 50
        points."* Quickly, Newton yells out, *"Three!"* What number would you
        choose? Justify and explain your answer.

C-42.   Use your solving skills to complete parts (a) and (b) below.

   a.   Solve $\frac{x+3}{x-1} - \frac{x}{x+1} = \frac{8}{x^2-1}$ for x.

   b.   In part (a), the result of solving the equation is $x = 1$, but what happens
        when you substitute 1 for x? What does this mean in relation to the
        solutions for this equation?

C-43.   Use your knowledge of graphing short cuts to determine the number of points
        of intersections of this system. You do not need to solve it.

$$y = (x+2)^2 - 1$$
$$y = \tfrac{1}{2}x + 2$$

C.1.3 How can I measure variability?

Standard Deviation

Today you will use an example from the study of biology to reveal the importance of describing the spread (variability) of data and not just a measure of the center.

C-44. A biologist is trying to determine which type of sugar is more successful in growing a particular eukaryotic cell. She measured the diameter of the cell and collected the data below (in micrometers, μm).

Sugar W: 10, 32, 32, 34, 34, 36, 37, 39, 39, 40, 41, 43, 43, 44, 45, 46, 46, 49, 70   *checksum 760*

Sugar P: 10, 10, 15, 20, 25, 28, 30, 32, 35, 40, 45, 48, 50, 52, 55, 60, 65, 70, 70   *checksum 760*

a. Make a combination histogram and boxplot for each type of sugar. (Use an interval of 10 to 80 with a bin width of 10.)

b. Find the mean and median of both collections of data.

c. The two sets of data are obviously not the same. Which statistic(s) differentiate between these two data sets? You do not need to calculate the statistic. If the biologist wants to consistently grow large cells, which sugar should she use?

C-45. MEASURING SPREAD

a. One way to measure the spread of data is to calculate the **range** (maximum minus minimum). What range of cell sizes did each type of sugar grow in problem C-44? Why is the range often not a useful measure of spread?

b. Another method for measuring the spread is the average distance to the mean, called the **mean absolute deviation**. Find the distance each value is from the mean (remember to use absolute value because distances are positive!), and find the mean distance. Compare the mean absolute deviation of Sugar W to Sugar P.

Problem continued from previous page. →

C-45.   *Problem continued from previous page.*

      c.   A mean absolute deviation should not be calculated if the data has outliers or is not symmetric. Why?

      d.   When the data is not symmetric or has outliers, the interquartile range (IQR) can be used to measure spread. Find and compare the IQR of the two sugars. If you need a reminder, reread the Math Notes box at the end of Lesson C.1.1.

C-46.   STANDARD DEVIATION

In addition to the methods in the previous problem, standard deviation is yet another measure of how much variability there is in a data set. **Standard deviation** is the average of all the distances to the mean. Instead of taking the absolute value to force the distances to the mean to be positive, statisticians square the distances to make them positive. After finding the average, then the square root of the average is taken so that the units come out right.

Without using your graphing calculator, find the standard deviation of each sugar in problem C-44. Compare the variability (the spread) of the two sugars using the standard deviation.

C-47.   Find the standard deviation for your team's tosses from the "Forty Holes of Golf" event from problem C-1 in Lesson C.1.1. Compare your result with the other teams in your class. Now which team was most consistently close to the hole?

C-48.   The standard deviation was probably not an appropriate way to report the spread of your team's golfing data. Why not? What would have been better?

C-49.   Your teacher will demonstrate how to find the standard deviation using your graphing calculator. Verify the standard deviations of the two sugars that you calculated in problem C-46 using your graphing calculator.

C-50. **LEARNING LOG**

In your Learning Log, describe how to compute the
standard deviation of a set of data. Make up five pieces of
data and include an example. When is it best not to use the
standard deviation as a measure of spread? Title this entry "Standard
Deviation" and include today's date.

METHODS AND **M**EANINGS

Describing Spread (of a Data Distribution)

MATH NOTES

A distribution of data can be summarized by describing its center,
shape, spread, and outliers. You have learned three ways to
describe the spread.

Interquartile Range (IQR)
The variability, or spread, in the distribution can be numerically
summarized with the interquartile range (IQR). The IQR is found by
subtracting the first quartile from the third quartile. The IQR is the range
of the middle half of the data. IQR can represent the spread of any data
distribution, even if the distribution is not symmetric or has outliers.

Standard Deviation
Either the interquartile range or standard deviation can be used to represent
the spread if the data is symmetric and has no outliers. The standard
deviation is the square root of the average of the distances to the mean,
after the distances have been made positive by squaring.

For example, for the data 10 12 14 16 18 kilograms:

- The mean is 14 kg.
- The distances of each data value to the mean are $-4, -2, 0, 2, 4$ kg.
- The distances squared are $16, 4, 0, 4, 16$ kg^2.
- The mean distance-squared is 8 kg^2.
- The square root is 2.83. Thus the standard deviation is 2.83 kg.

Range
The range (maximum minus minimum) is usually not a very good way to
describe the spread because it considers only the extreme values in the
data, rather than how the bulk of the data is spread.

C-51. An environmental engineering group has collected core samples from the earth to determine if they are contaminated. The samples were weighed, as follows:

15 40 69 65 10   60 34 20 43 40   10 25 44
65 32 45 30 36   45 50 35 39 50   46 55 31   *checksum 1034*

Determine if the mean and standard deviation is an appropriate way to summarize this data. If so, find the mean and standard deviation with your calculator. If not, use the median and IQR. Consider the precision of the measurement of weight when deciding how many decimal places to use in your answer.

C-52. A farmer wonders if his crops grow better in sun or in shade. He measures the amount of fruit gathered from a sample of 50 trees growing in full sun and from a sample of 50 trees growing in mostly shade. The five-number summaries, (minimum, Q1, median, Q3, maximum), follow:

Amount of fruit gathered from sunny trees: (10.8, 13.3, 22.1, 58.1, 100) bushels

Amount of fruit gathered from shady trees: (10.9, 18.5, 29.3, 61.5, 127) bushels

a. On the same set of axes on grid paper, create a boxplot for each type of tree. Compare the center, shape, spread, and outliers of amount of fruit from sunny trees to the amount from shady trees.

b. The farmer wants to summarize the amount of fruit from each type of orchard with a mean and standard deviation. Is that appropriate? Explain.

C-53. Based on the graph, give a possible equation for the parabola.

a.

(0, 0)   (4, 0)

b.

(−2, 0)   (2, 0)

c.

$(-\frac{1}{2}, 0)$ $(\frac{3}{2}, 0)$

Core Connections Algebra 2

C-54. Find all of the points at which the parabolas below intersect. Write your solution(s) in (x, y) form.

$$y = x^2 + 5x - 4$$
$$y = x^2 + x - 12$$

C-55. Solve the equations and inequalities below. Check your solutions, if possible.

a. $|5x + 8| \geq -4$

b. $x^2 + x - 20 < 0$

c. $2x^2 - 6x = -5$

d. $\frac{5}{9} - \frac{x}{3} = \frac{4}{9}$

C-56. Match the histogram to its corresponding boxplot.

a.

b.

c.

d.

e.

i.

ii.

iii.

iv.

v.

C-57. You roll three different-colored dice and use the numbers on the dice to determine the lengths of the sides of a triangle. For example, 3-3-5 would be an isosceles triangle with base 5. What is the probability of building a right triangle?

C-58. Find the value of x in each triangle.

a.

b.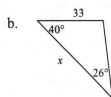

C-59. Graph the piecewise function $f(x) = \begin{cases} 2^x & \text{if } x \geq 0 \\ |x| & \text{if } x < 0 \end{cases}$.

Appendix C Closure   What have I learned?

Reflection and Synthesis

The activities below offer you a chance to reflect about what you have learned in this appendix. As you work, look for concepts that you feel very comfortable with, ideas that you would like to learn more about, and topics you need more help with. Look for connections between ideas as well as connections with material you learned previously.

①   TEAM BRAINSTORM

What have you studied in this appendix? What ideas were important in what you learned? With your team, brainstorm a list. Be as detailed as you can. To help get you started, a list of Learning Log entries and Math Notes boxes are below.

What topics, ideas, and words that you learned *before* this appendix are connected to the new ideas in this chapter? Again, be as detailed as you can.

How long can you make your list? Challenge yourselves. Be prepared to share your team's ideas with the class.

Learning Log Entries
- Lesson C.1.1 – Representing Data Graphically
- Lesson C.1.2 – Describing Single-Variable Data
- Lesson C.1.3 – Standard Deviation

Math Notes
- Lesson C.1.1 – Interquartile Range and Boxplots
- Lesson C.1.2 – Describing Shape (of a Data Distribution)
- Lesson C.1.3 – Describing Spread (of a Data Distribution)

②   MAKING CONNECTIONS

Below is a list of the vocabulary used in this appendix. Make sure that you are familiar with all of these words and know what they mean. Refer to the glossary or index for any words that you do not yet understand.

5-number summary	bar graph	boxplot
center	circle ("pie") graph	dot plot
histogram	IQR	mean
mean absolute deviation	median	outlier
quartile	range	scatterplot
shape	spread	standard deviation
statistic		

Make a concept map showing all of the connections you can find among the key words and ideas listed above. To show a connection between two words, draw a line between them and explain the connection. A word can be connected to any other word as long as you can justify the connection.

While you are making your map, your team may think of related words or ideas that are not listed here. Be sure to include these ideas on your concept map.

③   PORTFOLIO: EVIDENCE OF MATHEMATICAL PROFICIENCY

Your teacher will explain how to obtain two sets of data. Showcase your skills for comparing data by making combination histograms and boxplots and comparing the center, shape, spread, and outliers. Explain how you chose between using the median and IQR, and using the mean and standard deviation.

④ WHAT HAVE I LEARNED?

Most of the problems in this section represent typical problems found in this appendix. They serve as a gauge for you. You can use them to determine which types of problems you can do well and which types of problems require further study and practice. Even if your teacher does not assign this section, it is a good idea to try these problems and find out for yourself what you know and what you still need to work on.

Solve each problem as completely as you can. The table at the end of the closure section has answers to these problems. It also tells you where you can find additional help and practice with problems like these.

CL C-60. Jet Set claims that they are more "on time" than National Airways because National was delayed over an hour a couple times. Arin did not believe Jet Set was more "on time" so he looked up the data for both airlines during the last two weeks. Below is the data he found for departure delays. Negative numbers indicate that a flight departed earlier than scheduled.

National Airways:
69, 22, –3, –7, 2, 25, 7, 0, –3, 14, –4, 0, –1, –9, –2, 4, 12, 25, 65, –10
checksum 206

Jet Set:
6, –5, 33, 4, 37, 10, 23, 5, 21, 31, 2, –5, 35, 42, 19 –8, 25, 15
checksum 290

a. Compare the center, shape, spread, and outliers of the data sets. Use the values you calculate to make an argument as to which airline is on time more often. Use a bin width of 10 minutes on your histograms.

b. Arin wants to summarize his findings with just two numbers: the center and spread. Can he use mean and standard deviation, or should he use median and IQR? Justify your choice, then summarize the data for Arin.

CL C-61.   Given the system of equations: $y = (x+2)^2$
$$y = -2x - 4$$

    a.   How many points of intersection should there be?

    b.   Use your algebra skills to verify the answer to (a) and find the exact coordinates of the point(s) of intersection.

CL C-62.   For the parabola $y = 2x^2 - 12x + 6$:

    a.   Is the vertex is a maximum or minimum? Explain your reasoning.

    b.   Determine the coordinates of the vertex.

    c.   Make a sketch of the graph without using a calculator.

CL C-63.   Without graphing, determine all of the points of intersections of these two equations.

$$y = -5x - 7$$
$$y = x^2 - 3x - 10$$

CL C-64.   Check your answers using the table at the end of the closure section. Which problems do you feel confident about? Which problems were hard? Use the table to make a list of topics you need help on and a list of topics you need to practice more.

Answers and Support for Closure Activity #4
What Have I Learned?

Note: MN = Math Note, LL = Learning Log

Problem	Solution	Need Help?	More Practice
CL C-60.	a. Median delay for Jet Set is about 16 minutes longer than for National. National's delays were skewed with a peak at about −5 minutes, meaning they had a lot of flights that left early or had only a little delay, while Jet Set's delays were uniformly distributed. Jet Set had more variability in delays than National did; the IQR for Jet Set's delays was 6 minutes wider than for National's IQR. National did have two extreme outliers. Even though National had two very large delays in the last couple weeks, their overall performance makes them more "on time" than Jet Set. Jet Set's claims are misleading because they focused only on the outliers rather than on overall performance.	Lesson C.1.2 MN: C.1.2 and C.1.3 LL: C.1.2 National Time (min)	Problems C-26, C-35, C-44, C-51, and C-52
	b. Although the distribution for Jet Set is symmetric with no outliers, National is skewed with outliers. Since he wants to compare data, he needs to use the same statistics for both airlines. Arin must use median and IQR. Median delay for National is 1 minute with an IQR of 21 minutes, while Jet Set has median delay if 17 minutes with an IQR of 27 minutes.	 Jet Set Time (min)	
CL C-61.	a. 2 b. (−2,0), (−4,4)	Chapter 4	Problem C-43

Problem	Solution	Need Help?	More Practice
CL C-62.	a. Parabola opens up so the vertex is a minimum. b. (3, 12) c. See graph at right.	Chapter 2	Problems C-19, C-29, and C-53
CL C-63.	(−3, 8) and (1, −12)	Chapter 4	Problem C-54

Core Connections Algebra 2
Checkpoint Materials

Note to Students (and their Teachers)

Students master different skills at different speeds. No two students learn exactly the same way at the same time. At some point you will be expected to perform certain skills accurately. Most of the Checkpoint problems incorporate skills that you should have developed in previous courses. If you have not mastered these skills yet it does not mean that you will not be successful in this class. However, you may need to do some work outside of class to get caught up on them.

Starting in Chapter 2 and finishing in Chapter 12, there are 18 problems designed as Checkpoint problems. Each one is marked with an icon like the one above. After you do each of the Checkpoint problems, check your answers by referring to this section. If your answers are incorrect, you may need some extra practice to develop that skill. The practice sets are keyed to each of the Checkpoint problems in the textbook. Each has the topic clearly labeled, followed by the answers to the corresponding Checkpoint problem and then some completed examples. Next, the complete solution to the Checkpoint problem from the text is given, and there are more problems for you to practice with answers included.

Remember, looking is not the same as doing! You will never become good at any sport by just watching it, and in the same way, reading through the worked examples and understanding the steps is not the same as being able to do the problems yourself. How many of the extra practice problems do you need to try? That is really up to you. Remember that your goal is to be able to do similar problems on your own confidently and accurately. This is your responsibility. You should not expect your teacher to spend time in class going over the solutions to the Checkpoint problem sets. If you are not confident after reading the examples and trying the problems, you should get help outside of class time or talk to your teacher about working with a tutor.

Checkpoint Topics

6A. Multiplying and Dividing Rational Expressions

6B. Adding and Subtracting Rational Expressions

7A. Finding x- and y-Intercepts of a Quadratic Function

7B. Completing the Square to Find the Vertex of a Parabola

8A. Solving and Graphing Inequalities

8B. Solving Complicated Equations

9A. Writing and Solving Exponential Equations

9B. Finding the Equation for the Inverse of a Function

10. Rewriting Expressions with and Solving Equations with Logarithms

11. Solving Rational Equations

Checkpoint 6A
Problem 6-73
Multiplying and Dividing Rational Expressions

Answers to problem 6-73: a: $\frac{x+3}{x+4}$, b: $\frac{1}{x(x+2)}$

Multiplication or division of rational expressions follows the same procedure used with numerical fractions. However, it is often necessary to factor the polynomials in order to simplify them. Factors that are the same in the numerator and denominator are equal to 1. For example: $\frac{x^2}{x^2}=1$, $\frac{(x+2)}{(x+2)}=1$ and $\frac{(3x-2)}{(3x-2)}=1$ but $\frac{5-x}{x-5}=\frac{-(x-5)}{x-5}=-1$.

When dividing rational expressions, change the problem to multiplication by inverting (flipping) the second expression (or any expression that follows a division sign) and completing the process as you do for multiplication.

In both cases, the simplification is only valid provided that the denominator is not equal to zero. See the examples below.

Example 1: Multiply $\frac{x^2+6x}{(x+6)^2}\cdot\frac{x^2+7x+6}{x^2-1}$ **and simplify the result.**

Solution:

After factoring, the expression becomes:
$$\frac{x(x+6)}{(x+6)(x+6)}\cdot\frac{(x+6)(x+1)}{(x+1)(x-1)}$$

After multiplying, reorder the factors:
$$\frac{(x+6)}{(x+6)}\cdot\frac{(x+6)}{(x+6)}\cdot\frac{x}{(x-1)}\cdot\frac{(x+1)}{(x+1)}$$

Since $\frac{(x+6)}{(x+6)}=1$ and $\frac{(x+1)}{(x+1)}=1$, simplify:
$$1\cdot1\cdot\frac{x}{x-1}\cdot1 \Rightarrow \frac{x}{x-1} \text{ for } x\neq-6,-1, \text{ or } 1.$$

Example 2: Divide $\frac{x^2-4x-5}{x^2-4x+4}\div\frac{x^2-2x-15}{x^2+4x-12}$ **and simplify the result.**

Solution:

First change to a multiplication expression by inverting (flipping) the second fraction:
$$\frac{x^2-4x-5}{x^2-4x+4}\cdot\frac{x^2+4x-12}{x^2-2x-15}$$

After factoring, the expression is:
$$\frac{(x-5)(x+1)}{(x-2)(x-2)}\cdot\frac{(x+6)(x-2)}{(x-5)(x+3)}$$

Reorder the factors (if you need to):
$$\frac{(x-5)}{(x-5)}\cdot\frac{(x-2)}{(x-2)}\cdot\frac{(x+1)}{(x-2)}\cdot\frac{(x+6)}{(x+3)}$$

Since $\frac{(x-5)}{(x-5)}=1$ and $\frac{(x-2)}{(x-2)}=1$, simplify:
$$\frac{(x+1)}{(x-2)}\cdot\frac{(x+6)}{(x+3)}$$

Thus, $\frac{x^2-4x-5}{x^2-4x+4}\div\frac{x^2-2x-15}{x^2+4x-12}=\frac{(x+1)}{(x-2)}\cdot\frac{(x+6)}{(x+3)}$ or $\frac{x^2+7x+6}{x^2+x-6}$ for $x\neq-3,$ 2, or 5.

Now we can go back and solve the original problems.

a. $\dfrac{x^2-16}{(x-4)^2} \cdot \dfrac{x^2-3x-18}{x^2-2x-24} \Rightarrow \dfrac{(x+4)(x-4)}{(x-4)(x-4)} \cdot \dfrac{(x-6)(x+3)}{(x-6)(x+4)} \Rightarrow \dfrac{(x+4)(x-4)(x-6)(x+3)}{(x+4)(x-4)(x-6)(x-4)} \Rightarrow \dfrac{x+3}{x-4}$

b. $\dfrac{x^2-1}{x^2-6x-7} \div \dfrac{x^3+x^2-2x}{x-7} \Rightarrow \dfrac{(x+1)(x-1)}{(x-7)(x+1)} \cdot \dfrac{(x-7)}{x(x+2)(x-1)} \Rightarrow \dfrac{(x+1)(x-1)(x-7)}{(x+1)(x-1)(x-7)x(x+2)} \Rightarrow \dfrac{1}{x(x+2)}$

Here are some more to try. Multiply or divide each pair of rational expressions.
Simplify the result. Assume the denominator is not equal to zero.

1. $\dfrac{x^2+5x+6}{x^2-4x} \cdot \dfrac{4x}{x+2}$

2. $\dfrac{x^2-2x}{x^2-4x+4} \div \dfrac{4x^2}{x-2}$

3. $\dfrac{x^2-16}{(x-4)^2} \cdot \dfrac{x^2-3x-18}{x^2-2x-24}$

4. $\dfrac{x^2-x-6}{x^2+3x-10} \cdot \dfrac{x^2+2x-15}{x^2-6x+9}$

5. $\dfrac{x^2-x-6}{x^2-x-20} \cdot \dfrac{x^2+6x+8}{x^2-x-6}$

6. $\dfrac{x^2-x-30}{x^2+13x+40} \cdot \dfrac{x^2+11x+24}{x^2-9x+18}$

7. $\dfrac{15-5x}{x^2-x-6} \div \dfrac{5x}{x^2+6x+8}$

8. $\dfrac{17x+119}{x^2+5x-14} \div \dfrac{9x-1}{x^2-3x+2}$

9. $\dfrac{2x^2-5x-3}{3x^2-10x+3} \cdot \dfrac{9x^2-1}{4x^2+4x+1}$

10. $\dfrac{x^2-1}{x^2-6x-7} \div \dfrac{x^3+x^2-2x}{x-7}$

11. $\dfrac{3x-21}{x^2-49} \div \dfrac{3x}{x^2+7x}$

12. $\dfrac{x^2-y^2}{x+y} \cdot \dfrac{1}{x-y}$

13. $\dfrac{y^2-y}{w^2-y^2} \div \dfrac{y^2-2y+1}{1-y}$

14. $\dfrac{y^2-y-12}{y+2} \div \dfrac{y-4}{y^2-4y-12}$

15. $\dfrac{x^2+7x+10}{x+2} \div \dfrac{x^2+2x-15}{x+2}$

Answers:

1. $\dfrac{4(x+3)}{x-4}$

2. $\dfrac{1}{4x}$

3. $\dfrac{x+3}{x-4}$

4. $\dfrac{x+2}{x-2}$

5. $\dfrac{x+2}{x-5}$

6. $\dfrac{x+3}{x-3}$

7. $\dfrac{-x-4}{x}$

8. $\dfrac{17(x-1)}{9x-1}$

9. $\dfrac{3x+1}{2x+1}$

10. $\dfrac{1}{x(x+2)}$

11. 1

12. 1

13. $\dfrac{-y}{w^2-y^2}$

14. $(y+3)(y-6)$

15. $\dfrac{x+2}{x-3}$

Checkpoint 6B
Problem 6-145
Adding and Subtracting Rational Expressions

Answers to problem 6-145: a: $\frac{2(x+1)}{x+3}$, b: $\frac{3x^2-5x-3}{(2x+1)^2}$

Addition and subtraction of rational expressions uses the same process as simple numerical fractions. First, if necessary find a common denominator. Second, convert the original fractions to equivalent ones with the common denominator. Third, add or subtract the new numerators over the common denominator. Finally, factor the numerator and denominator and simplify, if possible. Note that these steps are only valid provided that the denominator is not zero.

Example 1: $\frac{3}{2(n+2)} + \frac{3}{n(n+2)}$

Solution:

The least common multiple of $2(n+2)$ and $n(n+2)$ is $2n(n+2)$.

$\frac{3}{2(n+2)} + \frac{3}{n(n+2)}$

To get a common denominator in the first fraction, multiply the fraction by $\frac{n}{n}$, a form of the number 1. Multiply the second fraction by $\frac{2}{2}$.

$= \frac{3}{2(n+2)} \cdot \frac{n}{n} + \frac{3}{n(n+2)} \cdot \frac{2}{2}$

Multiply the numerator and denominator of each term. It may be necessary to distribute the numerator.

$= \frac{3n}{2n(n+2)} + \frac{6}{2n(n+2)}$

Add, factor, and simplify the result. (Note: $n \neq 0 \ or \ -2$)

$= \frac{3n+6}{2n(n+2)} \Rightarrow \frac{3(n+2)}{2n(n+2)} \Rightarrow \frac{3}{2n}$

Example 2: $\frac{2-x}{x+4} + \frac{3x+6}{x+4}$

Solution:

$\frac{2-x}{x+4} + \frac{3x+6}{x+4} \Rightarrow \frac{2-x+3x+6}{x+4} \Rightarrow \frac{2x+8}{x+4} \Rightarrow \frac{2(x+4)}{x+4} \Rightarrow 2$

Example 3: $\frac{3}{x-1} - \frac{2}{x-2}$

Solution:

$\frac{3}{x-1} - \frac{2}{x-2} \Rightarrow \frac{3}{x-1} \cdot \frac{x-2}{x-2} - \frac{2}{x-2} \cdot \frac{x-1}{x-1} \Rightarrow \frac{3x-6-2x+2}{(x-1)(x-2)} \Rightarrow \frac{x-4}{(x-1)(x-2)}$

Now we can go back and solve the original problems.

a. $\dfrac{4}{x^2+5x+6}+\dfrac{2x}{x+2}\Rightarrow\dfrac{4}{(x+3)(x+2)}+\dfrac{2x}{(x+2)}\cdot\dfrac{(x+3)}{(x+3)}\Rightarrow\dfrac{2x^2+6x+4}{(x+2)(x+3)}\Rightarrow\dfrac{2(x+2)(x+1)}{(x+2)(x+3)}\Rightarrow\dfrac{2(x+1)}{(x+3)}$

b. $\dfrac{3x^2+x}{(2x+1)^2}-\dfrac{3}{(2x+1)}\Rightarrow\dfrac{3x^2+x}{(2x+1)^2}-\dfrac{3}{(2x+1)}\cdot\dfrac{(2x+1)}{(2x+1)}\Rightarrow\dfrac{3x^2+x-6x-3}{(2x+1)^2}\Rightarrow\dfrac{3x^2-5x-3}{(2x+1)^2}$

Here are a few more to try. Add or subtract each expression and simplify the result. In each case assume the denominator does not equal zero.

1. $\dfrac{x}{(x+2)(x+3)}+\dfrac{2}{(x+2)(x+3)}$

2. $\dfrac{x}{x^2+6x+8}+\dfrac{4}{x^2+6x+8}$

3. $\dfrac{b^2}{b^2+2b-3}+\dfrac{-9}{b^2+2b-3}$

4. $\dfrac{2a}{a^2+2a+1}+\dfrac{2}{a^2+2a+1}$

5. $\dfrac{x+10}{x+2}+\dfrac{x-6}{x+2}$

6. $\dfrac{a+2b}{a+b}+\dfrac{2a+b}{a+b}$

7. $\dfrac{3x-4}{3x+3}-\dfrac{2x-5}{3x+3}$

8. $\dfrac{3x}{4x-12}-\dfrac{9}{4x-12}$

9. $\dfrac{6a}{5a^2+a}-\dfrac{a-1}{5a^2+a}$

10. $\dfrac{x^2+3x-5}{10}-\dfrac{x^2-2x+10}{10}$

11. $\dfrac{6}{x(x+3)}+\dfrac{2x}{x(x+3)}$

12. $\dfrac{5}{x-7}+\dfrac{3}{4(x-7)}$

13. $\dfrac{5x+6}{x^2}-\dfrac{5}{x}$

14. $\dfrac{2}{x+4}-\dfrac{x-4}{x^2-16}$

15. $\dfrac{10a}{a^2+6a}-\dfrac{3}{3a+18}$

16. $\dfrac{3x}{2x^2-8x}+\dfrac{2}{x-4}$

17. $\dfrac{5x+9}{x^2-2x-3}+\dfrac{6}{x^2-7x+12}$

18. $\dfrac{x+4}{x^2-3x-28}-\dfrac{x-5}{x^2+2x-35}$

19. $\dfrac{3x+1}{x^2-16}-\dfrac{3x+5}{x^2+8x+16}$

20. $\dfrac{7x-1}{x^2-2x-3}-\dfrac{6x}{x^2-x-2}$

Answers:

1. $\dfrac{1}{x+3}$

2. $\dfrac{1}{x+2}$

3. $\dfrac{b-3}{b-1}$

4. $\dfrac{2}{a+1}$

5. 2

6. 3

7. $\dfrac{1}{3}$

8. $\dfrac{3}{4}$

9. $\dfrac{1}{a}$

10. $\dfrac{x-3}{2}$

11. $\dfrac{2}{x}$

12. $\dfrac{23}{4(x-7)}=\dfrac{23}{4x-28}$

13. $\dfrac{6}{x^2}$

14. $\dfrac{1}{x+4}$

15. $\dfrac{9}{a+6}$

16. $\dfrac{7}{2(x-4)}=\dfrac{7}{2x-8}$

17. $\dfrac{5(x+2)}{(x-4)(x+1)}=\dfrac{5x+10}{x^2-3x-4}$

18. $\dfrac{14}{(x-7)(x+7)}=\dfrac{14}{x^2-49}$

19. $\dfrac{4(5x+6)}{(x-4)(x+4)^2}$

20. $\dfrac{x+2}{(x-3)(x-2)}=\dfrac{x+2}{x^2-5x+6}$

Checkpoint 7A
Problem 7-67
Finding the x- and y-Intercepts of a Quadratic Function

Answers to problem 7-67: y-intercept: $(0,-17)$, x-intercepts: $(-2+\sqrt{21},0)$ and $(-2-\sqrt{21},0)$

The y-intercepts of an equation are the points at which the graph crosses the y-axis. To find the y-intercept of an equation, substitute $x=0$ into the equation and solve for y.

The x-intercepts of an equation are the points at which the graph crosses the x-axis. To find the x-intercepts of an equation, substitute $y=0$ into the equation and solve for x. For a quadratic, you can do this by factoring and using the Zero Product Property or by using the Quadratic Formula, as well as other methods.

Example 1: Find the x-intercepts of the graph of the equation $y = x^2 + 4x - 12$.

Solution: If $y=0$, then:
$$0 = x^2 + 4x - 12$$
By factoring and using the Zero Product Property:
$$0 = (x+6)(x-2)$$
$$x+6 = 0 \quad \text{or} \quad x-2 = 0$$
$$x = -6 \quad \text{or} \quad x = 2$$

Answers: The x-intercepts are $(-6, 0)$ and $(2, 0)$.

Example 2: Find the x-intercepts of the graph of the equation $y = 2x^2 - 3x - 3$.

Solution: If $y=0$, then:
$$0 = 2x^2 - 3x - 3$$

Since we cannot factor the trinomial we use the Quadratic Formula to solve for x.

If $ax^2 + bx + c = 0$ then:
$$x = \frac{-b \pm \sqrt{b^2 - 4ac}}{2a}.$$

Substitute $a = 2$, $b = -3$, $c = -3$.
$$x = \frac{-(-3) \pm \sqrt{(-3)^2 - 4(2)(-3)}}{2(2)}$$

Simplify.
$$x = \frac{3 \pm \sqrt{9+24}}{4} = \frac{3 \pm \sqrt{33}}{4}$$

Find $\sqrt{33}$ approximately:
$$\approx \frac{3 \pm 5.745}{4}, \text{ so } \frac{3+5.745}{4} \text{ and } \frac{3-5.745}{4}.$$

Answers: Simplify the fractions and the x-intercepts are approximately $(2.19, 0)$ and $(-0.69, 0)$. They can be expressed in exact form as $\left(\frac{3+\sqrt{33}}{4}, 0\right)$ and $\left(\frac{3-\sqrt{33}}{4}, 0\right)$.

Core Connections Algebra 2

Now we can find the x- and y-intercepts in the original problem.

Find the x- and y-intercepts of the graph of $y = x^2 + 4x - 17$.

Solution: To find the y-intercept, let $x = 0$ so $y = (0)^2 + 4(0) - 17 = -17$.
To find the x-intercept, let $y = 0$ so $0 = x^2 + 4x - 17$.
Since we cannot factor we use the Quadratic Formula with $a = 1$, $b = 4$, and $c = -17$.

$$x = \frac{-4 \pm \sqrt{4^2 - 4(1)(-17)}}{2(1)} = \frac{-4 \pm \sqrt{16+68}}{2} = \frac{-4 \pm \sqrt{84}}{2} = \frac{-4 \pm 2\sqrt{21}}{2} = -2 \pm \sqrt{21}$$

Answers: The y-intercept is $(0, -17)$. The x-intercepts are $(-2 \pm \sqrt{21}, 0)$, or approximately $(2.58, 0)$ and $(-6.58, 0)$.

Here are some more to try. Find the x- and y-intercepts for the graphs of each equation.

1. $y = x^2 + 2x - 15$ 2. $y = 2x^2 + 7x + 3$

3. $y = 3x^2 - 5x + 2$ 4. $y = 4x^2 - 8x$

5. $y = 2x^2 - 9x - 35$ 6. $y = 2x^2 - 11x + 5$

7. $3x^2 + 2 + 7x = y$ 8. $8x^2 + 10x + 3 = y$

9. $y + 2 = x^2 - 5x$ 10. $(x - 3)(x + 4) - 7x = y$

11. $-4x^2 + 8x + 3 = y$ 12. $0.009x^2 - 0.86x + 2 = y$

13. $y = 2x^3 - 50x$ 14. $y = 3x^2 + 4x$

Answers:

1. $(3,0), (-5,0)$, and $(0,-15)$ 2. $\left(-\frac{1}{2},0\right), (-3,0)$, and $(0,3)$

3. $\left(\frac{2}{3},0\right), (1,0)$, and $(0,2)$ 4. $(0,0), (2,0)$, and $(0,0)$

5. $(7,0), \left(-\frac{5}{2},0\right)$, and $(0,-35)$ 6. $(5,0), \left(\frac{1}{2},0\right)$, and $(0,5)$

7. $\left(-\frac{1}{3},0\right), (-2,0)$, and $(0,2)$ 8. $\left(-\frac{3}{4},0\right), \left(-\frac{1}{2},0\right)$, and $(0,3)$

9. $\left(\frac{5 \pm \sqrt{33}}{2},0\right)$ or $(\approx 5.37, 0), (\approx -0.37, 0)$, and $(0,-2)$

10. $\left(\frac{-6 \pm \sqrt{84}}{2}, 0\right)$ or $(\approx 7.58, 0), (\approx -1.58, 0)$, and $(0,-12)$

11. $\left(\frac{-8 \pm \sqrt{112}}{-8}, 0\right)$ or $(\approx -0.32, 0), (\approx 2.32, 0)$, and $(0,3)$

12. $\left(\frac{0.86 \pm \sqrt{0.6676}}{0.018}, 0\right)$ or $(\approx 2.39, 0), (\approx 93.17, 0)$, and $(0,2)$

13. $(0,0), (5,0), (-5,0)$, and $(0,0)$ 14. $(0,0), \left(-\frac{4}{3},0\right)$, and $(0,0)$

Checkpoint 7B
Problem 7-131
Completing the Square to Find the Vertex of a Parabola

Answers to problem 7-131:   Graphing form: $y = 2(x-1)^2 + 3$, vertex $(1, 3)$
See graph in solution that follows examples.

If a quadratic function is in graphing form then the vertex can be found easily and a sketch of the graph can be made quickly. If the equation of the parabola is not in graphing form, the equation can be rewritten in graphing form by completing the square.

First, recall that $y = x^2$ is the parent equation for quadratic functions and the general equation can be written in graphing form as $y = a(x-h)^2 + k$ where (h, k) is the vertex, and relative to the parent graph the function has been:

- Vertically stretched, if the absolute value of a is greater than 1.

- Vertically compressed, if the absolute value of a is less than 1.

- Reflected across the x-axis, if a is less than 0.

Example 1: Complete the square to change $y = x^2 + 8x + 10$ into graphing form and name the vertex.

Solution: Use an area model to make $x^2 + 8x$ into a perfect square. To do this, use half of the coefficient of the x-term on each side of the area model, and complete the upper right corner of the square, as shown at right.

$+4$	$4x$	16
x	x^2	$4x$
	x	$+4$

Your square shows that $(x+4)^2 = x^2 + 8x + 16$. Your original expression is $x^2 + 8x + 10$, which is 6 fewer than $(x+4)^2$. So you can write $y = x^2 + 8x + 10 = (x+4)^2 - 6$.

Because the function is now in graphing form, $y = a(x-h)^2 + k$, you know the vertex is (h, k), in this case $(-4, -6)$.

Example 2: Complete the square to change $y = x^2 + 5x + 7$ into graphing form and name the vertex.

Solution: We need to make $x^2 + 5x$ into a perfect square. Again, we take half of the coefficient of x and fill in the upper right of the area model, as shown at right.

$+2.5$	$2.5x$	6.25
x	x^2	$2.5x$
	x	$+2.5$

The area model shows that $(x+2.5)^2 = x^2 + 5x + 6.25$. Your original expression, $y = x^2 + 5x + 7$, is 0.75 more than $(x+2.5)^2$.
So you can write: $y = x^2 + 5x + 7 = (x+2.5)^2 + 0.75$ and the vertex is $(-2.5, 0.75)$.

Example 3: **Complete the square to change $y = 2x^2 - 6x + 2$ into graphing form and name the vertex.**

Solution: This problem is different because the x^2-term has a coefficient. First factor the 2 out of the quadratic expression so that an x^2-term remains, as follows: $y = 2x^2 - 6x + 2 = 2(x^2 - 3x + 1)$. Then make $x^2 - 3x$ into a perfect square as before:

	$-1.5x$	2.25
-1.5		
x	x^2	$-1.5x$
	x	-1.5

Since $(x - 1.5)^2 = x^2 - 3x + 2.25$, the original expression $x^2 - 3x + 1$ is 1.25 less than $(x - 1.5)^2$. You can write:

The vertex is $(1.5, -2.5)$.

$y = 2x^2 - 6x + 2$

$y = 2(x^2 - 3x + 1)$

$y = 2\left((x - 1.5)^2 - 1.25\right)$

which can be distributed to give

$y = 2(x - 1.5)^2 - 2.5$

Now we can go back and solve the original problem.

Complete the square to change the equation $y = 2x^2 - 4x + 5$ to graphing form, identify the vertex of the parabola, and sketch its graph.

Solution: Factor out the coefficient of x^2, resulting in $y = 2\left(x^2 - 2x + \frac{5}{2}\right)$. Make a perfect square out of $x^2 - 2x$:

	$-1x$	1
-1		
x	x^2	$-1x$
	x	-1

Since $(x - 1)^2 = x^2 - 2x + 1$, the original expression $x^2 - 2x + \frac{5}{2}$ is $\frac{3}{2}$ more than $(x - 1)^2$. You can write:

Because the function is now in graphing form, $y = a(x - h)^2 + k$, you know the vertex is $(h, k) = (1, 3)$.

$y = 2x^2 - 4x + 5$

$y = 2\left(x^2 - 2x + \frac{5}{2}\right)$

$y = 2\left((x - 1)^2 + \frac{3}{2}\right)$

which can be distributed to give

$y = 2(x - 1)^2 + 3$

To sketch the graph, we start by plotting the vertex, $(1, 3)$. From the standard form, $y = 2x^2 - 4x + 5$, we see that the y-intercept is $(0, 5)$, because when $x = 0$, $y = 5$. By symmetry, $(2, 5)$ must also be a point. Thus we get the graph at the right. If desired, additional points can be found by recognizing that the shape of this parabola is the shape of $y = x^2$ stretched by a factor of 2.

Answer: Graphing form: $y = 2(x - 1)^2 + 3$;
Vertex: $(1, 3)$;
See graph at right.

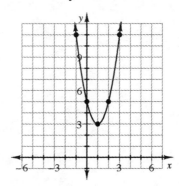

Here are some more to try. Write each equation in graphing form. If needed, complete the square to do so. Then state the vertex, y-intercept, and the stretch factor and sketch a graph.

1. $y = x^2 - 6x + 9$

2. $y = x^2 + 3$

3. $y = x^2 - 4x$

4. $y = x^2 + 2x - 3$

5. $y = x^2 + 5x + 1$

6. $y = x^2 - \frac{1}{3}x$

7. $y = 3x^2 - 6x + 1$

8. $y = 5x^2 + 20x - 16$

9. $y = -x^2 - 6x + 10$

Answers:

1. $y = (x - 3)^2$; $(3, 0)$; $(0, 9)$; $a = 1$

2. $y = (x - 0)^2 + 3$; $(0, 3)$; $(0, 3)$; $a = 1$

3. $y = (x - 2)^2 - 4$; $(2, -4)$; $(0, 0)$; $a = 1$

4. $y = (x + 1)^2 - 4$; $(-1, -4)$; $(0, -3)$ $a = 1$

5. $y = \left(x + \frac{5}{2}\right)^2 - 5\frac{1}{4}$; $\left(-\frac{5}{2}, -5\frac{1}{4}\right)$; $(0, 1)$; $a = 1$

6. $y = \left(x - \frac{1}{6}\right)^2 - \frac{1}{36}$; $\left(\frac{1}{6}, -\frac{1}{36}\right)$; $(0, 0)$; $a = 1$

7. $y = 3(x - 1)^2 - 2$; $(1, -2)$; $(0, 1)$; $a = 3$

8. $y = 5(x + 2)^2 - 36$; $(-2, -36)$; $(0, -16)$; $a = 5$

9. $y = -(x + 3)^2 + 19$ $(-3, 19)$; $(0, 10)$; $a = -1$

Checkpoint 8A
Problem 8-127
Solving and Graphing Inequalities

Answers to problem 8-127:

a.

b.

There are several methods for graphing different types of inequalities but there is one way that works for all types: Solve as you would an equation then use the solutions to break the graph into regions. If testing a point from a region makes the inequality "true," shade in that region as it is part of the solution. If a point from the region makes the inequality "false," then that region is not part of the solution.

Example 1: Graph $x^2 + 5x + 4 < 0$.

Solution: Change the inequality into an equation and solve.

$$x^2 + 5x + 4 = 0$$
$$(x+4)(x+1) = 0$$
$$x = -4 \text{ or } x = -1$$

Place the solutions on a number line to break the line into three regions. Use open circles since the original problem is a strict inequality. Test one point from each region in the original inequality. For example testing $x = -5$ we find:

$$(-5)^2 + 5(-5) + 4 < 0$$

$$4 < 0 \text{ False}$$

So that region is not shaded in. Continue in the same manner with one point from each of the other regions.

test	test	test
$x = -5$	$x = -2$	$x = 0$
F	T	F

The solution may also be written $-4 < x < -1$.

Example 2: Graph the system $y \le x + 1$
$$y \ge x^2 - 4$$

Solution: Graph the line $y = x + 1$ and check the point $(0, 0)$. The point makes the first inequality "true" so the shading is in the $(0, 0)$ region or below the line.

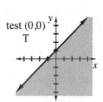

Next graph the parabola $y = x^2 - 4$ and again finding the point $(0, 0)$ to be "true" in the inequality, the shading is inside the parabola. The overlapping shaded region is the solution to the system.

Now we can go back and solve the original problems.

a. $|x+1| \geq 3$

Solution: If $|x+1| = 3$ then $x+1 = \pm 3$ or $x = 2, -4$. Using solid dots to divide the number line into three regions and testing a point from each region gives the answer graph at right. This can also be written as: $x \leq -4$ or $x \geq 2$.

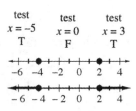

b. Graph: $y \leq -2x+3$ $y \geq x$ $x \geq -1$

Solution: Start by looking at the equation of the line that marks the edge of each inequality. The first has slope -2 and y-intercept $(0, 3)$. Checking $(0, 1)$ gives a true statement so we shade below the solid line. The second line has slope 1 and y-intercept $(0, 0)$. Again checking $(0, 1)$ gives a true statement, so we shade above the solid line. The third is a vertical line at $x = -1$. Checking a point tells us to shade the right side. The overlapping shading is a triangle with vertices $(-1, 5), (1, 1)$, and $(-1, -1)$. See the answer graph at right.

Here are a few more to try. In problems 1 through 6, graph each inequality. In problems 7 through 14 graph the solution region for each system of inequalities.

1. $|2x+3| \leq 7$

2. $x^2 - 2x - 3 > 0$

3. $4 - x^2 \leq 0$

4. $|4r - 2| > 8$

5. $3m^2 \leq 9m$

6. $-|x+3| < 10$

7. $y \leq -x+2$
$\quad y \leq 3x-6$

8. $y \geq \frac{2}{3}x+4$
$\quad y \leq \frac{7}{12}x+5$

9. $x < 3$
$\quad y \geq -2$

10. $y \leq 4x+16$
$\quad y \geq -\frac{4}{3}x-4$

11. $y \geq x^2 - 4$
$\quad y < -3x+1$

12. $y < 2x+5$
$\quad y \geq |x+1|$

13. $y < x^2 - 2x - 3$
$\quad y \leq \frac{1}{2}x+3$

14. $y \leq -\frac{1}{2}x+2$
$\quad y \geq (x+1)^2 - 3$

Answers:

1.
-5 2

2.
-1 3

3.
-2 2

4.
$-\frac{3}{2}$ $\frac{5}{2}$

5.
0 3

6.
all numbers

7.
(0, 2)
(0, −6)
x
y

8.
(0, 5)
(0, 4)
x
y

9.
$x = 3$
$y = −2$
x
y

10.
(0, 16)
(0, −4)
x
y

11.
(−2, 0)
(0, 1)
(2, 0) x
y

12.
(0, 5)
(−1, 0)
x
y

13.
(0, 3)
(0, −1)
(3, 0) x
y

14.
(0, 2)
$\left(-1-\sqrt{3}, 0\right)$
$\left(\sqrt{3}-1, 0\right)$
x
y

Checkpoint 8B
Problem 8-174
Solving Complicated Equations

Answers to problem 8-174: a: $x = 5$ or 1, b: $x = 4$ or 0, c: $x = 7$, d: $x = 1$

Often the best way to solve a complicated equation is to use a method such as the Looking Inside or Undoing Methods. Checking your answer(s) is important because sometimes solutions are accurately found but will not work in the original equation. These answers are called extraneous solutions.

Example 1: Solve $3(x+1)^3 - 1 = 80$

Solution: In this case we will undo everything.

		check
$3(x+1)^3 - 1 = 80$ original problem		$3(2+1)^3 = 81$
$3(x+1)^3 = 81$ add 1 to undo -1		$3(3)^3 = 81$
$(x+1)^3 = 27$ division undoes multiplication		$3(27) = 81$
$x+1 = 3$ cube root undoes cubing		$81 = 81$
$x = 2$ subtract 1 to undo $+1$		

Example 2: Solve $|2x + 5| = x + 4$

Solution: In this case we will use the Look Inside Method and the fact that absolute value of a quantity and its opposite are the same.

$$2x + 5 = x + 4 \quad \text{or} \quad -(2x+5) = x + 4$$
$$x = -1 \qquad\qquad\qquad -2x - 5 = x + 4$$
$$-3x = 9$$
$$x = -3$$

checks

$$|2(-1)+5| = -1+4 \qquad |2(-3)+5| = -3+4$$
$$|3| = |3| \qquad\qquad\qquad |-1| = |1|$$
$$3 = 3 \text{ True} \qquad\qquad\qquad 1 = 1 \text{ True}$$

The solutions are $x = -1$, $x = -3$.

Now we can go back and solve the original problems.

a.
$$2|x-3|+7=11$$
$$2|x-3|=4$$
$$|x-3|=2$$
$$x-3=2 \text{ or } -(x-3)=2$$
$$x=5 \text{ or } x=1$$

checks

$$2|5-3|+7=11 \qquad 2|1-3|+7=11$$
$$2|2|+7=11 \qquad 2|-2|+7=11$$
$$4+7=11 \text{ True} \qquad 4+7=11 \text{ True}$$

The solutions are $x=5$, $x=1$.

b.
$$4(x-2)^2=16$$
$$(x-2)^2=4$$
$$x-2=\pm2$$
$$x=2\pm2=4 \text{ or } 0$$

checks

$$4(4-2)^2=16 \qquad 4(0-2)^2=16$$
$$4(2)^2=16 \qquad 4(-2)^2=16$$
$$4(4)=16 \text{ True} \qquad 4(4)=16 \text{ True}$$

The solutions are $x=4$, $x=0$.

c.
$$\sqrt{x+18}=x-2$$
$$(\sqrt{x+18})^2=(x-2)^2$$
$$x+18=x^2-4x+4$$
$$0=x^2-5x-14$$
$$0=(x-7)(x+2)$$
$$x=7 \text{ or } x=-2$$

checks

$$\sqrt{7+18}=7-2 \qquad \sqrt{-2+18}=-2-2$$
$$\sqrt{25}=5 \text{ True} \qquad \sqrt{16}=-4 \text{ False}$$

The only solution is $x=7$.

d.
$$|2x+5|=3x+4$$
$$2x+5=3x+4 \text{ or } -(2x+5)=3x+4$$
$$x=1 \qquad \text{or} \qquad x=-\tfrac{9}{5}$$

checks

$$|2(1)+5|=3(1)+4 \qquad |2(-\tfrac{9}{5})+5|=3(-\tfrac{9}{5})+4$$
$$|7|=7 \text{ True} \qquad |-\tfrac{18}{5}+\tfrac{25}{5}|=-\tfrac{27}{5}+\tfrac{20}{5}$$
$$|\tfrac{7}{5}|=-\tfrac{7}{5} \text{ False}$$

The only solution is $x=1$.

Here are some more to try. Solve each equation and check your solutions.

1. $|x+4|+3=17$

2. $|3w-6|-2=19$

3. $\sqrt{3w+4}-2=2$

4. $\sqrt{3x+13}=x+5$

5. $\sqrt[3]{x}-2=5$

6. $(x+1)^2+1=6$

7. $|2y-4|=12$

8. $|3m+5|=5m+2$

9. $\sqrt{y+7}+5=y$

10. $\sqrt{5-m}=m+1$

11. $\frac{2(x-1)^2}{3}-7=1$

12. $3(x-2)^3=81$

13. $|2m+5|=m+4$

14. $|2y+8|=3y+7$

15. $\sqrt{x+7}-x=1$

16. $\sqrt{y+2}=y$

17. $\sqrt[4]{x+1}+2=5$

18. $\frac{1}{2}(x+5)^3+1=10$

19. $\sqrt{x}+2=x$

20. $\sqrt{x}+2=\sqrt{x+6}$

Answers:

1. $x=-18,10$ 2. $w=-5,9$ 3. $w=4$ 4. $x=-3,-4$

5. $x=343$ 6. $x=-1\pm\sqrt{5}$ 7. $y=-4,8$ 8. $m=\frac{3}{2}$

9. $y=9$ 10. $m=1$ 11. $x=1\pm\sqrt{12}$ 12. $x=5$

13. $m=-1,-3$ 14. $y=1$ 15. $x=2$ 16. $y=2$

17. $x=80$ 18. $x=-5+\sqrt[3]{18}$ 19. $x=4$ 20. $x=\frac{1}{4}$

Checkpoint 9A
Problem 9-41
Writing and Solving Exponential Equations

Answers to problem 9-41:

a. The more rabbits you have, the more new ones you get, a linear model would grow by the same number each year. A sine function would be better if the population rises and falls, but more data would be needed to apply this model.

b. $R = 80,000(5.4772...)^t$ c. ≈ 394 million

d. 1859, it seems okay that they grew to 80,000 in 7 years, *if* they are growing exponentially.

e. No, since it would predict a huge number of rabbits now. The population probably leveled off at some point or dropped drastically and rebuilt periodically.

Exponential functions are equations of the form $y = ab^x + c$ where a represents the initial value, b represents the multiplier, c represents the horizontal asymptote, and x often represents the time. Some problems simply involve substituting in the given information into the equation and then doing calculations. If you are trying to solve for the time (x), then you will usually need to use logarithms. If you need to find the multiplier (m), then you will need to find a root. Note that we often assume that $c = 0$, unless we are told otherwise.

Example 1: Lunch at our favorite fast food stands cost \$6.50. The price has steadily increased 4% per year for many years.

Question 1: What will lunch cost in 10 years?

Solution: In this case, we can use \$6.50 as the initial value and the multiplier is 1.04, so the equation for the situation is $y = 6.50(1.04)^x$. The time we are interested in here is 10 years. Substituting into the equation, $y = 6.50(1.04)^{10} = \$9.62$.

Question 2: What did it cost 10 years ago?

Solution: Using the same equation, only using -10 for the years, $y = 6.50(1.04)^{-10} = \$4.39$.

Question 3: How long before lunch costs \$10?

Solution: Again, we use the same equation, but this time we know the y-value, but not the value of x. To solve for x, we use logarithms, as shown in the work at right.

$$\$10 = 6.50(1.04)^x$$
$$1.04^x = \tfrac{10}{6.5}$$
$$\log 1.04^x = \log\left(\tfrac{10}{6.5}\right)$$
$$x \log 1.04 = \log\left(\tfrac{10}{6.5}\right)$$
$$x = \frac{\log\left(\tfrac{10}{6.5}\right)}{\log 1.04} \approx 11$$

Answer: About 11 years.

Example 2: **Tickets for a big concert first went on sale three weeks ago for $60. This week people are charging $100. Write an equation that represents the cost of the tickets w weeks from the time that they went on sale. Assume that they continue to increase in the same way.**

Solution: To find the multiplier, we can use what we are given. The initial value is $60, the time is 3 weeks, and the final value is $100. This gives $100 = 60k^3$. Solving for k gives $k = \sqrt[3]{\frac{100}{60}} \approx 1.186$.

Answer: The equation is approximately $y = 60(1.186)^w$.

Now we can go back and solve parts (b), (c), and (d) of the original problem.

When rabbits were first brought to Australia, they had no natural enemies. There were about 80,000 rabbits in 1866. Two years later, in 1868, the population had grown to over 2,400,000!

b. Write an exponential equation for the number of rabbits t years after 1866.

Solution: For 1866, 80000 would be the initial value, time would be 2 years, and the final amount would be 2400000, which gives the equation $2400000 = 80000m^2$. Solving for m, we get $30 = m^2$ so $m = \sqrt{30} \approx 5.477$. Thus the equation is approximately $R = 80,000(5.477)^t$.

c. How many rabbits do you predict would have been present in 1871?

Solution: The initial value is still 80,000, the multiplier ≈ 5.477, and now the time is 5 years. This gives $80,000(5.477)^5 \approx 394$ million.

d. According to your model, in what year was the first pair of rabbits introduced into Australia?

Solution: In this situation, we use 2 as the initial value, 80000 as the final value, and the multiplier is still 5.477 but now the time is not known. Using these values, we get $80000 = 2(5.477)^x$, which is solved at right. The answer 6.23 tells us that approximately 6.23 years had passed between the time of the first pair of rabbits, and the time when there were 80000. Thus, rabbits would have been introduced sometime in 1859.

$$80000 = 2(5.477)^x$$
$$40000 = (5.477)^x$$
$$\log(5.477)^x = \log 40000$$
$$x\log(5.477) = \log 40000$$
$$x = \frac{\log(40000)}{\log(5.477)} \approx 6.23$$

Here are some more to try:

1. A DVD loses 60% of its value every year it is in the store. The DVD costs $80 new. Write a function that represents its value in t years. What is it worth after 4 years?

2. Inflation is at a rate of 7% per year. Evan's favorite bread now costs $1.79. What did it cost 10 years ago? How long before the cost of the bread doubles?

3. A bond that appreciates 4% per year will be worth $146 in five years. Find the current value.

4. Sixty years ago, when Sam's grandfather was a kid, he could buy his friend dinner for $1.50. If that same dinner now costs $25.25 and inflation was consistent, write an equation that models the cost for the dinner at different times.

5. A two-bedroom house in Omaha is now worth $110,000. If it appreciates at a rate of 2.5% per year, how long will it take to be worth $200,000?

6. A car valued at $14,000 depreciates 18% per year. After how many years will the value have depreciated to $1000?

Answers:

1. $y = 80(0.4)^t$, $2.05

2. $0.91, 10.2 years

3. $120

4. $y = 1.50(1.048)^x$

5. 24.2 years

6. 13.3 years

Checkpoint 9B

Problem 9-111

Finding the Equation for the Inverse of a Function

Answers to problem 9-111:

a. $f^{-1}(x) = \frac{1}{3}\left(\frac{x-5}{2}\right)^2 + 1 = \frac{1}{12}(x-5)^2 + 1$ for $x \geq 5$

b. See graph at right.

To find the equation for the inverse of a function, you can interchange the x and y variables and then solve for y. This also means that the coordinates of points that are on the graph of the function will be reversed on the graph of the inverse. Here are some examples:

Example 1: Write the equation for the inverse of $y = 2(x+3)$.

Solution: We can interchange the x and the y to get the equation of the inverse. To get our final answer, we solve for y, as shown at right.

$$2(y+3) = x$$
$$(y+3) = \frac{x}{2}$$
$$y = \frac{x}{2} - 3$$

Answer: $y = \frac{x}{2} - 3$

Example 2: Write the equation for the inverse of $y = \frac{1}{2}(x+4)^2 + 1$.

Solution: Again, we can interchange the x and the y to get the equation of the inverse and then solve for y to get our answer in $y =$ form, as shown at right.

Answer: $y = -4 \pm \sqrt{2x-2}$. Note that because of the $\pm$, this inverse is not a function.

$$x = \frac{1}{2}(y+4)^2 + 1$$
$$\frac{1}{2}(y+4)^2 = x-1$$
$$(y+4)^2 = 2x-2$$
$$y+4 = \pm\sqrt{2x-2}$$
$$y = -4 \pm \sqrt{2x-2}$$

Example 3: Write the equation for the inverse of $y = -\frac{2}{3}x + 6$.

Solution: Interchanging the x and the y, we get $x = -\frac{2}{3}y + 6$. Solving for y gives
$$y = -\frac{3}{2}(x-6) = -\frac{3}{2}x + 9.$$

Answer: $y = -\frac{3}{2}x + 9$

Example 4: Write the equation for the inverse of $y = \sqrt{x-2}+3$.

Solution: Again, we exchange x and y and then solve for y, as shown at
right.

$$x = \sqrt{y-2}+3$$
$$\sqrt{y-2} = x-3$$

The original function is half of a sleeping parabola, so the
inverse is only half of a parabola as well. Thus the domain of
the inverse is restricted to $x \geq 3$.

$$y-2 = (x-3)^2$$
$$y = (x-3)^2 + 2$$

Answer: $y = (x-3)^2 + 2$ in the domain $x \geq 3$.

Now we can go back and solve the original problem.

Find the equation for the inverse of the function $y = 2\sqrt{3(x-1)}+5$. Then sketch the graph
of both the original and the inverse.

Solution: Interchanging x and y we get $x = 2\sqrt{3(y-1)}+5$. We then
solve for y, as shown at right. This equation is simplified to
get $y = \frac{(x-5)^2}{12}+1$.

$$x = 2\sqrt{3(y-1)}+5$$
$$2\sqrt{3(y-1)} = x-5$$
$$\sqrt{3(y-1)} = \tfrac{x-5}{2}$$

Note that the domain and range of the inverse are the
interchanged domain and range of the original function. In
other words, the original function has a domain of $x \geq 1$ and
range of $y \geq 5$. The domain of the inverse, then, is $x \geq 5$
and the range is $y \geq 1$.

$$3(y-1) = \left(\tfrac{x-5}{2}\right)^2$$
$$y-1 = \tfrac{1}{3}\left(\tfrac{x-5}{2}\right)^2$$
$$y = \tfrac{1}{3}\left(\tfrac{x-5}{2}\right)^2 + 1$$

As you can see by the graph at right, the points on the inverse
graph, have interchanged coordinates from the points on the
graph of the original function. For example, two points on
the original graph are (1, 5) and (4, 11). The corresponding
points on the graph of the inverse are (5, 1) and (11, 4).

Answer: $y = \frac{(x-5)^2}{12}+1$ in the domain $x \geq 5$.

Here are some more to try. Find an equation for the inverse of each function.

1. $y = 3x - 2$

2. $y = \frac{x+1}{4}$

3. $y = \frac{1}{3}x + 2$

4. $y = x^3 + 1$

5. $y = 1 + \sqrt{x + 5}$

6. $y = 3(x + 2)^2 - 7$

7. $y = 2\sqrt{x - 1} + 3$

8. $y = \frac{1}{2+x}$

9. $y = \log_3(x + 2)$

Answers:

1. $y = \frac{x+2}{3}$

2. $y = 4x - 1$

3. $y = 3x - 6$

4. $y = \sqrt[3]{x - 1}$

5. $y = (x - 1)^2 - 5$

6. $y = -2 \pm \sqrt{\frac{x+7}{3}}$

7. $y = \left(\frac{x-3}{2}\right)^2 + 1$

8. $y = \frac{1}{x} - 2$

9. $y = 3^x - 2$

Checkpoint 10
Problem 10-176
Rewriting Expressions with and Solving Equations with Logarithms

Answers to problem 10-176: a: $\log_2(5x)$, b: $\log_2(5x^2)$, c: 17, d: $-\frac{9}{20} = -0.45$,
e: 15, f: 4

First a review of the properties based on the inverse relationship of exponentials and logarithms:

The following definitions and properties hold true for all positive $m \neq 1$.

Definition of logarithms: $\log_m(a) = n$ means $m^n = a$

Product Property: $\qquad \log_m(a \cdot b) = \log_m(a) + \log_m(b)$

Quotient Property: $\qquad \log_m(\frac{a}{b}) = \log_m(a) - \log_m(b)$

Power Property: $\qquad \log_m(a^n) = n \cdot \log_m(a)$

Inverse relationship: $\qquad \log_m(m)^n = n$ and $m^{\log m (n)} = n$

Example 1: Write as a single logarithm: $3\log_5(x) + \log_5(x+1)$

Solution: $3\log_5(x) + \log_5(x+1) = \log_5(x^3) + \log_5(x+1)$ by the Power Property
$$= \log_5(x^3(x+1)) \qquad \text{by the Product Property}$$
$$= \log_5(x^4 + x^3) \qquad \text{by simplifying}$$

Example 2: Solve $\log_2(x) - \log_2(3) = 4$

Solution: $\log_2(x) - \log_2(3) = 4 \qquad$ problem
$$\log_2\left(\tfrac{x}{3}\right) = 4 \qquad \text{by the Quotient Property}$$
$$2^4 = \tfrac{x}{3} \qquad \text{by the definition of logarithms}$$
$$48 = x \qquad \text{multiply both sides by 3}$$

Now we can go back and solve the original problems.

a. $\log_2(30x) - \log_2(6)$

   $\log_2(\frac{30x}{6}) = \log_2(5x)$

b. $2\log_3(x) + \log_3(5)$

   $\log_3(x^2) + \log_3(5)$

   $\log_3(x^2 \cdot 5) = \log_3(5x^2)$

c. $\log_7(3x - 2) = 2$

   $7^2 = 3x - 2$

   $49 = 3x - 2 \Rightarrow x = 17$

d. $\log(2x + 1) = -1$

   $10^{-1} = 2x + 1$

   $\frac{1}{10} = 2x + 1 \Rightarrow x = -\frac{9}{20} = -0.45$

e. $\log_5(3y) + \log_5(9) = \log_5(405)$

   $\log_5(3y \cdot 9) = \log_5(405)$

   $\log_5(27y) = \log_5(405)$

   $27y = 405 \Rightarrow y = 15$

f. $\log(x) + \log(x + 21) = 2$

   $\log(x^2 + 21x) = 2$

   $x^2 + 21x = 10^2$

   $x^2 + 21x - 100 = 0$

   $(x + 25)(x - 4) = 0$

   $x = -25, x = 4$

   $x = 4$

   $x = -25$ is an extraneous solution

Here are some more to try. In problems 1 through 8, write each expression as a single logarithm. In problems 9 through 26 solve each equation.

1. $\log_3(5) + \log_3(m)$

2. $\log_2(q) - \log_2(z)$

3. $\log_6(r) + 3\log_6(x)$

4. $\log(90) + \log(4) - \log(36)$

5. $\log_4(16x) - \log_4(x)$

6. $\log(\sqrt{x}) + \log(x^2)$

7. $\log_5(\sqrt{x}) + \log_5(\sqrt[3]{x})$

8. $\log_5(x-1) + \log_5(x+1)$

9. $\log_4(2x+3) = \frac{1}{2}$

10. $\log_5(3x+1) = 2$

11. $\log_9(9^2) = x$

12. $16^{\log_{16}(5)} = y$

13. $8^{\log_8(x)} = 3$

14. $\log_5(5^{0.3}) = y$

15. $\log_2(x) = 3\log_2(4) + \log_2(5)$

16. $\log_6(x) + \log_6(8) = \log_6(48)$

17. $\log_2(144) - \log_2(x) = \log_2(9)$

18. $\log_2(36) - \log_2(y) = \log_2(12)$

19. $\log_5(3x-1) = -1$

20. $\log_2(x) - \log_2(3) = 4$

21. $\frac{1}{3}\log(3x+1) = 2$

22. $\log_2(5) + \frac{1}{2}\log_2(x) = \log_2(15)$

23. $\frac{1}{2}\log(y) = 2\log(2) + \log(16)$

24. $\log_2(x^2 + 2x) = 3$

25. $2\log_4(x) - \log_4(3) = 2$

26. $\log_7(x+1) + \log_7(x-5) = 1$

Answers:

1. $\log_3(5m)$ 2. $\log_2(\frac{q}{z})$ 3. $\log_6(rx^3)$ 4. $\log(10) = 1$

5. $\log_4(16) = 2$ 6. $\log(x^{5/2})$ 7. $\log_5(x^{5/6})$ 8. $\log_5(x^2 - 1)$

9. $-\frac{1}{2}$ 10. 8 11. 2 12. 5

13. 3 14. 0.3 15. 320 16. 6

17. 16 18. 3 19. $\frac{2}{5}$ 20. 48

21. 333,333 22. 9 23. 4096 24. −4, 2

25. $\sqrt{48} = 4\sqrt{3}$ 26. 6

Checkpoint 11

Problem 11-95

Solving Rational Equations

Answers to problem 11-95: a: $x = \pm 2\sqrt{3}$, b: $x = 2$, c: $x = \frac{2}{9}$, d: $x = \frac{-1 \pm \sqrt{13}}{6} \approx 0.434$ or -0.768

To solve rational equations (equations with fractions) it is usually best to first multiply everything by the common denominator to remove the fractions, a method known as **Fraction Busters**. After you have done this, you can solve the equation using your usual strategies. Following are a few examples.

Example 1: Solve $\frac{24}{x+1} = \frac{16}{1}$.

Solution: The common denominator in this case is $(x+1)$.
Multiplying both sides of the equation by $(x+1)$
removes all fractions from the equation. You can
then simplify and solve for x. This process is
demonstrated at right.

$$(x+1)\left(\frac{24}{x+1}\right) = (x+1)\left(\frac{16}{1}\right)$$
$$24 = 16(x+1)$$
$$24 = 16x + 16$$
$$8 = 16x$$
$$x = \frac{1}{2}$$

Answer: $x = \frac{1}{2}$

Example 2: Solve $\frac{5}{2x} + \frac{1}{6} = 8$.

Solution: Again, we multiply both sides of the equation by the
common denominator, which, in this case, is $6x$. We
must be careful to remember to distribute so that we
multiply each term on both sides of the equation by $6x$.
Then we simplify and solve, as shown at right.

$$6x\left(\frac{5}{2x} + \frac{1}{6}\right) = 6x(8)$$
$$6x \cdot \frac{5}{2x} + 6x \cdot \frac{1}{6} = 48x$$
$$15 + x = 48x$$
$$15 = 47x$$
$$x = \frac{15}{47}$$

Answer: $x = \frac{15}{47}$

Now we can go back and solve the original problems.

a. $\frac{x}{3} = \frac{4}{x}$

$3x\left(\frac{x}{3}\right) = 3x\left(\frac{4}{x}\right)$

$x^2 = 12$

$x = \pm\sqrt{12} = \pm 2\sqrt{3}$

$x \approx \pm 3.46$

b. $\frac{x}{x-1} = \frac{4}{x}$

$x(x-1)\left(\frac{x}{x-1}\right) = x(x-1)\left(\frac{4}{x}\right)$

$x^2 = 4(x-1)$

$x^2 - 4x + 4 = 0$

$(x-2)(x-2) = 0$

$x = 2$

c. $\frac{1}{x} + \frac{1}{3x} = 6$

$3x\left(\frac{1}{x} + \frac{1}{3x}\right) = 3x(6)$

$3x\left(\frac{1}{x}\right) + 3x\left(\frac{1}{3x}\right) = 18x$

$3 + 1 = 18x$

$x = \frac{2}{9}$

d. $\frac{1}{x} + \frac{1}{x+1} = 3$

$x(x+1)\left(\frac{1}{x} + \frac{1}{x+1}\right) = x(x+1)(3)$

$x(x+1)\left(\frac{1}{x}\right) + x(x+1)\left(\frac{1}{x+1}\right) = x(x+1)(3)$

$x + 1 + x = 3x^2 + 3x$

$0 = 3x^2 + x - 1$

Using the Quadratic Formula,

$x \approx -0.434, -0.768$

Here are some more to try. Solve each of the following rational equations.

1. $\frac{3x}{5} = \frac{x-2}{4}$

2. $\frac{4x-1}{x} = 3x$

3. $\frac{2x}{5} - \frac{1}{3} = \frac{137}{3}$

4. $\frac{4x-1}{x+1} = x - 1$

5. $\frac{x}{3} = x + 4$

6. $\frac{x-1}{5} = \frac{3}{x+1}$

7. $\frac{x+6}{3} = x$

8. $\frac{2x+3}{6} + \frac{1}{2} = \frac{x}{2}$

9. $\frac{3}{x} + \frac{5}{x-7} = -2$

10. $\frac{2x+3}{4} - \frac{x-7}{6} = \frac{2x-3}{12}$

Answers:

1. $x = -\frac{10}{7}$

2. $x = \frac{1}{3}, 1$

3. $x = 115$

4. $x = 0, 4$

5. $x = -6$

6. $x = \pm 4$

7. $x = 3$

8. $x = 6$

9. $x = \frac{3 \pm \sqrt{51}}{2}$

10. $x = -13$

Glossary

3-dimensional coordinate system   In three dimensions the z-axis is perpendicular to the x-y plane at $(0,0)$. Points in 3-dimensions are represented with coordinates (x, y, z). The first octant where x,-y, and-z are positive is shown at right with the point $(2, 3, 1)$. (p. 257)

30°-60°-90 triangle   A special right triangle with acute angle measures of 30° and 60°. The side lengths are always in the ratio of $1:\sqrt{3}:2$. (p. 320)

45°-45°-90 triangle   A special right triangle with acute angle measures of 45°. The side lengths are always in the ratio of $1:1:\sqrt{2}$. (p. 320)

absolute value   The absolute value of a number is the distance of the number from zero. Since the absolute value represents a distance without regard to direction, it is always a positive real number. For example, $|-7| = 7$, and $|7| = 7$. The absolute value of a complex number is its distance from zero in the complex plane. For a complex number $a + bi$, $|a + bi| = \sqrt{a^2 + b^2}$. For example, $|3 - 2i| = \sqrt{3^2 + (-2)^2} = \sqrt{13}$. (p. 404)

algebraic strategies   Using algebraic strategies means to write an algebraic representation of the problem and then to rewrite those expressions to get equivalent, but more useful results that lead to a solution for the problem or that reveal more information to help solve it.

amplitude   The amplitude of a cyclic graph is one-half the distance between the highest and lowest points. In the graph at right, a is the amplitude. (p. 360)

angle   An angle is formed by two rays joined at a common endpoint (the vertex). In geometric figures, angles are usually formed by two segments with a common endpoint.

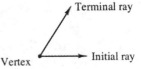

angles of rotation.   Angles with one vertex at the origin and formed by counter-clockwise rotation from the positive x-axis, are referred to as angles of rotation in standard position. For an angle θ, in standard position, the positive x-axis is the initial ray and the terminal ray may point in any direction. The measure of such an angle may have any real value. (p. 319)

Angle Sum and Difference Identities   Trigonometric identities that involve angle sums or differences. They are: $\sin(x \pm y) = \sin(x)\cos(y) \pm \cos(x)\sin(y)$ and $\cos(x \pm y) = \cos(x)\cos(y) \mp \sin(x)\sin(y)$. (p. 649)

annual Occurring once every year.

appreciation An increase in value. (p. B38)

arccosine of *x* See *cosine inverse* ($\cos^{-1} x$).

arcsine of *x* See *sine inverse* ($\sin^{-1} x$).

arctangent of *x* See *tangent inverse* ($\tan^{-1} x$).

area For a 2-dimensional region, the number of non-overlapping square units needed to cover the region.

area model See *generic rectangle*. (p. 126)

argument Used with sigma notation for sequences to describe the nth term. In the expression, $\sum_{k=1}^{10} (2k+1)$ the expression $2k+1$ is the argument. (p. 519)

arithmetic sequence In an arithmetic sequence the difference between sequential terms is constant. Each term of an arithmetic sequence can be generated by adding the common difference to the previous term. For example in the sequence, $4, 7, 10, 13, \ldots$, the common difference is 3. (p. A34)

arithmetic series An arithmetic series is the sum of the terms of an arithmetic sequence. Given the arithmetic sequence $3, 7, 11, \ldots, 43$, the corresponding arithmetic series is $3 + 7 + 11 + \ldots + 43$. (p. 510)

association A relationship between two (or more) variables. An association between numerical variables can be displayed on a scatterplot, and described by its form, direction, strength, and outliers. Possible association between two categorical variables can be studied in a relative frequency table. Also see *scatterplot*.

asymptote A line that a graph of a curve approaches as the *x*-values approach positive or negative infinity. An asymptote is often represented by a dashed line on a graph. For example, the graph at right has an asymptote at $y = -2$. (p. 37)

average See *mean*.

average rate of change The average rate of change of a function over an interval is the change in the value of the dependent quantity divided by the change in the independent quantity. It is the change in the *y*-value divided by the change in the *x*-value for two distinct points on the graph, which is the slope of the line through these two distinct points. (p. 137)

axes In a coordinate plane, the two perpendicular number lines that intersect at the origin $(0, 0)$. The x-axis is horizontal and the y-axis is vertical. In 3-dimensions a third number line, the z-axis is perpendicular to the x-y plane at the origin $(0, 0, 0)$. See *coordinate axes* and *3-dimensional coordinate system* for an illustration.

b When the equation of a line is expressed in $y = mx + b$ form, the parameter b gives the y-intercept of the line. For example, the y-intercept of the line $y = -\frac{1}{3}x + 7$ is $(0, 7)$.

bar graph A bar graph is a set of rectangular bars that have height proportional to the number of data elements in each category. Usually the bars are separated from each other. It is a way of displaying one-variable data that can be put into categories (like what color you prefer, your gender, or the state you were born in). Also see *histogram*.

base When working with an exponential expression in the form a^b, a is called the base. For example, 2 is the base in 2^5. (5 is the exponent, and 32 is the value.) Also see *exponent*.

best-fit line See *line of best fit*.

bias A systematic inaccuracy in data due to a process that favors certain outcomes. (p. 442)

biased wording Words used in a survey question that intentionally or unintentionally influence results. (p. 443)

bin width An interval, or the width of a bar, on a histogram. (p. C11)

binomial An expression that is the sum or difference of exactly two terms, each of which is a monomial. For example, $-2x + 3y^2$ is a binomial. (p. 135)

The Binomial Theorem The formula for the expansion of $(x + y)^n$ is called the Binomial Theorem. $(x + y)^n = {_nC_n}x^n + {_nC_{n-1}}x^{n-1}y + {_nC_{n-2}}x^{n-2}y^2 + \ldots + {_nC_1}xy^{n-1} + {_nC_0}y^n$
For example, $(x + y)^3 = {_3C_3}x^3 + {_3C_2}x^2y + {_3C_1}xy^2 + {_3C_0}y^3 = 1x^3 + 3x^2y + 3xy^2 + 1y^3$. (p. 544)

bound The highest or lowest value that a statistical prediction is within. Also see *margin of error* and *boundary line*. (p. 589)

boundary line or curve (1) A line or curve on a two-dimensional graph that divides the graph into two regions. A boundary line or curve is used when graphing inequalities with two variables. For example, the inequality $y < -\frac{2}{3}x + 2$ is graphed at right. The dashed boundary line has equation $y = -\frac{2}{3}x + 2$. A boundary line is also sometimes called a "dividing line." (2) A line drawn parallel to and above or below the least squares regression line at a distance equivalent to the largest residual. The line determines the upper or lower limit on the values that a prediction is likely to be. (p. 197)

$$y < -\frac{2}{3}x + 2$$

boundary point The endpoint of a ray or segment on a number line where an inequality is true. For strict inequalities (that is, inequalities involving < or >), the point is not part of the solution. We find boundary points by solving the equality associated with our inequality. For example, the solution to the equation $2x + 5 = 11$ is $x = 3$, so the inequality $2x + 5 \geq 11$ has a boundary point at 3. The solution to that inequality is illustrated on the number line at right. A boundary point is also sometimes called a "dividing point." (p. 186)

boxplot A graphic way of displaying the five number summary of a distribution of data: minimum, first quartile, median, third quartile, and maximum. A **modified boxplot** displays outliers separately from the boxplot. Also see *five number summary*. (p. C5)

census The process of measuring every member of the population. (p. 445)

center (of a data distribution) A number that represents the middle of a data set, or that represents a "typical" value of the set. Two ways to measure the center of a data set are the mean and the median. When dealing with measures of center, it is often useful to consider the distribution of the data. For symmetric distributions with no outliers, the mean or median can represent the middle, or "typical" value, of the data well. However, in the presence of outliers or non-symmetrical data distributions, the median may be a better measure. Also see *mean* and *median*. (p. C12)

circle In a plane, the set of all points equidistant from a single point. The general equation of a circle is $(x - h)^2 + (y - k)^2 = r^2$ where the point (h, k) is the center of the circle of radius r.

circle graph A way of displaying data that can be put into categories (like what color you prefer, your gender, or the state you were born in). A circle graph shows the proportion each category is of the whole.

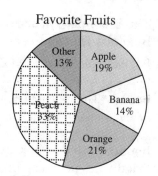

Favorite Fruits

circular functions The periodic functions based on the unit circle, including $y = \sin x$, $y = \cos x$, and $y = \tan x$. See *sine function*, *cosine function*, and *tangent function*.

closed question A question that limits respondents to some set number of responses from which to choose. (p. 444)

closed set A set of numbers is said to be closed under an operation if the result of applying the operation to any two numbers in the set produces a number in the set. For example, the whole numbers are a closed set under addition, because if you add any two whole numbers the result is always a whole number. However, the whole numbers are not closed under division: if you divide any two whole numbers you do not always get a whole number. (p. 139)

closure properties A closure properties states that a particular set of numbers is a closed set under a specific operation. For example, the closure property of rational numbers states that the product or sum of two rational numbers is a rational number. For example, $\frac{1}{2}$ and $\frac{3}{4}$ are both rational numbers; $\frac{1}{2} + \frac{3}{4}$ is $\frac{5}{4}$; and $\frac{5}{4}$ is a rational number. Also, 2.2 and 0.75 are both rational numbers; $2.2 \cdot 0.75$ is 1.65; and 1.65 is a rational number.

coefficient When variable(s) are multiplied by a number, the number is called a coefficient of that term. The numbers that are multiplied by the variables in the terms of a polynomial are called the coefficients of the polynomial. For example, 3 is the coefficient of $3x^2$. (p. 135)

cofunction A trigonometric function whose value for the complement of an angle is equal to the value of a given trigonometric function of the angle itself. For example, the cofunction of sine is cosine and the cofunction of tangent is cotangent. (p. 651)

cofunction identities Trigonometric identities that relate sine and cosine, tangent and cotangent, and secant and cosecant. The value of a trigonometric function of an angle equals the value of the co-function of the complement of the angle. (p. 651)

coincide Two graphs coincide if they have all their points in common. For example, the graphs of $y = 2x + 4$ and $3y = 6x + 12$ coincide; both graphs are lines with a slope of 2 and a y-intercept of 4. When the graphs of two equations coincide, those equations share all the same solutions and have an infinite number of intersection points.

combination A combination is the number of ways we can select items from a larger set without regard to order. For instance, choosing a committee of 3 students from a group of 5 volunteers is a combination since the order in which committee members are selected does not matter. We write $_nC_r$ to represent the number of combinations of n things taken r at a time (or n choose r). For instance, the number of ways to select a committee of 3 students from a group of 5 is $_5C_3$. You can use Pascal's Triangle to find $_5C_3$ or use permutations and divided by the number of arrangements $\frac{_5P_3}{_3P_3} = \frac{5!}{3!2!}$. Formulas for combinations include: $_nC_r = \frac{_nP_r}{r!} = \frac{n!}{r!(n-r)!}$. (p. 503)

combination histogram and box plot A way to visually represent a distribution of data. The box plot is drawn with the same x-axis as the histogram.

composite function   A function that is created as the result of using the outputs of one function as the inputs of another can be seen as a composite function. For example the function $h(x) = |\log x|$ can be seen as the composite function $f(g(x))$ where $f(x) = |x|$ and $g(x) = \log x$. See *composition*. (p. 225)

composition   When the output of one function is used as the input for a second function, a new function is created which is a composition of the two original functions. If the first function is $g(x)$ and the second is $f(x)$, the composition can be written as $f(g(x))$ or $f \circ g(x)$. Note that the order in which we perform the composition matters, and $g(f(x))$ will usually be a different function.

compound interest   Interest that is paid on both the principal and the previously accrued interest. (p. 550)

compress   A term used informally to describe the relationship of a graph to its parent graph when the graph increases or decreases more slowly than the parent. For example, the solid parabola shown at right is a compressed version of its parent, shown as a dashed curve. (p. 66)

conjugate   Every complex number $a + bi$ has a conjugate, $a - bi$, and both the sum and product of the conjugates are real. Similarly, an irrational number that can be written $a + \sqrt{b}$ where a and b are rational, has a conjugate, $a - \sqrt{b}$, and the product and sum of these conjugates are rational. (p. 396)

constant term   A number that is not multiplied by a variable. In the expression $2x + 3(5 - 2x) + 8$, the number 8 is a constant term. The number 3 is not a constant term, because it is multiplied by a variable inside the parentheses. (p. 135)

constraint   A limitation or restriction placed on a function or situation, either by the context of the situation or by the nature of the function.

continuous   For this course, when the points on a graph are connected and it makes sense to connect them, we say the graph is continuous. Such a graph will have no holes or breaks in it. This term will be more completely defined in a later course. (p. 668)

continuously compounded interest   For this course, continuously compounded interest can be thought of as interest that is computed and added to the balance of an account every instant.

control limit   The upper and lower limits of a critical measurement that determines acceptable quality in a manufacturing process. See *statistical process control*. (p. 599)

convenience sampling   A subgroup of the population for which it was easy to collect data. A convenience sample is not a random sample. (p. 456)

composite function   A function that is created as the result of using the outputs of one function as the inputs of another can be seen as a composite function. For example the function $h(x) = |\log x|$ can be seen as the composite function $f(g(x))$ where $f(x) = |x|$ and $g(x) = \log x$. See *composition*. (p. 225)

composition   When the output of one function is used as the input for a second function, a new function is created which is a composition of the two original functions. If the first function is $g(x)$ and the second is $f(x)$, the composition can be written as $f(g(x))$ or $f \circ g(x)$. Note that the order in which we perform the composition matters, and $g(f(x))$ will usually be a different function.

compound interest   Interest that is paid on both the principal and the previously accrued interest. (p. 550)

compress   A term used informally to describe the relationship of a graph to its parent graph when the graph increases or decreases more slowly than the parent. For example, the solid parabola shown at right is a compressed version of its parent, shown as a dashed curve. (p. 66)

conjugate   Every complex number $a + bi$ has a conjugate, $a - bi$, and both the sum and product of the conjugates are real. Similarly, an irrational number that can be written $a + \sqrt{b}$ where a and b are rational, has a conjugate, $a - \sqrt{b}$, and the product and sum of these conjugates are rational. (p. 396)

constant term   A number that is not multiplied by a variable. In the expression $2x + 3(5 - 2x) + 8$, the number 8 is a constant term. The number 3 is not a constant term, because it is multiplied by a variable inside the parentheses. (p. 135)

constraint   A limitation or restriction placed on a function or situation, either by the context of the situation or by the nature of the function.

continuous   For this course, when the points on a graph are connected and it makes sense to connect them, we say the graph is continuous. Such a graph will have no holes or breaks in it. This term will be more completely defined in a later course. (p. 668)

continuously compounding interest   For this course, continuously compounding interest can be thought of as interest that is computed and added to the balance of an account every instant.

control limit   The upper and lower limits of a critical measurement that determines acceptable quality in a manufacturing process. See *statistical process control*. (p. 599)

convenience sampling   A subgroup of the population for which it was easy to collect data. A convenience sample is not a random sample. (p. 456)

coordinate axes   For two dimensions, two perpendicular number lines, the *x*- and *y*-axes, that intersect where both are zero and that provide the scale(s) for labeling each point in a plane with its horizontal and vertical distance and direction from the origin $(0, 0)$. In three dimensions, a third number line, the *z*-axis, is perpendicular to a plane and intersects it at origin $(0, 0, 0)$. The *z*-axis provides the scale for the height of a point above or below the plane. See *3-dimensional coordinate system.*

coordinates   The numbers in an ordered pair (a, b) or triple (a, b, c) used to locate a point in the plane or in space in relation to a set of coordinate axes.

correlation coefficient, *r*   A measure of how much or how little data is scattered around the least squares regression line. It is a measure of the strength of an association that has already been determined to be linear. The correlation coefficient takes on values between −1 and 1. The closer to 1 or −1 the correlation coefficient is, the less scattered the data is around the LSRL.

cosecant   The cosecant is the reciprocal of the sine. (p. 651)

cosine function   For any real number θ, the cosine of θ, denoted $\cos\theta$, is the *x*-coordinate of the point on the unit circle reached by a rotation angle of θ radians in standard position. The general equation for the cosine function is $y = a\cos b(x - h) + k$. The graph of this function has amplitude a, period $\frac{2\pi}{b}$, horizontal shift h, and vertical shift k. (p. 327)

cosine inverse ($\cos^{-1} x$)   Read as the inverse of cosine *x*, $\cos^{-1} x$ is the measure of the angle with cosine *x*. We can also write $y = \arccos x$. Note that the notation refers to the inverse of the cosine function, *not* $\frac{1}{\cos x}$. Because $y = \cos^{-1} x$ is equivalent to $x = \cos y$ and there are infinitely many angles *y* such that $\cos y = x$, the inverse *function* is restricted to select the *principal* value of *y* such that $0 \le y \le \pi$. The graph of the inverse cosine function is at right. (p. 636)

cosine ratio   In a right triangle the ratio $\frac{\text{adjacent side}}{\text{hypotenuse}}$ is known as the cosine of the acute angle. At right, $\cos B = \frac{a}{c}$ since the side length *a* is adjacent to angle *B*. (p. 327)

cotangent   The cotangent is the reciprocal of the tangent. The graph of the cotangent function is at right. (p. 651)

counterexample   An example showing that a statement has at least one exception; that is, a situation in which the statement is false. For example, the number 4 is a counterexample to the hypothesis that all even numbers are greater than 7. (p. 283)

cubic   A cubic polynomial is a polynomial of the form $y = ax^3 + bx^2 + cx + d$. "Cube" refers to the third (3) power.

cube root   In the equation $a = b^3$, the value b that is multiplied by itself three times to give the value a. For example, the cube root of 8 is 2 because $8 = 2 \cdot 2 \cdot 2 = 2^3$. This is written $\sqrt[3]{8} = 2$.

cycle   One cycle of a graph of a trigonometric function is the shortest piece that represents all possible outputs. The length of one cycle is the distance along the x-axis needed to generate all possible output values or the distance around the unit circle needed to generate all possible outcomes.

cyclic function   The term cyclic function is sometimes used to describe trigonometric functions, but it also includes any function that sequentially repeats its outputs at regular intervals. (p. 349)

data distribution   See *distribution*.

degree   One degree is an angle measure that is $\frac{1}{360}$ of a full circle or $\frac{\pi}{180}$ radians. (p. 333)

degree of a polynomial   The degree of a monomial is the sum of the exponents of its variables. For example, the degree of $3x^2y^5z$ is 8. For a polynomial the degree is the degree of the monomial term with the highest degree. Example: for the polynomial $2x^5y^2 - 4x^4z^6 + x^7z$ the degree is 10. (p. 374)

degree of a polynomial in one variable   The highest power of the variable. The degree of a polynomial function also indicates the maximum number of factors of the polynomial and provides information for predicting the number of "turns" the graph can take. (p. 374)

dependent variable   When one quantity depends for its value on one or more others, it is called the dependent variable. For example, we might relate the speed of a car to the amount of force you apply to the gas pedal. Here, the speed of the car is the dependent variable; it depends on how hard you push the pedal. The dependent variable appears as the output value in an $x \to y$ table, and is usually placed relative to the vertical axis of a graph. We often use the letter y and the vertical y-axis for the dependent variable. When working with functions or relations, the dependent variable represents the output value. In Statistics, the dependent variable is often called the response variable. Also see *independent variable*. (p. 6)

depreciation   A decrease in value possibly because of normal wear and tear, age, decay, decrease in price. (p. B38)

description of a function   A complete description of a function includes: a description of the shape of the graph, where it increasing and/or decreases, all the intercepts, domain and range, description of special points, and description of lines of symmetry.

difference of squares A polynomial that can be factored as the product of the sum and difference of two terms. The general pattern is $x^2 - y^2 = (x+y)(x-y)$. For example, the difference of squares $4x^2 - 9$ can be factored as $(2x+3)(2x-3)$. (p. 128)

difference of cubes A polynomial of the form $x^3 - y^3$. It can be factored as follows: $x^3 - y^3 = (x-y)(x^2 + xy + y^2)$. For example, the difference of cubes $8x^3 - 27$ can be factored as $(2x-3)(4x^2 + 6x + 9)$. (p. 427)

dilation A transformation which vertically compresses or stretches the graph of a function. For example, the graph of $g(x) = 2(x^2 + 3x - 5)$ is a dilation of the function $f(x) = x^2 + 3x - 5$ by a factor of 2.

dimensions The dimensions of a flat region or space tell how far it extends in each direction. For example, the dimensions of a rectangle might be 16 cm wide by 7 cm high.

direction (of an association) If one variable in a relationship increases as the other variable increases, the direction is said to be a positive association. If one variable decreases as the other variable increases, there is said to be a negative association. If there is no apparent pattern in the scatterplot, then the variables have no association. When describing a linear association, you can use the slope, and its numerical interpretation in context, to describe the direction of the association.

discrete graph A graph that consists entirely of separated points is called a discrete graph. For example, the graph shown at right is discrete. Also see *continuous*. (p. A10)

discriminant For quadratic equations in standard form $ax^2 + bx + c = 0$, the discriminant is $b^2 - 4ac$. If the discriminant is positive, the equation has two roots; if the discriminant is zero, the equation has one root; if the discriminant is negative, the equation has no real-number roots. For example, the discriminant of the quadratic equation $2x^2 - 4x - 5$ is $(-4)^2 - 4(2)(-5) = 56$, which indicates that that equation has two roots (solutions). (p. 396)

distance formula An application of the Pythagorean Theorem to find the distance between two points in a plane. The distance between any two points (x_1, y_1) and (x_2, y_2) is $\sqrt{(x_2 - x_1)^2 + (y_2 - y_1)^2}$. In the example at right the distance is $\sqrt{4^2 + 5^2}$. (p. 76)

distribution The statistical distribution of a variable is a description (usually a list, table, or graph) of the number of times each possible outcome occurs. A distribution of data is often summarized using its center, shape, spread, and outliers, and can be displayed with a combination histogram and boxplot. (p. C13)

Distributive Property We use the Distributive Property to write a product of expressions as a sum of terms. The Distributive Property states that for any numbers or expressions a, b, and c, $a(b+c) = ab + ac$. For example, $2(x+4) = 2 \cdot x + 2 \cdot 4 = 2x + 8$. We can demonstrate this with a generic rectangle.

dividing line See *boundary line*.

dividing point See *boundary point*.

domain The set of all input values for a relation or function. For example, the domain of the relation graphed at right is $x \geq -3$. For variables, the domain is the set of numbers the variable may represent. Also see *input*. (p. 6)

dot plot A way of displaying one-variable data that has an order and can be placed on a number line. Dot plots are generally used when the data is discrete (separate and distinct) and numerous pieces of data are of equal value.

Dot Plot

Double Angle Identities Trigonometric identities that involve doubling angle measures. They are: $\sin(2x) = 2\sin(x)\cos(x)$ and $\cos(2x) = \cos^2(x) - \sin^2(x)$. (p. 651)

double-peaked See *shape (of a data display)*. (p. C13)

double root A root of a function that occurs exactly twice. If an expression of the form $(x-a)^2$ is a factor of a polynomial, then the polynomial has a double root at $x = a$. The graph of the polynomial does not pass through the x-axis at $x = a$ but is tangent to the axis at $x = a$. (p. 380)

double root

e In mathematics, the base of a natural logarithm. $e \approx 2.71828\ldots$ (p. 548)

Elimination Method A method for solving a system of equations. The key step in using the Elimination Method is to add or subtract both sides of two equations to eliminate one of the variables. For example, the two

$$5x + 2y = 10$$
$$2x - 2y = 4$$

equations in the system at right can be added together to get the simplified result $7x = 14$. We can solve this equation to find x, then substitute the x-value back into either of the original equations to find the value of y.

Equal Values Method A method for solving a system of equations. To use the equal values method, take two expressions that are each equal to the same variable and set those expressions equal to each other. For

$$y = -2x + 5$$
$$y = x - 1$$

example, in the system of equations at right, $-2x + 5$ and $x - 1$ each equal y. So we write $-2x + 5 = x - 1$, then solve that equation to find x. Once we have x, we substitute that value back into either of the original equations to find the value of y.

equation   A mathematical sentence in which two expressions appear on either side of an "equals" sign (=), stating that the two expressions are equivalent. For example, the equation $7x + 4.2 = -8$ states that the expression $7x + 4.2$ has the value -8. In this course, an equation is often used to represent a rule relating two quantities. For example, a rule for finding the area y of a tile pattern with figure number x might be written $y = 4x - 3$.

equivalent   Two expressions are equivalent if they have the same value. For example, $2 + 3$ is equivalent to $1 + 4$. Two equations are equivalent if they have all the same solutions. For example, $y = 3x$ is equivalent to $2y = 6x$. Equivalent equations have the same graph. (pp. 123, 133)

evaluate   To evaluate an expression, substitute the value(s) given for the variable(s) and perform the operations according to the order of operations. For example, evaluating $2x + y - 10$ when $x = 4$ and $y = 3$ gives the value 1.

even function   A function where $f(-x) = f(x)$ for all values of x defined for the function. The graph of the function will be symmetric about the y-axis. (p. 108)

event   One or more results of an experiment.

excluded value   A value that is undefined for a given function and therefore excluded from the domain of the function. (p. 152)

expected value   The expected value for an outcome is the product of the probability of the outcome and the value placed on that outcome. The expected value of an event is the sum of the expected values for its possible outcomes. For example, in a lottery where 7 numbers are drawn from 77 and you have to have chosen all seven to win, the probability that your ticket is the $1,000,000 winner is $\frac{1}{2404808340}$ and the expected value is $0.000416.

experiment   A process that applies a treatment (change) to a group of subjects to determine if there is a measureable difference from another group. If an experiment properly implements randomization, controls (balances) the effects of lurking variables between the groups, and is replicated with many subjects, cause and effect can often be determined. (p. 461)

explicit equation (for a sequence)   An equation for a term in a sequence that determines the value of any term $t(n)$ directly from n, without necessarily knowing any other terms in the sequence. Also see *recursive equation*. (p. A25)

exponent   In an expression of the form a^b, b is called the exponent. For example, in the expression 2^5, 5 is called the exponent. (2 is the base, and 32 is the value.) The exponent indicates how many times to use the base as a multiplier. For example, in 2^5, 2 is used 5 times: $2^5 = 2 \cdot 2 \cdot 2 \cdot 2 \cdot 2 = 32$. For exponents of zero, the rule is: for any number $x \neq 0$, $x^0 = 1$. For negative exponents, the rule is: for any number $x \neq 0$, $x^{-n} = \frac{1}{x^n}$, and $\frac{1}{x^{-n}} = x^n$. Also see *laws of exponents*. (pp. B20, B36)

exponential function An exponential function in this course has an equation of the form $y = ab^x + c$, where a is the initial value, b is positive and is the multiplier, and $y = c$ is the equation of the horizontal asymptote. An example of an exponential function is graphed at right. (p. 57)

expression An expression is a combination of individual terms separated by plus or minus signs. Numerical expressions combine numbers and operation symbols; algebraic (variable) expressions include variables. For example, $4 + (5 - 3)$ is a numerical expression. In an algebraic expression, if each of the following terms, $6xy^2$, 24, and $\frac{y-3}{4+x}$, are combined, the result may be $6xy^2 + 24 - \frac{y-3}{4+x}$. An expression does not have an "equals" sign. (p. 135)

extraneous solution Sometimes in the process of solving equations, multiplying or squaring expressions involving a variable will lead to a numerical result that does not make the original equation true. This false result is called an extraneous solution. For example, in the process of solving the equation $\sqrt{x+3} = 9 - x$ both sides of the equation are squared to get $x + 3 = x^2 - 19x + 81$ which has solutions 6 and 13. 6 is a solution of the original equation, but 13 is extraneous, because $\sqrt{13+3} \neq 9 - 13$. (p. 173)

extrapolate A prediction made outside the range of the observed data. Often extrapolations are not very reliable predictions.

$f^{-1}(x)$ Read this as "f inverse of x," the inverse function for $f(x)$. (p. 219)

factor A factor is part of a product. A polynomial expression $p(x)$ is a factor of another polynomial expression $P(x)$ when there is a polynomial $q(x)$ such that $p(x)q(x) = P(x)$. In the equation $3x^2 - 9x + 6 = 3(x-2)(x-1)$, the expressions $(x-2)$, $(x-1)$, and 3 are factors.

Factor Theorem States that if a is a root of a polynomial then $x - a$ is a factor, and if $x - a$ is a factor then a is a root. For example, the polynomial $x^2 - 5x - 6 = (x-6)(x+1)$ and the roots are 6 and –1. (p. 418)

factored completely A polynomial is factored completely if none of the resulting factors can be factored further using integer coefficients. For example, $-2(x+3)(x-1)$ is the completely factored form of $-2x^2 - 4x + 6$. (p. 371)

factored form A quadratic equation in the form $a(x+b)(x+c) = 0$, where a is nonzero, is said to be in factored form. For example, $-7(x+2)(x-1.5) = 0$ is a quadratic equation in factored form. (p. 371)

factorial A shorthand notation for the product of a list of consecutive positive integers from the given number down to $1: n! = n(n-1)(n-2)(n-3) \cdot \ldots \cdot 3 \cdot 2 \cdot 1$. For example, $5! = 5 \cdot 4 \cdot 3 \cdot 2 \cdot 1 = 120$. (p. 648)

family of functions   A group of functions that have at least one common characteristic, usually the shape and the form of the equation. For example the quadratic family of functions have graphs that are parabolas, and equations of the form $y = ax^2 + bx + c$. Examples of other families are linear functions, exponential functions, and absolute value functions. (p. 98)

Fibonacci Sequence   The sequence of numbers $1, 1, 2, 3, 5, 8, 13, \dots$. Each term of the Fibonacci sequence (after the first two terms) is the sum of the two preceding terms. (p. A26)

first quartile (Q1)   The median of the lower half of a set of data which has been written in numerical order. (p. C5)

first term form (of a sequence)   An equation of a sequence written in first term form uses the first term of the sequence and its common difference or ratio. The first term form of an arithmetic sequence is $a_n = a_1 + d(n-1)$, where a_1 is the first term and d is the common difference. The first term form of a geometric sequence is $a_n = a_1 r^{n-1}$, where a_1 is the first term and r is the common ratio. (p. B40)

five number summary   A way of summarizing the center and spread of a one-variable distribution of data. The five number summary includes the minimum, first quartile, median, third quartile, and maximum of the set of data. Also see *boxplot*. (p. C5)

form (of an association)   The form of an association can be linear of non-linear. The form can contain cluster of data. A residual plot can help determine if a particular form is appropriate for modeling the relationship.

fraction   The quotient of two quantities in the form $\frac{a}{b}$ where b is not equal to 0. (p. 142)

fractional exponents   Raising a number to a fractional exponent indicates a power as well as a root. $x^{a/b} = \sqrt[b]{x^a} = (\sqrt[b]{x})^a$. (p. B36)

function   A relationship in which for each input value there is one and only one output value. For example, the relationship $f(x) = x + 4$ is a function; for each input value (x) there is exactly one output value. In terms of ordered pairs (x, y), no two ordered pairs of a function have the same first member (x). See also *description of a function* and *function notation*. (p. 6)

function notation   When a rule expressing a function is written using function notation, the function is given a name, most commonly "*f*," "*g*," or "*h*." The notation $f(x)$ represents the output of a function, named *f*, when x is the input. It is pronounced "*f* of *x*." For example, $g(2)$, pronounced "*g* of 2", represents the output of the function *g* when $x = 2$. If $g(x) = x^2 + 3$, then $g(2) = 7$. (p. 6)

Fundamental Theorem of Algebra   The Fundamental Theorem of Algebra states that a polynomial of degree n with (real or) complex coefficients has exactly n roots, which may be real or complex. This also means that the polynomial has n linear factors since for every root a, $(x - a)$ is a linear factor. (p. 418)

general equation   If $y = f(x)$ is a parent equation, then the general equation for that function is given by $y = af(x - h) + k$ where (h, k) is the point corresponding to $(0, 0)$ in the parent graph and, relative to the parent graph, the function has been: 1) vertically stretched if the absolute value of a is greater than 1; 2) vertically compressed if the absolute value of a is less than 1; and/or 3) reflected across the x-axis if a is less than 0. (p. 98)

generator   The generator of a sequence tells what you do to each term to get the next term. Note that this is different from the function for the nth term of the sequence. The generator only tells you how to find the following term, when you already know one term. In an arithmetic sequence the generator is the common difference; in a geometric sequence it is the multiplier or common ratio. (p. A34)

generic rectangle   A type of diagram used to visualize multiplying expressions without algebra tiles. Each expression to be multiplied forms a side length of the rectangle, and the product is the sum of the areas of the sections of the rectangle. For example, the generic rectangle at right can be used to multiply $(2x + 5)$ by $(x + 3)$.

$$(2x + 5)(x + 3) = 2x^2 + 11x + 15$$

area as a product   area as a sum

geometric sequence   A geometric sequence is a sequence that is generated by a multiplier. This means that each term of a geometric sequence can be found by multiplying the previous term by a constant. For example: $5, 15, 45\ldots$ is the beginning of a geometric sequence with generator (common ratio) 3. In general a geometric sequence can be represented $a, ar, ar^2, \ldots + ar^{n-1}$. (p. 537)

geometric series   The sum of a geometric sequence is a geometric series, for example: $5 + 15 + 45 + \ldots$ The sum of the first n terms of a geometric sequence, $a + ar + ar^2 + ar^3 + \ldots + ar^{n-1}$ is given by the formula at right. (p. 510)

$$S = \frac{a(r^n - 1)}{r - 1}$$

Giant One   A fraction that is equal to 1. Multiplying any fraction by a Giant One will create a new fraction equivalent to the original fraction. (p. 152)

graph   The graph of an equation is the set of points representing the coordinates that make the equation true. The direction to "graph an equation" or "draw a graph" means use graph paper, scale your axes appropriately, label key points, and plot points accurately. This is different from *sketching* a graph. The equation $y = \frac{1}{3}(x - 2)^2(x + 3)$ is graphed at right. (p. 9)

graphing form   A form of the equation of a function or relation that clearly shows key information about the graph. For example, the graphing form for the general equation of a quadratic function (also called vertex form) is $y = a(x - h)^2 + k$. The vertex (h, k), orientation (whether a is positive or negative) and amount of stretch or compression based on $|a| > 1$ or $|a| < 1$ can be appear in the equation. (p. 68)

growth factor   One way to analyze how the output value in a mathematical relation changes as the input value increases. Growth can be represented by constant addition, as the slope of a linear function or the constant difference in an arithmetic sequence, or by multiplication as the base of an exponential function or the multiplier in a geometric sequence. (p. 10)

(h, k)   In this course h and k are used as parameters in general equations for families of functions $f(x) = af(x - h) + k$ and families of relations to represent the horizontal and vertical shifts of the parent graph. The point (h, k) represents location of a point that corresponds to $(0, 0)$ for parent graphs where $(0, 0)$ is on the graph.

half-life   When material decays, the half-life is the time it takes until only half the material remains. (p. B19)

histogram   A way of displaying one-variable data that is like a bar graph in that the height of the bars is proportional to the number of elements. However, a histogram is for numerical data. Each bin (bar) of a histogram represents the number of data elements in a range of values, such as the number of people who take from 15 minutes up to, but not including, 30 minutes to get to school. Each bin should the same width and the bins should touch each other. Also see *bar graph*. (p. C11)

horizontal   Parallel to the horizon. The x-axis of a coordinate graph is the horizontal axis.

horizontal lines   Horizontal lines are "flat" and run left to right in the same direction as the x-axis. Horizontal lines have equations of the form $y = b$, where b can be any number. For example, the graph at right shows the horizontal line $y = 3$. The slope of any horizontal line is 0. The x-axis has the equation $y = 0$ because $y = 0$ everywhere on the x-axis.

horizontal shift   Used with parent graphs and general equations for functions and relations such as $y = a(x - h)^2 + k$. This type of transformation is a horizontal translation of a graph that moved left or right in relation to its parent graph. The horizontal shift will be h units to the right if h is positive, to the left if h is negative. (p. 66)

hypotenuse   The longest side of a right triangle, the side opposite the right angle.

identity (trigonometric) Equations that are true for all values for which the functions are defined. For example $\sin^2 x + \cos^2 x = 1$ which is true for all values of x, or $\cot x = \frac{1}{\tan x}$ which is true whenever the tangent and cotangent are defined.

imaginary numbers The set of numbers created by multiplying the imaginary number i by every possible real number. The imaginary number i is defined as the square root of -1, or $i = \sqrt{-1}$. Therefore $i^2 = -1$. They are not positive, negative, or zero. These numbers are solutions of equations of the form $x^2 = $ (a negative number). In general, imaginary numbers follow the rules of real number arithmetic (e.g. $i + i = 2i$). (p. 392)

independent variable When one quantity changes in a way that does not depend on the value of another quantity, the value that changes independently is represented with the independent variable. For example, we might relate the speed of a car to the amount of force you apply to the gas pedal. Here, the amount of force applied may be whatever the driver chooses, so it represents the independent variable. The independent variable appears as the input value in an $x \rightarrow y$ table, and is usually placed relative to the horizontal axis of a graph. We often use the letter x and the horizontal x-axis for the independent variable. When working with functions or relations, the independent variable represents the input value. In Statistics, the independent variable is often called the explanatory variable. Also see *dependent variable*. (p. 6)

index (plural indices) In summation notation, the indices are the numbers below and above the sigma that indicate which term to start with and which to end with. For a series they show the first and last replacement values for n. When the symbol above sigma is ∞ the series continues without ending. (p. 519)

Example: $\displaystyle\sum_{n=1}^{8} 5n - 7 = -2 + 3 + 8 + ... + 33$.

inequality An inequality consists of two expressions on either side of an inequality symbol. For example, the inequality $7x + 4.2 < -8$ states that the expression $7x + 4.2$ has a value less than -8. (p. 197)

inequality symbols The symbol $\leq$ read from left to right means "less than or equal to." The symbol $\geq$ read from left to right means "greater than or equal to." The symbols $<$ and $>$ mean "less than" and "greater than," respectively. For example, "$7 < 13$" means that 7 is less than 13.

inequalities with absolute value If k is any positive number, an inequality of the form: $|f(x)| > k$ is equivalent to the statement $f(x) > k$ or $f(x) < -k$; and $|f(x)| < k$ is equivalent to the statement $-k < f(x) < k$. For example, you can solve the inequality, $|5x - 6| > 4$ by solving the two inequalities $5x - 6 > 4$ or $5x - 6 < -4$. (p. 193)

inference A statistical prediction.

infinite geometric series An infinite geometric series is a geometric series which never ends. The sum of such a series with an initial value a and common ratio r, with $-1 < r < 1$, is given by the formula at right. (p. 537)

$$S = \frac{a}{1-r}$$

infinity The concept that something is without limit or unending. The symbol for infinity is ∞. Note that infinity is an idea, not a number, even though it is often treated as such. (p. 18)

initial value The initial value of a sequence is the first term of the sequence. (p. 57)

input A replacement value for a variable in a function or relation. The first number in an ordered pair. The set of all possible input values is the domain of a function. (p. 26)

integer Any whole number or the opposite of a whole number: $\dots -3, -2, -1, 0, 1, 2, 3, \dots$

integral roots Roots (or zeros) of functions that are integers. (p. 414)

Integral Zero Theorem For any polynomial with integral coefficients, if an integer is a zero of the polynomial, it must be a factor of the constant term. (p. 418)

intercepts Points where a graph crosses the axes. x-intercepts are points at which the graph crosses the x axis and y-intercepts are points at which the graph crosses the y axis. On the graph at right the x-intercept is $(3, 0)$ and the y-intercept is $(0, 6)$. (p. 10)

interest An amount paid which is a percentage of the principal. For example, a savings account may offer 4% annual interest rate, which means they will pay $4.00 in interest for a principal of $100 kept in the account for one year. (p. B15)

interquartile range (IQR) A way to measure the spread of data. It is calculated by subtracting the first quartile from the third quartile.

intersection A point of intersection is a point that the graphs of two or more equations have in common. Graphs may intersect in one, two, several, many or no points. The set of coordinates of a point of intersection are a solution to the equation for each graph. (p. 21)

interval A set of numbers between two given numbers.

inverse circular functions See *inverse trigonometric functions*.

inverse function A function that "undoes" what the original function does. It can also be seen as the x-y interchange of the function. The inverse of a function performs in reverse order the inverse operation for each operation of the function. The graph of an inverse function is a reflection of the original function across the line $y = x$. For example, $y = x^3 + 2$ is equivalent to $x = \sqrt[3]{y-2}$, its inverse function is written $y = \sqrt[3]{x-2}$. (p. 216)

inverse operations Subtraction is the inverse operation for addition and vice versa, division for multiplication, square root for squaring, and more generally taking the nth root for raising to the nth power.

inverse trigonometric functions For each trigonometric function $\sin(x), \cos(x)$, and $\tan(x)$, there is an inverse function written $\sin^{-1}(x), \cos^{-1}(x)$, and $\tan^{-1}(x)$. Note: This symbol does not mean $\frac{1}{\sin(x)}$. It is a new function that "undoes" the original trig function, thus giving a specific angle measure when the input is $\sin x, \cos x$, or $\tan x$. For example: $\sin^{-1}(-\frac{1}{2}) = -\frac{\pi}{6}$. Note that the range of the inverse function is restricted to outputs for y such that $-\frac{\pi}{2} \le y \le \frac{\pi}{2}$ for $\sin x$, $-\frac{\pi}{2} < y < \frac{\pi}{2}$ for $\tan x$ and $0 \le y \le \pi$ for $\cos x$. Also see *cosine inverse*, *sine inverse*, and *tangent inverse*. (p. 629)

investigating a function To investigate a function means to make a complete graph of the function and to write down everything you know about the function. Some things to consider are: domain, range, intercepts, asymptotes, inverse, and symmetry. (p. 33)

irrational numbers The set of numbers that cannot be expressed in the form $\frac{a}{b}$, where a and b are integers and $b \ne 0$. For example, π and $\sqrt{2}$ are irrational numbers. (p. 389)

Law of Cosines For any $\triangle ABC$, $a^2 = b^2 + c^2 - 2bc\cos A$. (p. 29)

Law of Large Numbers A theorem stating that as the number of trials of a random process increases (for example, as the number of trials in a simulation increases), the results will approach the theoretical value closer. (p. 567)

Law of Sines For any $\triangle ABC$, $\frac{\sin A}{a} = \frac{\sin B}{b} = \frac{\sin C}{c}$. (p. 29)

laws of exponents The laws of exponents we study in this course are: (pp. B20, B36)

Law	Examples	
$x^m x^n = x^{m+n}$ for all x	$x^3 x^4 = x^{3+4} = x^7$	$2^5 \cdot 2^{-1} = 2^4$
$\frac{x^m}{x^n} = x^{m-n}$ for $x \ne 0$	$x^{10} \div x^4 = x^{10-4} = x^6$	$\frac{5^4}{5^7} = 5^{-3}$
$(x^m)^n = x^{mn}$ for all x	$(x^4)^3 = x^{4 \cdot 3} = x^{12}$	$(10^5)^6 = 10^{30}$
$x^0 = 1$ for $x \ne 0$	$\frac{y^2}{y^2} = y^0 = 1$	$9^0 = 1$
$x^{-1} = \frac{1}{x}$ for $x \ne 0$	$\frac{1}{x^2} = (\frac{1}{x})^2 = (x^{-1})^2 = x^{-2}$	$3^{-1} = \frac{1}{3}$
$x^{m/n} = \sqrt[n]{x^m}$ for $x \ge 0$	$\sqrt{k} = k^{1/2}$	$y^{2/3} = \sqrt[3]{y^2}$

least squares regression line (LSRL)   A unique best-fit line that is found by making the squares of the residuals as small as possible.

line   Graphed, a line is made up of an infinite number of points, is one-dimensional and extends without end in two directions. In two dimensions a line is the graph of an equation of the form $ax + by = c$.

line of best fit   A line that represents, in general, data on a scatterplot. The line of best fit is a model of numerical two-variable data that helps describe the data. It is also used to make predictions for other data. Also see *least square regression line*. (p. A9)

line of symmetry   A line that divides a figure into two congruent shapes which are reflections of each other across the line. (p. 217)

linear equation   An equation with at least one variable of degree one and no variables of degree greater than one. The graph of a linear equation of two variables is a line in the plane. $ax + by = c$ is the standard form of a linear equation. (p. 10)

linear factor   A factor of the form $(ax + b)$.

linear function   A polynomial function of degree one or zero, with general equation $f(x) = a(x - h) + k$. The graph of a linear function is a line. (p. 41)

linear inequality   An inequality with a boundary line represented by a linear equation. (p. 197)

linear programming   A method for solving a problem with several conditions or constraints that can be represented as linear equations or inequalities. (p. 195)

linear regression   A method for finding a best-fit line through a set of points on a scatterplot. Also see *regression* and *least squares regression line*.

locator point   A locator point is a point which gives the position of a graph with respect to the axes. For a parabola, the vertex is a locator point. (p. 82)

Log base 10 $\log_{10} m = n$ if $10^n = m$. See *common logarithm*. (p. 282)

Log-Power Property   See *Power Property of Logs*.

Log-Product Property   See *Product Property of Logs*.

Log-Quotient Property   See *Quotient Property of Logs*.

logarithm   The logarithm of a given number, x, with respect to a base, b, is the exponent to which b must be raised to give x. For example, since we know that $32 = 2^5$, it follows that 5 is the logarithm, base 2, of 32, or $\log_2 32 = 5$. (p. 233)

logarithmic and exponential notation $m = \log_b(n)$ is the logarithmic form of the exponential equation $b^m = n$ ($b > 0$).

logarithmic functions   Inverse exponential functions. The base of the logarithm is the same base as that of the exponential function. For instance $y = \log_2 x$ can be read as "y is the exponent needed for base 2 to get x," and is equivalent to $x = 2^y$. The short version is stated "log, base 2, of x," and written $\log_2 x$. (p. 240)

Looking Inside   "Looking Inside" is a method of solving one-variable equations containing parentheses or an absolute value symbol. To use "looking inside," we first determine what the value of the entire expression inside the parentheses (or absolute value symbol) must be. We then use that fact to solve for the value of the variable. For example, to use "looking inside" to solve the equation $4(x + 2) = 36$, we first determine that $x + 2$ must equal 9. We then solve the equation $x + 2 = 9$ to find that $x = 7$. (p. 170)

lower control limit (LCL)   See *control limit*. (p. 599)

lurking variable   A hidden variable that was not part of the statistical study under investigation. Sometimes a lurking variable explains the true cause of an association between two other variables that are linked. (p. 461)

m   When the equation of a line is expressed in $y = mx + b$ form, the parameter m gives the slope of the line. For example, the slope of the line $y = -\frac{1}{3}x + 7$ is $-\frac{1}{3}$.

margin of error   Half of the spread between the upper and lower bounds of a statistical prediction. For example, if we predict weight is likely to be between an upper bound of 12 kg and lower bound of 18 kg, the margin of error is 3 kg, and we could write our prediction of the weight as 15 ± 3 kg. (p. 584)

maximize   Make as large as possible. (p. 192)

maximum point   The highest point on a graph. For example, the vertex of a downwardly oriented parabola.

maximum value   The largest value in the range of a function. For example, the y-coordinate of the vertex of a downwardly oriented parabola. (p. C5)

mean   The arithmetic mean, or average, of several numbers is one way of defining the "center" or "middle" or "typical value" of a set of numbers. The mean represents the center of a set of data well if the distribution of the data is symmetric and has no outliers. To find the mean of a numerical data set, add the values together then divide by the number of values in the set. For example, the mean of the numbers 1, 5, and 6 is $(1 + 5 + 6) \div 3 = 4$.

measure of central tendency Mean and median are measures of central tendency, representing the "center" or "middle" or "typical value" of a set of data. See *center (of a data distribution)*.

mean absolute deviation A way to measure the spread, or the amount of variability, in a set of data. The mean absolute deviation is the average of the distances to the mean, after the distances have been made positive with the absolute value. The standard deviation is a much more commonly used measure of spread than the mean absolute deviation. (p. C17)

median The middle number of a set of data which has been written in numerical order. If there is no distinct middle, then the mean of the two middle numbers is the median. The median is generally more representative of the "middle" or of a "typical value" than the mean if there are outliers or if the distribution of the data in not symmetric. (p. C5)

midline The horizontal axis of the graph of a trigonometric function. The midline is halfway between the maximum and minimum values of the function. (p. 360)

minimize Make as small as possible.

minimum point The lowest point on a graph. For example, the vertex of an upwardly oriented parabola.

minimum value The smallest value in the range of a function. For example, the y-coordinate of the vertex of an upwardly oriented parabola. (p. C5)

model A mathematical summary (often an equation) of a trend in data, after making assumptions and approximations to simplify a complicated situation. Models allow us to describe data to others, compare data more easily to other data, and allow us to make predictions. For example, mathematical models of weather patterns allow us to predict the weather. No model is perfect, but some models are better at describing trends than other models. Regressions are a type of model. Also see *regression*. (p. 113)

modified boxplot See *boxplot*. (p. C13)

monomial An expression with only one term. It can be a number, a variable, or the product of a number and one or more variables. For example, 7, $3x$, $-4ab$, and $3x^2y$ are each monomials.

multiple representations web An organizational tool we use to keep track of connections between the four representations of relationships between quantities emphasized in this course. In this course, we emphasize four different ways of representing a numerical relationship: with a graph, table, situation (pattern), or rule (equation or inequality). (p. 9)

multiplicative identity   The number 1 is called the multiplicative identity because multiplying any number by 1 does not change the number. For example, $7(1) = 7$.

Multiplicative Identity Property   The Multiplicative Identity Property states that multiplying any expression by 1 leaves the expression unchanged. That is, $a(1) = a$. For example, $437x \cdot 1 = 437x$.

multiplier   In a geometric sequence the number multiplied times each term to get the next term is called the multiplier or the common ratio or generator. The multiplier is also the number you can multiply by in order to increase or decrease an amount by a given percentage in one step. For example, to increase a number by 4%, the multiplier is 1.04. We would multiply the number by 1.04. The multiplier for decreasing by 4% is 0.96. (p. A34)

natural logarithm   A logarithm base e. Abbreviated "ln". (p. 548)

negative exponent   The value of a number raised to a negative exponent is the reciprocal of the number raised to the absolute value of the exponent. $x^{-a} = \frac{1}{x^a}$ for $x \neq 0$. (p. B36)

non-function   A relation that has more than one output for one or more of its inputs.

normal distribution   A distribution of data that can be modeled with the normal probability density function. See *normal probability density function*. (p. 477)

normal probability density function   A very specific function that is used to model single-peaked, symmetric, bell-shaped data. (p. 485)

observational study   A study where data is collected by observing an existing situation without the researcher (or observer) imposing any type of change or treatment. (p. 461)

observed value   An actual measurement, as opposed to a prediction made from a model.

odd function   A function where $f(-x) = -f(x)$ for all values of x defined for the function. The graph of the function will be symmetric about the origin. (p. 108)

open question   A question that allows respondents to offer any answer they like. (p. 444)

one-dimensional   Not having any width or depth. Lines and curves are one-dimensional.

ordered pair   A pair of numbers written (x, y) used to represent the coordinates of a point in an xy-plane where x represents the horizontal distance from 0 and y is the vertical. The input and output values of a function or relation can be represented as ordered pairs where x is the input, and y is the output.

ordered triple Three real numbers written in order (x, y, z) represent a point in space or replacement values for a situation involving three variables. See *3-dimensional coordinate system*. (p. 263)

orientation Used informally in this course to describe some graphs. For example the direction a parabola opens might be referred to as its orientation. When describing the graph of a polynomial function, a positive orientation would mean the graph eventually continues upward as the value of x increases, as in the example above right. A negative orientation would mean it eventually heads downward as the value of x continues to increase, as in the example below right. (p. 358)

origin The point on a coordinate plane where the x- and y-axes intersect is called the origin. This point has coordinates $(0, 0)$. The point assigned to zero on a number line is also called the origin. (p. 258)

outlier A number in a set of data that is far away from the bulk of the data. (p. C13)

output Used to describe the result of applying a function or relationship rule to an input value. For the function $f(x) = x^2 - 73$ when the input is 10, the output is 27. Function notation shows how the function operates on the input to produce the output: $f(10) = 10^2 - 73 = 27$. (p. 26)

parabola The set of all points that are equidistant from a single point (the focus) and a line (the directrix). The general equation for a parabola that is a function (or a quadratic function) in graphing (or vertex) form, is $y = a(x - h)^2 + k$. The general equation of a quadratic function in standard form is $y = ax^2 + bx + c$. A general equation for parabolas that are not functions, "sleeping" parabolas, is $x - h = a(y - k)^2$. (p. 66)

parallel Two lines in a plane are parallel if they never intersect. Parallel lines have the same slope. Two line segments in a plane are parallel if they lie on lines that never intersect. Two lines in space are parallel if they lie in the same plane and they do not intersect. There is a constant distance between parallel lines.

parameter In a general equations where x and y represent the inputs and outputs of the function, variables such as $a, b, c, m, h,$ and k are often referred to as parameters, and they are often replaced with specific values. For example, in the equation $y = a(x - h)^2 + k$ representing all parabolas that are functions, the $a, h,$ and k are (variable) parameters that give the shape and location, while x and y are the independent and dependent variables. (p. 41)

parent graph The simplest version of a family of graphs. For instance, the graph of $y = x^2$, is considered the parent graph for parabolas that are functions. (p. 98)

Pascal's Triangle   The array of numbers at right. The triangular pattern continues downward. This array shows all the values of $_nC_r$ where n is the row number when the vertex is $_0C_0$. r is the number of places to the right in row n (when the counting begins with 0). For instance, $_5C_2$ is equal to 10. (p. 540)

```
        1
      1   1
    1   2   1
  1   3   3   1
1   4   6   4   1
1  5  10  10  5  1
```

percent   A ratio that compares a number to 100. Percents are often written using the "%" symbol. For example, 0.75 is equal to $\frac{75}{100}$ or 75%.

percentile   A percentile ranking indicates the percentage of scores which are below the score in question. For example, if you scored at the 90th percentile on a test, your score was higher than the scores of 90% of the other test takers. (p. 482)

perfect square   Usually, a quadratic polynomial $ax^2 + bx + c$ that can be rewritten as the second power of a binomial, $(cx+d)^2$. For example, $x^2 - 6x + 9$ is a perfect square that can be rewritten as $(x-3)^2$. Also, any polynomial of even degree that can be rewritten as the square of one polynomial factor. For numbers, a whole number that can be written as the second power of another whole number. For example, 1, 4, 9, 16, and 25 are perfect squares.

perfect square form   A quadratic equation in the form $(ax+b)^2 = c$, where a is nonzero, is said to be in perfect square form. For example, $(2x+3)^2 = 20$ is a quadratic equation in perfect square form. (p. 68)

perfect square trinomials   Trinomials of the form $a^2x^2 + 2abx + b^2$, where a and b are nonzero real numbers, are known as perfect square trinomials and factor as $(ax+b)^2$. For example, the perfect square trinomial $9x^2 - 24x + 16$ can be factored as $(3x-4)^2$.

perimeter   The distance around a figure on a flat surface.

Perimeter =
$5 + 8 + 4 + 6 = 23$ units

period   The length of one cycle of a graph, as shown by the dashed line in the graph at right. (p. 360)

periodic function   A function which has a repetitive section or cycle such as the sine, cosine and tangent functions. In a periodic function, the cyclic pattern continues forever both to the left and to the right.

permutation   A permutation is an arrangement in which the order of selection matters. For example a batting line-up is a permutation because it is an ordered list of players. If each of five letters, A, B, C, D, E is printed on a card, the number of 3-letter sequences can you make by selecting three of the five cards is a permutation. Permutations can be represented with tree diagrams, decision charts, and their value calculated by using the formula for $_nP_r = \frac{n!}{(n-r)!}$. In the example given above, $_5P_3 = \frac{5!}{2!} = \frac{5 \cdot 4 \cdot 3 \cdot 2 \cdot 1}{2 \cdot 1} = 5 \cdot 4 \cdot 3 = 60$. (p. 503)

perpendicular   Two lines, rays, or line segments that intersect to form a right angle. A line and a plane can also be perpendicular if the line does not lie in the plane, but intersects it and forms a right angle with every line in the plane that passes through the point of intersection.

piecewise function   A function composed of parts of two or more functions. Each part is a function with a restricted (limited) domain. (p. 105)

placebo   A treatment with no effect. A placebo is sometimes used in experiments involving people so that the psychological effects of participating in an experiment are the same in all the treatment groups. (p. 462)

plane   A plane is an undefined term in geometry. It is a two-dimensional flat surface that extends without end. It is made up of points and has no thickness. The part of a plane outlined by its *xy*-, *xz*- and *yz*-traces is often used to represent a plane on a 3-dimensional coordinate system. (p. 263)

point   An undefined term in geometry. A point has no dimensions but can be located by its coordinates on a number line, in a plane, or in space. (p. 263)

Point-Slope form $y - k = m(x - h)$ is called the point slope form of a linear equation or function because it shows the slope m and a point (h, k) that is on the graph of the line. For example, given a line that has slope $\frac{5}{3}$ and contains the point with coordinates $(3, -4)$ its equation can be written $y + 4 = \frac{5}{3}(x - 3)$. (p. 92)

polynomial   An algebraic expression that involves at most the operations of addition, subtraction, and multiplication. A polynomial in one variable is an expression that can be written as the sum of terms of the form: (any number) $\cdot$ $x^{(\text{whole number})}$. These polynomials are usually arranged with the powers of x in order, starting with the highest, left to right. The numbers that multiply the powers of x are called the coefficients of the polynomial. See *degree of a polynomial* for an example. (p. 135)

population   A collection of objects or group of people about whom information is gathered. (p. 445)

power   A number or variable raised to an exponent in the form x^n. See *exponent*.

power model or power curve   A best-fit curve of the form $y = ax^b$ that represents data on a scatterplot.

Power Property of Logs $\log_m(a^n) = n\log_m(a)$. For example, $\log_3 625 = 4\log_3 5$. (p. 289)

predicted value (of an association)   The dependent (y-value) that is predicted for an independent (x-value) by the best-fit model for an association.

principal   Initial investment or capital. An initial value.

probability   The probability that an event A. with a finite number of equally likely outcomes, will occur is the number of outcomes for event A divided by the total number of equally likely outcomes. This can be written as $\frac{\text{number of outcomes for event A}}{\text{total number of possible outcomes}}$. A probability p is a ratio, $0 \le p \le 1$. (p. 567)

process control   See *statistical process control*. (p. 598)

Product Property of Logs $\log_m(a \cdot b) = \log_m(a) + \log_m(b)$. For example, $\log_3 30 = \log_3 5 + \log_3 6$. (p. 289)

profit   The amount of money after expenses have been accounted for.

proportion   Equal ratios are described as a proportion. For example, the equation $\frac{x-8}{2x+1} = \frac{5}{6}$. (p. 472)

Pythagorean Identity   For trigonometric functions, $\cos^2 x + \sin^2 x = 1$ for any value of x. (p. 343)

quadrants   The coordinate plane is divided by its axes into four quadrants. The quadrants are numbered as shown in the first diagram at right. When graphing data that has no negative values, we sometimes use a graph showing only the first quadrant.

4-quadrant graph: 1st-quadrant graph:

quadratic equation   Any equation where at least one term has degree 2 and no term has degree higher than 2. The standard equation $Ax^2 + By^2 + Cxy + Dx + Ey + F = 0$ represents all quadratic relations in one or two variables. (p. 24)

quadratic expression   An expression that can be written in the form $ax^2 + bx + c$, where a, b, and c are real numbers and a is nonzero. For example, $3x^2 - 4x + 7.5$ is a quadratic expression.

Quadratic Formula   This formula gives you the solutions $x = \frac{-b \pm \sqrt{b^2 - 4ac}}{2a}$, for a quadratic equation in one variable that can be written in the standard form $ax^2 + bx + c = 0$. (p. 24)

quadratic function   A quadratic equation that can be written $y = ax^2 + bx + c$ is also a quadratic function where x is the independent variable and y is the dependent variable. Its graph is a parabola with a vertical orientation. The graphing form of a quadratic function is $f(x) = a(x - h)^2 + k$.

quarterly   Occurring four times a year. (p. B14)

quartile   Along with the median, the quartiles divide a set of data into four groups of the same size. Also see *boxplot*. (p. C5)

quotient   The result of a division problem is a quotient with a remainder (which could be 0). When a polynomial $p(x)$ is divided by a polynomial $d(x)$ the polynomial $q(x)$ will be the quotient with a remainder $r(x)$. The product of $q(x)$ and $d(x)$ plus the remainder $r(x)$ will equal the original polynomial. $p(x) = d(x)q(x) + r(x)$.

Quotient Property of Logs $\log_m(\frac{a}{b}) = \log_m(a) - \log_m(b)$. For example, $\log_3 \frac{37}{5} = \log_3 37 - \log_3 5$. (p. 289)

R^2 See *R-squared*.

radian measure   An arc of a unit circle equal to the length of the radius of the circle is one radian. The central angle for this arc has measure one radian. 1 radian = $\frac{180}{\pi}$ degrees. (p. 334)

radical   An expression in the form $\sqrt{a}$, where $\sqrt{a}$ is the positive square root of a. For example, $\sqrt{49} = 7$. Also see *square root*. (p. 68)

radicand   The expression under a radical sign. For example, in the expression $3 + 2\sqrt{x-7}$, the radicand is $x - 7$.

random sample   A sample which was chosen as a result of a random process. A random sample can represent the whole population well.

range (of a data set)   The range of a set of data is the difference between the highest and lowest values. (p. C19)

range (of a function)   The range of a function is the set of possible outputs for a function. It consists of all the values of the dependent variable, that is every number that y can represent for the function $f(x) = y$. (p. 18)

ratio   The comparison of two quantities or expressions by division.

rational equation   An equation that includes at least one rational expression. For example, $5 - \frac{x+2}{x} = 7$. (p. 608)

rational expression   An expression in the form of a fraction in which the numerator and denominator are polynomials. For example, $\frac{x-7}{x^2+8x-9}$ is a rational expression. (p. 135)

rational function   A function that contains at least one rational expression. For example, $f(x) = \frac{5}{x-3}$. (p. 138)

rational number   A number that can be written as a fraction $\frac{a}{b}$ where a and b are integers and $b \neq 0$.

real numbers   The set of all rational numbers and irrational numbers is referred to as the set of real numbers. Any real number can be represented by a point on a number line. (p. 389)

rebound height   The height a ball reaches after a bounce.

rebound ratio   The ratio of the height a ball bounces after one bounce to the height from which it dropped. (p. A8)

reciprocal   The multiplicative inverse of a number or an expression.

reciprocal trigonometric functions   The functions $y = \frac{1}{\sin x} = \csc x$, $y = \frac{1}{\cos x} = \sec x$, and $y = \frac{1}{\tan x} = \cot x$. (p. 636)

rectangular numbers   The terms of the sequence $0, 2, 6, 12, 20, \dots$. These numbers are called rectangular because they count the number of dots in rectangular arrays with the dimensions $n(n+1)$ where $n = 0, 1, 2, 3, 4, \dots$

recursive equation (for a sequence)   An equation for a term in a sequence that requires knowing other terms in the sequence first. For example, the equation for the Fibonacci sequence is recursive because you need to know the previous two terms to find any other term. The equation for the Fibonacci sequence is $t(n) = t(n-2) + t(n-1)$, $t(1) = 1$, $t(2) = 1$. Also see *explicit equation*. (p. A34)

recursive sequence   A sequence which can be described by a recursive equation. See *recursive equation*. (p. A34)

reference angle   For every angle of rotation in standard position, the reference angle is the angle in the first quadrant $0 \leq \theta \leq \frac{\pi}{2}$ whose cosine and sine have the same absolute values as the cosine and sine of the original angle. (p. 338)

reflective symmetry   A type of symmetry where one half of the image is a reflection across a line of the other half of the image. You can fold the image on the line of symmetry and have both halves match exactly. Also see *line of symmetry*.

regression   A method for finding a best-fit line or curve through a set of points on a scatterplot. The most common type of regression is finding the least squares regression line. In this course we also do curved regressions: exponential regressions (fitting $y = a \cdot b^x$), quadratic regressions (fitting $y = ax^2 + bx + c$) and power regressions (fitting $y = ax^b$).

relation   Functions are also relations, but relations are not necessarily functions. The equations for parabolas, ellipses, hyperbolas, and circles are all relations but only the equations that describe vertically oriented parabolas are functions.

relative frequency   A ratio or percent. If 60 people are asked, and 15 people prefer "red," the relative frequency of people preferring red is $\frac{15}{60} = 25\%$. (p. 472)

relative maximum (minimum)   A function that has a "peak" (or "valley") at a point P is said to have a relative maximum (minimum) at the point P. This is the point where the function changes direction.

relative maximum

relative minimum

remainder   When dividing polynomials in one variable, the remainder is what is left after the constant term of the quotient has been determined. The degree of the remainder must be less than the degree of the divisor.   In the example below the remainder is $3x - 3$.
$(x^4 + 3x^3 - x^2 + x - 7) \div (x^2 + x + 1) = x^2 + 2x - 4 + \frac{3x-3}{x^2+x+1}$.   Also see *quotient*. (p. 410)

Remainder Theorem   For any number c, when a polynomial $p(x)$ is divided by $(x - c)$, the remainder is $p(c)$. For example, if the polynomial $p(x) = x^4 - x^3 + 20x - 48$ is divided by $(x - 5)$, the remainder is $p(5) = 552$. (p. 418)

triple root

repeated root   A root of a polynomial that occurs more than once. The root r will occur as many times as $(x - r)$ is a factor of the polynomial. See *double root* and *triple root*. (p. 380)

double root

residual   The distance a prediction is from the actual observed measurement in an association. The residual is the y-value predicted by the best-fit model subtracted from the actual observed y-value. A residual can be graphed with a vertical segment that extends from the observed point to the line or curve made by the best-fit model. It has the same units as the y-axis.

residual plot   A display of the residuals of an association. A residual plot is created in order to analyze the appropriateness of a best-fit model. If a model fits the data well, no apparent pattern will be made by the residuals—the residuals will be randomly scattered.

rewrite   To rewrite an equation or expression is to write an equivalent equation or expression. Rewriting could involve using the Distributive Property, following the Order of Operations, using properties of 0 or 1, substitution, inverse operations, Properties of Logarithms, or use of trigonometric identities. We usually rewrite in order to change expressions or equations into more useful forms or sometimes, just simpler forms. (p. 170)

right angle   An angle with measure 90°.

right triangle   A triangle with a right angle.

roots of a function   The number r is a root (or zero) of the function
$f(x)$ if $f(r) = 0$. A root may be a real or a complex number. Real roots
occur where the graph of the function $f(x)$ crosses the x-axis. Complex
roots must be found algebraically. (p. 382)

R-squared   The correlation coefficient squared, and usually expressed as a percent. R^2
is a measure of the strength of a linear relationship. Its interpretation is that $R^2\%$ of the
variability in the dependent variable can be explained by a linear relationship with the
independent variable. The rest of the variability is explained by other variables not part of
the study.

rule   An algebraic representation or a written description of a mathematical relationship.

sample   A subset (group) of a given population with the same characteristics as the whole
population. (p. 445)

sample space   With probability, all the possible outcomes.

scatter   The variability in data. When the scatter of data forms a pattern, we can often
describe and model the data. Random scatter has no discernable pattern. (Note that
random scatter does not mean evenly scattered—randomly scattered data often forms
clusters and gaps.) See *variability* and *spread*.

scatterplot   A way of displaying two-variable numerical data
where two measurements are taken for each subject (like
height and forearm length, or surface area of cardboard and
volume of cereal held in a cereal box). To create a scatterplot,
the two values for each subject are written as coordinate pairs
and graphed on a pair of coordinate axes (each axis
representing a variable). Also see *association*.

secant   The reciprocal of the cosine. (p. 651)

sequence   A function in which the independent variable is a positive integer (sometimes
called the "term number"). The dependent variable is the term value. A sequence is
usually written as a list of numbers. (p. A34)

series   The sum of the terms of a sequence. (p. 500)

set   A collection of data or items. (p. 139)

shape (of a data distribution)   Statisticians use the following words to describe the overall shape of a data distribution: symmetric, skewed, single-peaked, double-peaked, and uniform. Examples are shown below. (p. 765)

symmetric   skewed   single-peaked   double-peaked   uniform

sigma   The Greek letter Σ which is used to mean sum. Using Σ provides a way to write a short, compact mathematical representation for a series. See *summation notation*. (p. 519)

simple interest   Interest paid on the principal alone. (p. B15)

simplify   To rewrite an expression or equation as an equivalent expression or equation in a form that is considered to be simpler or less cumbersome than the original.

simulation (probability)   When conducting an experiment with an event that is unrealistic to perform, a simulation can be used. A simulation is a similar experiment that has the same probabilities as the original experiment. (p. 565)

sine function   For any real number θ, the sine of θ, denoted $\sin\theta$, is the y-coordinate of the point on the unit circle reached by a rotation angle of θ radians in standard position. The general equation for the sine function is $y = a\sin b(x-h)+k$. This function has amplitude a, period $\frac{2\pi}{b}$, horizontal shift h, and vertical shift k. (p. 360)

sine inverse ($\sin^{-1} x$)   Read as the inverse of sine x, $\sin^{-1} x$ is the measure of the angle with sine x. We can also write $y = \arcsin x$. Note that the notation refers to the inverse of the sine function, *not* $\frac{1}{\sin x}$. Because $y = \sin^{-1} x$ is equivalent to $x = \sin y$ and there are infinitely many angles y such that $\sin y = x$, the inverse *function* is restricted to select the *principal* value of y such that $-\frac{\pi}{2} \le y \le \frac{\pi}{2}$. The graph of the inverse function, $y = \sin^{-1} x$ with $\frac{\pi}{2} \le y \le \frac{\pi}{2}$ is at right. (p. 636)

sine ratio   In a right triangle the ratio $\frac{\text{opposite side}}{\text{hypotenuse}}$ is known as the sine of the acute angle. At right, $\sin B = \frac{b}{c}$ since the side length b is opposite angle B. (p. 317)

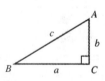

single-peaked   See *shape (of a data display)*. (p. C13

sketch a graph   To sketch the graph of an equation means to show the approximate shape of the graph in the correct location with respect to the axes with key points clearly labeled. (p. 8)

skewed (data display)   See *shape (of a data display)*. (p. C13)

"sleeping" parabola   A "sleeping" parabola is a parabola which opens to the left or right, rather than upward or downward. These parabolas are not the graphs of functions. (p. 102)

slope   The ratio of the vertical change to the horizontal change between any two points on a line. For any two points (x_1, y_1) and (x_2, y_2) on a given line, the slope is $\frac{y_2 - y_1}{x_2 - x_1}$. For example, the slope of a line between points with coordinates $(3, -5)$ and $(-7, 2)$ is $\frac{2-(-5)}{-7-3} = -\frac{7}{10}$. (p. 10)

Slope-Intercept Form   A linear equation written in the form $y = mx + b$ is written in slope-intercept form. In this form, m is the slope of the line and the point $(0, b)$ is the y-intercept. (p. 10)

solution   Of an equation or inequality is a number or expression that makes the equation or inequality true when substituted for the variable. To find the numerical solution means to identify all the numbers that make a mathematical equation or inequality true. There may be any number of solutions for an equation or inequality, from 0 to infinitely many. Solutions to equations and inequalities in one variable are single numbers. For two variables they are ordered pairs, for three variables ordered triples. Equations with no solutions, such as $|x - 5| = -3$, are never true. Equations with one, several, or many solutions, such as $x(x + 3)(x - 7) = 0$ are sometimes true, and equations or identities such as $5(2x - 4) = 10x - 20$ are always true. (p. 200)

solve   (1) To find all the solutions to an equation or an inequality (or a system of equations or inequalities). For example, solving the equation $x^2 = 9$ gives the solutions $x = 3$ and $x = -3$. (2) Solving an equation for a variable gives an equivalent equation that expresses that variable in terms of other variables and constants. For example, solving $2y - 8x = 16$ for y gives $y = 4x + 8$. The equation $y = 4x + 8$ has the same solutions as $2y - 8x = 16$, but $y = 4x + 8$ expresses y in terms of x and some constants. (p. 169)

special right triangles   A right triangle with particular notable features that can be used to solve problems. Sometimes, these triangles can be recognized by the angles, such as the 45°-45°-90° triangle (also known as an "isosceles right triangle") and a 30°-60°-90° triangle. (p. 320)

spread (of a data distribution)   A measure of the amount of variability, or how "spread out" a set of data is. Some ways to measure spread are the range, the mean absolute deviation, the standard deviation, and the interquartile range. For symmetric distributions with no outliers, the standard deviation or the interquartile range can represent the spread of the data well. However, in the presence of outliers or non-symmetrical data distributions, the interquartile range may be a better measure. Also see *variability*. (p. C19)

square root   A number a is a square root of b if $a^2 = b$. For example, the number 9 has two square roots, 3 and –3. A negative number has no real square roots; a positive number has two; and zero has just one square root, namely, itself. Other roots, such as cube root, will be studied in other courses. Also see *radical*. (p. 83)

standard deviation A way to measure the spread, or the amount of variability, in a set of data. The standard deviation is the square root of the average of the distances to the mean, after the distances have been made positive by squaring. The standard deviation represents the spread of a set of data well if the distribution of the data is symmetric and has no outliers. (p. 771)

Standard Form (linear function) A linear equation written in the form $Ax + By = C$ is written in standard form. For linear functions, $B \neq 0$. (p. 10)

Standard Form (quadratic function) The standard form for the equation of a quadratic function is $y = ax^2 + bx + c$ where $a \neq 0$. (p. 68)

Standard Form (quadratic relations in general) The standard for parabolas, ellipses, and hyperbolas with axes parallel to the x- or y-axes is $Ax^2 + By^2 + Cx + Dy + E = 0$.

standard position An angle is in standard position if its vertex is located at the origin and one ray is on the positive x-axis. (p. 343)

standard window The graphing window on a calculator set to show the x- and y-axes for values $-10 \leq x \leq 10$ and $-10 \leq y \leq 10$.

statistic A numerical fact or calculation that is formed from data. For example, a mean or a correlation coefficient is a statistic. With a capital "S," Statistics is the field of study which is concerned with summarizing data, and using probability to make predictions from data with natural variability. (p. 445)

statistical process control The process of checking whether manufacturing quality remains stable over time. A process is "in control" if critical measurements of quality remain within the upper control limit and lower control limit as expected. (p. 598)

statistical test A method of making decisions based on a statistical analysis of data. (p. 581)

step function A special kind of piecewise function (a function composed of parts of two or more functions). A step function has a graph that is a series of line segments that often looks like a set of steps. (p. B24)

stoplight icon The icon (shown at right) will appear periodically throughout the text. Problems that display this icon contain errors of some type.

strength (of an association) A description of how much scatter there is in the data away from the line or curve of best fit. If an association is linear, the correlation coefficient, r, or R-squared can be used to numerically describe and interpret the strength.

streak Consecutive identical outcomes in a probabilistic situation. For example, if a baseball team wins four consecutive games, they have a winning streak of 4. (p. 572)

study See *observational study*. (p. 461)

stretch factor Used to describe the effect of a in the graphing form of a quadratic, cubic, absolute value, or exponential function. For $a > 1$ or $a < -1$ the outputs increase or decrease faster than the outputs for the parent functions, and the graphs are described as being stretched upwards or downwards in relation to the parent graph. (p. 66)

subjects The people or items being measured in a statistical study.

substitution Replacing a variable or expression with a number, another variable, or another expression. For example, when evaluating the function $f(x) = 5x - 1$, for $x = 3$, substitute 3 for x to get $f(3) = 5(3) - 1 = 14$.

Substitution Method A method for solving a system of equations by replacing one variable with an expression involving the remaining variable(s). For example, in the system of equations at right the first equation tells you that y is equal to $-3x + 5$. We can substitute $-3x + 5$ in for y in the second equation to get $2(-3x + 5) + 10x = 18$, then solve this equation to find x. Once we have x, we substitute that value back into either of the original equations to find the value of y.

$$y = -3x + 5$$
$$2y + 10x = 18$$

sum The result of adding two or more numbers. For example, the sum of 4 and 5 is 9.

sum of cubes A polynomial of the form $x^3 + y^3$. It can be factored as follows: $x^3 + y^3 = (x + y)(x^2 - xy + y^2)$. For example, the sum of cubes $27y^3 + 64$ can be factored as $(3y + 4)(9y^2 - 12y + 16)$. (p. 427)

summation notation A convenient way to represent a series is to use summation notation. The Greek letter sigma, Σ, indicates a sum.
For example, $\sum_{n=1}^{4} 3n = 3(1) + 3(2) + 3(3) + 3(4) = 30$. (p. 519)
The numbers below and above the sigma are called the indices. The index below, $n = 1$, tells us what value to start with for n. The top index tells us how high the value can go. In the example shown above, n starts at 1 and increases to 4.

symmetry A figure that appears not to change when reflected across a line is said to have reflection symmetry. A figure that appears not to change when rotated through an angle of less than $360°$ is described as having rotation symmetry.

system of equations A system of equations is a set of equations with more than one unknown or variable. The systems we solve most often in this course have two or three equations and two or three variables. Systems of equations are often solved using substitution or elimination to reduce the number of variables. A system of quadratic equations is shown at right. (p. 171)

$$y = x^2 + 8x - 4$$
$$y = 2x^2 + 5x - 8$$

system of inequalities   A system of inequalities is a set of inequalities with the same variables. Solving a system of inequalities means finding one or more regions on the coordinate plane whose points represent solutions to each of the inequalities in the system. There may be zero, one, or several such regions for a system of inequalities. For example, the shaded region at right is a graph of the system of inequalities that appears below it. (p. 187)

$$y \le x^2 + x - 6$$
$$y > \tfrac{2}{3}x$$

tangent function   For any real number θ, the tangent of θ, denoted $\tan\theta$, is the slope of the line containing the ray which represents a rotation of θ radians in standard position. The general equation for the tangent function is $y = a\tan b(x - h) + k$. This function has period of $\frac{\pi}{b}$, vertical asymptotes at $\frac{\pi}{2b} + h \pm \frac{n\pi}{b}$ for $n = 1, 2, \ldots$, horizontal shift h, and vertical shift k. (p. 341)

tangent inverse ($\tan^{-1} x$)   Read as the inverse of tangent x, $\tan^{-1} x$ is the measure of the angle that has tangent x. We can also write $y = \arctan x$. Note that the notation refers to the inverse of the tangent function, *not* $\frac{1}{\tan x}$. Because $y = \tan^{-1} x$ is equivalent to $x = \tan y$ and there are infinitely many angles y such that $\tan y = x$, the inverse *function* is restricted to select the *principal* value of y such that $\frac{\pi}{2} < x < \frac{\pi}{2}$. The graph of the inverse tangent function is at right. (p. 636)

tangent ratio   In a right triangle the ratio $\frac{\text{opposite side}}{\text{adjacent side}}$ is known as the tangent of an acute angle. At right, $\tan B = \frac{b}{a}$ since the side of length b is opposite angle B and the side length a is adjacent to angle B.

term   A single number, variable, or product of numbers and variables. A monomial is a term. Also a component of a sequence. (p. 135)

term number   In a sequence, a number that gives the position of a term in the sequence. A replacement value for the independent variable in a function that determines the sequence. See *sequence*. (p. A18)

theoretical probability   A probability calculation based on counting possible outcomes.

third quartile (Q3)   The median of the upper half of a set of data which has been written in numerical order. (p. C5)

three-dimensional   An object that has height, width, and depth. (p. 257)

transcendental number   A number that is not the root of *any* polynomial equation with rational coefficients. Transcendental numbers are very common. The most prominent examples of transcendental numbers are π and e.   (p. 548)

transformation (of a function)   The conversion of a function to a corresponding function. Transformations often slide, reflect, stretch, and/or compress graphs of functions. For example, the transformation of $f(x) + k$ moves the graph of the function up or down by an amount k. The transformation $f(-x)$ reflects the graph of the function across the y-axis.   (p. 83)

translation   The result of moving a graph horizontally, vertically, or both but without changing its orientation.

treatment   Some type of change imposed on one or more groups in an experiment so that a direct comparison can be made.   (p. 461)

trend line   Another name for a line of best fit. See *line of best fit*.

trigonometric identities   The different trigonometric functions are related by many different equations, termed identities. A few examples of these identities are: $\cos(x) = \cos(-x)$ and $\sin(-x) = -\sin(x)$.   (p. 651)

trigonometric ratios   See *sine*, *cosine*, *tangent*, *secant*, *cosecant*, and *cotangent*.   (p. 29)

trinomial   A polynomial that is the sum or difference of exactly three terms, each of which is a monomial. For example, $x^2 + 6x + 9$ is a trinomial.

triple root   A root of a function that occurs exactly three times. If an expression of the form $(x - a)^3$ is a factor of a polynomial, then the polynomial has a triple root at $x = a$. The graph of the polynomial has an inflection point at $x = a$.   (p. 380)

two-dimensional   An object having length and width.   (p. 257)

Undoing   Using inverse operations and reversing the order of operations to solve an equation in one variable or to "undo" a function rule in order to write its inverse. For example, in the equation $y = x^3 - 7$, add y and write the cube root.   (p. 170)

uniform   See *shape (of a data display)*.   (p. C13)

unit circle   A circle with a radius of one unit is called a unit circle.   (p. 337)

upper control limit (UCL)   See *control limit*.   (p. 599)

variable A symbol used to represent one or more numbers. In this course, letters of the English alphabet are used as variables. For example, in the expression $3x - (8.6xy + z)$, the variables are $x, y,$ and z. (p. 41)

variability The inconsistency in measured data. Variability comes from two sources. Measurement error is the inconsistency in measurement of the same element repeated times and/or by different people. Element variability is the natural variation of the elements themselves. For example, even though in general people with larger shoe sizes are taller, not all people with the same shoe size have the same height. That is element variability. See *spread*. (p. 581)

vertex (of a parabola) The vertex of a parabola is the highest or lowest point on the parabola (depending on the parabola's orientation). See *parabola*. (p. 60)

vertex form The vertex form for the equation of a quadratic function (also called graphing form) is written $y = a(x - h)^2 + k$. (p. 68)

vertical shift Used to describe the location of a graph in relation to its parent graph, the shift is the vertical distance (up or down) of each point on the graph from the corresponding point on the parent graph. This type of transformation is a vertical translation. For example, each point on the graph of $y = x^2 + 2$ is two units higher that its corresponding point on $y = x^2$. In a general equation such as $y = a(x - h)^2 + k$ the vertical shift is represented by k. (p. 66)

volume For a three-dimensional figure the number of non-overlapping cubic units that will fit inside.

x-bar process control chart A plot of the mean measurement of samples over time. *x*-bar process control charts are used to monitor whether a manufacturing process is proceeding within limits as expected. (p. 599)

x-intercept A point where a graph intersects the *x*-axis. In two dimensions, the coordinates of the *x*-intercept are $(x, 0)$. In three dimensions they are $(x, 0, 0)$. See *intercept*. (p. 10)

x-y interchange The result of exchanging the x and y variables and then solving for y. The resulting equation is the inverse of the original function.

x → y table A table that represents pairs of related values. The input value x appears in the first row or column, and the output value, y, appears in the second. The $x \rightarrow y$ table at right contains input and output pairs for the equation $y = x^2 - 3$.

x	y
−3	6
−2	1
−1	−2
0	−3
1	−2
2	1

y-intercept A point where a graph intersects the y-axis. In two dimensions the coordinates of the y-intercept are $(0, y)$. In three dimensions, the coordinates are $(0, y, 0)$. See *intercept*. (p. 10)

z-score A z-score indicates how many standard deviations a data value is from the mean. More formally, $z = \frac{\text{data value} - \text{mean}}{\text{standard deviation}}$.

zero factorial Zero factorial is $1, 0! = 1$. (p. 648)

zero power The result of raising any number (except zero) to the zero power is 1. $x^0 = 1$ for any number $x \neq 0$. (p. B36)

Zero Product Property When the product of two or more factors is zero, at least one of the factors must equal zero. Used to solve equations in factored form. For example, given the equation $(x - 4)(x + 5) = 0$ you can see that 4 and −5 are solutions and that they are the only possible solutions because there are no other numbers that make either factor zero. (p. 24)

zeros of a function The roots of a function or the values of x for which the function value $y = 0$. The x-intercepts of the graph of a function in the real plane are zeros. These are also called the roots of the function. A function can have complex zeros. These complex zeros cause $y = 0$, but they are not x-intercepts since they do not exist in the real plane. See *roots of a function*. (p. 382)

Index
Student Version

Many of the pages referenced here contain a definition or an example of the topic listed, often within the body of a Math Notes box. Others contain problems that develop or demonstrate the topic. It may be necessary to read the text on several pages to fully understand the topic. Also, some problems listed here are good examples of the topic and may not offer any explanation. The page numbers below reflect the pages in the Student Version. References to Math Notes boxes are bolded.

THIS BOOK IS THE PROPERTY OF:

Book No._____

ISSUED TO	Year Used	CONDITION	
		ISSUED	RETURNED

PUPILS to whom this texbook is issued must not write on any part of it in any way, unless otherwise instructed by the teacher.